Stochastic Modeling

Theory and Reality from an Actuarial Perspective

ISBN 978-0-9813968-1-1

2nd printing

Association Actuarielle Internationale
International Actuarial Association

150 Metcalfe Street, Suite 601
Ottawa, Ontario
Canada K2P 1P1

www.actuaries.org
Tel: 1-613-236-0886   Fax: 1-613-236-1386

Email: secretariat@actuaries.org

Table of Contents

Introduction

As recently as the mid-1990s, most models used in financial analysis of insurance were deterministic. Based on sets of static parameters and assumptions, these models largely ignored random fluctuations that were likely to occur. Sensitivity analyses were performed but were generally limited to a fixed number of defined scenarios. This deterministic approach is rapidly being replaced by stochastic modeling that can better inform insurers on pricing, financial planning, and capital assessment strategies. Huge advancements in computing power have made it possible for actuaries and financial planners to better understand the increasingly complex risk profiles of insurers' evolving product design.

Rather than focus on a specific use of stochastic modeling, as many others have done, this book is intended to provide actuaries with a comprehensive resource that details current stochastic methods, provides background on the stochastic technique as well as their advantages and disadvantages.

Many of these techniques transcend international borders and will be relevant in any country. For this reason, we have not focused on any specific country or accounting framework. Parameters and assumptions may be illustrated for a specific region or country, in which case possible modifications have been noted. The goal of this book, however, is not to address all possible risk scenarios, nor generate specific factors for reserve loads, but rather to explain how an approach is derived. Readers can then develop their own parameters and assumptions based on current and historical experience for use in a specific and appropriate methodology.

Furthermore, because insurance products have and will continue to evolve differently around the world, certain products may be more or less advanced depending on the reader's location.

This book is presented by the International Actuarial Association (IAA) in collaboration with Milliman. It is intended for actuaries, actuarial students and other readers involved in actuarial modeling in both the life and non-life sectors.

Certain concepts, such as mean, standard deviation, and percentile distribution, will be illustrated but not defined. In many cases, technical formulas used in this document were obtained from other publications noted in the bibliography. Additional information on formulas, including their development, will not be discussed here and can be obtained from the source document. In addition, we are not promoting one method or technique over any other. Our goal is to illustrate

Huge advancements in computing power have made it possible for actuaries and financial planners to better understand the increasingly complex risk profiles of insurers' evolving product design.

commonly used methods employed in risk assessment. To this end, the book covers the following five major sections:

- **General methodology, including a discussion of "risk-neutral versus real-world" scenarios, techniques used, distributions and fitting, random number generation, and risk measures.**

- **Current applications, including economic scenarios, life, health, and non-life models, and country- or region-specific issues.**

- **Evaluation of results, including calibration, validation, audit, peer review, and communication.**

- **Seven case studies that show various applications of scenario development in real situations, including pricing, economic capital analysis, and embedded value analysis.**

- **References and additional resources available to the reader.**

This book is intended to be an on-going resource; however, stochastic modeling is expected to continue evolving following this publication. Still, we hope to remove much of the "black-box" mystique that surrounds these models by illustrating the methods that are currently known.

Acknowledgment

We would like to acknowledge the financial support we have received for this project from the following actuarial organizations:

- **The Actuarial Foundation (United States)**
- **Canadian Institute of Actuaries**
- **Casualty Actuarial Society**
- **Financial Reporting Section of the Society of Actuaries**
- **Het Actuarieel Genootschap (Dutch Actuarial Association)**
- **Institute of Actuaries of Australia**

In addition to their financial support, representatives from these organization participated in the IAA Ad Hoc Project Oversight Group, chaired by David Congram.

A book of this breadth and depth cannot be undertaken without broad international participation. The IAA would like to acknowledge Milliman who has assembled an international group of actuaries and economists to gather information and share their knowledge. We would like to thank the contributing authors to the book and the assistance of the IAA Ad Hoc Project Oversight Group, whose guidance and support were the impetus for completion of this document.

The opinions, viewpoints, and conclusions presented in this book are those of the contributing authors and are not necessarily those of the IAA, the supporting organisations, or Milliman, Inc. They should not be interpreted as prescribing actuarial standards of practice in any respect.

I. General Methodology

The often-quoted definition of actuarial science as "the quantification, analysis, and management of future contingent risk and its financial consequences"[1] was probably not made specifically in reference to stochastic modeling, but in many ways it could have been. We have only to consider the simplest of examples, such as the need to determine the present value at a fixed interest rate of $1 to be paid at the death of an individual at some future time, or the amount of payment an insurer might be obliged to make for the negligent action of one of its policyholders, to appreciate how this definition applies. In these and nearly all applications in actuarial science, we are faced with a range of possible future outcomes, some more likely than others, and are called upon to make assertions about quantities whose actual values are uncertain. This function – the determination of various possible values of unknown quantities – provides a broad definition of stochastic modeling.

I.A   Stochastic Models vs. Non-stochastic Models

A stochastic model is a mathematical simplification of a process – financial or otherwise – involving random variables. The primary purpose of a deterministic method is to provide a projection based on a single set of assumptions selected by the user. Depending on the purpose of the model, the single set of assumptions may represent an average expected outcome, a "stress" scenario, or some other single outcome the user is interested in understanding. Both of these are quite useful in understanding more about the processes they are modeling, but there are several aspects of modeling we can examine to determine when stochastic models should be used.

The primary purpose of a stochastic model is to simulate a distribution of possible outcomes that reflect the random variations in the inputs. In contrast, a non-stochastic, or deterministic, method is a mathematical simplification involving estimates of the input variables.

When should stochastic models be used?

As computing power has become cheaper and more widely available, the use of stochastic modeling has grown more and more popular. But to what extent has this growth been driven by necessity or the general perception that a more complex, computation-intensive model is better?

---

[1]   See for example CRUSAP Task Force (December 2006), "A Critical Review of the U.S. Actuarial Profession," p. 5. Retrieved September 6, 2009, from http://www.crusap.net/report.asp.

The situations for which stochastic modeling is required generally fall into the following categories:

▪ When required by regulation and/or standards of professionalism

Increasingly, government regulations, accounting standards, and/or professional guidelines dictate the use of stochastic modeling. In the United States, for example, the principles-based approach to calculation of statutory liabilities for life insurers requires stochastic modeling on many blocks of business. Stochastic techniques are also sometimes indicated for the calculation of risk-based capital.

▪ When analyzing extreme outcomes or "tail risks" that are not well understood

Scenarios intended to represent one-in-100-year events or one-in-1,000-year events are typically used to stress-test asset or liability portfolios. In some cases, such as a "Black Tuesday" stock market event, the modeler may even believe that he or she has a handle on the likelihood of an extreme event. But recent experience has proved differently in many cases.[2] How many would have included the "perfect storm" scenario of low interest rates and low equity returns of the early 2000s or an event that could cause the catastrophic losses of the World Trade Center terrorist attack? How many would have contemplated the 2008/2009 credit crisis that has affected the United States and European markets? Stochastic modeling would likely have revealed these scenarios, even if indicating they were extremely unlikely.

Yet financial risks are among the best understood risks with which actuaries deal. Mortality and morbidity risks are often much more complex, especially when considering the scope of assessing pandemic risk such as the 1918 Spanish flu event. Such an event could represent a 1-in-1,000 event, or it might not. Insufficient frequency data, rapidly evolving healthcare technology, and increasing globalization could alter the likelihood of a contemporary pandemic and call into question the credibility of using a few select stress scenarios to understand the true exposure. Another approach would be to develop a stochastic model that relies on a few well-understood parameters and is appropriately calibrated for the risk manager's intended modeling purpose.

▪ When using certain risk measures, such as Value at Risk (VaR) or Conditional Tail Expectation (CTE)

These risk measures, which quantify a company's exposure to tail risks, provide an understanding of how an observed phenomenon – interest rates, mortality, etc. – behaves in the tail. Stochastic modeling is required in order to completely describe the probability distribution of the tail.

▪ When certain percentiles are required

Assigning a percentile to a particular outcome is an excellent way of gaining insight into how extreme the occurrence of an event is. For example, would we rather know that the "Black Tuesday" stock market scenario represents an extreme event, or that the probability of stock market returns being worse than the "Black Tuesday" scenario is 0.005%? Stochastic modeling is the approach to use if probabilities are required.

Would we rather know that the "Black Tuesday" stock market scenario represents an extreme event, or that the probability of stock market returns being worse than the "Black Tuesday" scenario is 0.005%? Stochastic modeling is the approach to use if probabilities are required.

---

[2] Note that here and throughout the term "recent" will refer to the period of approximately 2007-2009, when this book was written.

- **When one wants to understand where stress tests fall in the broader spectrum of possible outcomes**

In many cases, stress tests are prescribed by regulators or other professional organizations. A prime example is the use of seven interest rate scenarios for cash flow testing of life insurance liabilities in the United States. These scenarios satisfy regulatory requirements, but provide little insight into a company's true risk exposure, especially if the stress scenarios fall between the 25th and 75th percentiles. Thorough risk management, however, requires an understanding of where the stress scenarios fall in the broader range of possible outcomes.

In other cases, knowing the range of reasonably possible outcomes is desirable, but not strictly required. When optional, stochastic modeling should be used at the discretion of the actuary, who must weigh the benefits of a sophisticated stochastic analysis against the increased costs.

When should use of stochastic models be questioned?

In still other cases, stochastic modeling may not be of sufficient value to justify the effort. Examples include:

- **When it is difficult or impossible to determine the appropriate probability distribution**

The normal or lognormal distributions are commonly used for many stochastic projections because of their relative ease of use. However, there are times when these distributions do not properly describe the process under review. In these situations a distribution should not be forced onto the variable. Indeed, there are many other distributions available as described in other parts of this book; the analysis of which distribution best describes the available information is a critical part of the overall modeling exercise. However, there are still times when it is impossible to determine the appropriate distribution.

- **When it is difficult or impossible to calibrate the model**

Calibration requires either credible historical experience or observable conditions that provide insight on model inputs. If neither is available, the model cannot be fully calibrated and the actuary should carefully consider whether its use is appropriate. Sometimes, an actuary is required to develop a model when no credible, observable data exists. Such a situation requires professional actuarial judgment and the lack of data on which to calibrate the model should be carefully considered.

- **When it is difficult or impossible to validate the model**

Stochastic models are less reliable if the model output cannot be thoroughly reviewed, comprehended, and compared to expectations. If the actuary must use a model from which the output cannot be reviewed and validated, professional actuarial judgment is required and other methods of review and checking should perhaps be considered. The method of review and checking will necessarily involve a careful consideration of the specifics of the situation.

When optional, stochastic modeling should be used at the discretion of the actuary, who must weigh the benefits of a sophisticated stochastic analysis against the increased costs.

Alternatives to stochastic models

When the use of stochastic models is impractical or not of sufficient value, some possible alternatives include:

- **Stress testing/scenario testing**

Stress testing (also known as scenario testing) examines the outcome of a projection under alternative sets of assumptions. In many cases, the alternative scenarios are intended to represent extreme scenarios, such as pandemic risk or stock market crashes. In this way, stress testing can provide some insights into the risk of an asset or liability portfolio. In other cases, the alternative scenarios are intended to gauge sensitivity of outcomes to certain assumptions. If an actuary lacks full confidence in a certain assumption, for example, a stress test of that assumption may help to understand its materiality. If the outcome of the projection is insensitive to the assumption, it may not make sense to invest the time and effort required for fine-tuning the assumption and/or stochastically modeling the assumption to understand the risk profile.

- **Static factors (or "load factors")**

In many cases, an actuary may rely on previously developed or commonly used "load factors" to account for risk. Under this approach, static factors (usually multiplicative) are applied to deterministic results to account for potential variability. For example, a factor, which accounts for variability in the liability assumptions, could be applied to a liability of $1 million developed via a deterministic or formulaic approach. In the United States, this approach was adopted by the National Association of Insurance Commissioners (NAIC) for the calculation of risk-based capital (RBC). However, there are widely recognized weaknesses to this approach, and many countries – the United States included – are moving away from this methodology. Weaknesses of load factors include, among other things, the inability to tailor the risk load to the specific block of business under consideration, the inability to apply professional judgment, and the possibility that the risk loads are not fully understood (e.g., what risk factors are reflected, and to what extent, in the risk load).

- **Ranges**

Ranges can be used to account for uncertainty of a "best" estimate or, alternatively, the variability of potential outcomes. A range of reasonable best estimates can be selected using multiple "reasonable" estimates or using a best estimate and assigning a range of reasonable estimates such as 90% to 110% of the point estimate. The factors should be based on informed judgment and/or past experience. A range designed for uncertainty of a "best" estimate is generally as narrow as reasonably possible, is focused on describing the central estimate itself, and is not intended as a description of the range of possible outcomes. On the other hand, a range designed to describe variability of potential outcomes is generally wider (how much depends on the target percentile width) and is focused on describing a particular confidence interval (or equivalent).

Disadvantages of stochastic models

Stochastic modeling has its advantages, many of which are fairly apparent from the above discussion, but it also has some limitations. These include:

- **The "black box" phenomenon**

Stochastic models are quite complex and often viewed as "black boxes" into which data and assumptions are entered and results are magically produced. This perception can be true, if the model is not properly understood.

- **Improper calibration or validation**

Users often fail to properly calibrate or validate the model. Improper calibration is often caused by a misunderstanding of the model's purpose or by the use of inappropriate historical data. Much like the "black box" phenomenon, improper validation is often related to a misunderstanding of the model.

- **Uses of inappropriate distributions or parameters**

Users of stochastic modeling often assume – blindly or with very limited empirical evidence – that a variable has a particular distribution. While many processes can approximate a normal distribution, more often than not the possible outcomes are skewed. Users of stochastic modeling should be cautioned against the uninformed use of a particular distribution, which can generate scenarios producing completely useless results. Such a misguided assumption can be especially problematic when examining tail risk.

Guidance on stochastic model implementation

Before we begin a discussion of the technical components of stochastic modeling, it is useful to outline the implementation steps. In general, the modeler needs to:

1. Describe the goals and all of the intended uses of the model.

2. Decide if stochastic modeling is necessary or if an alternative approach will yield equally useful results.

3. Determine which of the projection techniques (Monte Carlo, lattice methods, regime-switching models, etc.) should be used, if a stochastic model is deemed appropriate.

4. Decide on the risk metrics (VaR, CTE, etc.) to use.

5. Establish which risk factors need to be modeled stochastically.

6. Determine the approach for modeling these risk factors in terms of which distributions or models should be used, and how to parameterize or "fit" the distributions.

7. Determine the number of scenarios necessary to reach the point at which additional iterations provide no additional information about the shape of distribution. This point is often figured by performing several different runs – one with 100 scenarios, one with 1,000 scenarios, one with 2,000 scenarios, etc.

8. Calibrate the model.

9. Run the model.

> Stochastic models are quite complex and often viewed as "black boxes" into which data and assumptions are entered and results are magically produced. This perception can be true, if the model is not properly understood.

10. Validate the model and review output.

11. Conduct a peer review.

12. Communicate results.

We have already discussed the need to first determine whether the use of a stochastic model is appropriate. We now turn to a detailed discussion of various stochastic projection techniques.

I.B   Risk-neutral vs. Real-world

Stochastic models have a wide range of applications in insurance and finance. In many of these models, stochastically simulated variables include stock prices, security values, interest rates, or other parameters describing market prices of instruments, and trials (or paths or scenarios) of market prices or rates generated over time. The methodology for determining the stochastic evolution of such prices is referred to as an economic scenario generator (ESG).

The processes underlying an ESG may simply isolate a single-market variable that directly drives the value of the instruments in question, such as a single equity index. Or the ESG may involve the joint simulation of many variable combinations, such as multiple equity indices, several points on the yield curve, currency exchange rates, inflation rates, yield curves in multiple countries, and historical and implied volatilities.

We broadly distinguish between two classes of ESG: real-world and risk-neutral. It is important to note that real-world and risk-neutral scenarios should produce the same expected present value of cash flows.

Real-world scenarios use expected cash flows and a discount rate that reflects the risk believed to be associated with those cash flows. Risk-neutral scenarios use risk-adjusted cash flows and a risk-free discount rate. The risk-adjusted cash flows are adjusted in such a way as to ensure that the expected present value of cash flows between the risk-neutral and real-world scenarios are consistent.

Real-world scenarios can be connected with risk-neutral scenarios via the use of deflators, which establish an equivalence between these two methodologies. The concept of deflators is explored more thoroughly later in the document in Section I.B.5.

This overview of risk-neutral and real-world ESGs is meant to provide a basic context for the more technical discussion to follow. Extensive academic research and reference material also exists, which might help the reader better understand the subject.

It is important to note that real-world and risk-neutral scenarios should produce the same expected present value of cash flows. Real-world scenarios use expected cash flows and a discount rate that reflects the risk believed to be associated with those cash flows. Risk-neutral scenarios use risk-adjusted cash flows and a risk-free discount rate.

I.B.1   Risk-neutral Scenarios

Background

Risk-neutral scenarios are used to value cash flows for the primary purpose of reproducing prices observed in the market as of a specific date. One way to think of the risk-neutral measure is to consider it a representation of the probability distribution of underlying security prices if all investors were "risk-neutral" or indifferent to risk. Under this scenario, investors would not demand a premium for holding riskier assets, and all assets would be expected to earn the risk-free rate available over a given time period. Accordingly, in risk-neutral scenarios, the expected return of every asset is the risk-free rate associated with the given term. It should be noted that in construction of risk-neutral scenarios, it does not matter that risk premiums are observed or expected in the real-world; rather, the "risk-neutral world" is an alternate world where such premiums do not exist.

A well-established result of financial economics is the principle of risk-neutral valuation, which states that the value of any financial derivative is the mathematical expectation of the path-wise present value of cash flows under a risk-neutral measure (or probability distribution).[3] For some derivatives, there may be analytical solutions to the mathematical expectation. In many cases, however, there are not, and the solution can be estimated using Monte Carlo methods that simulate the underlying state variables and security prices, and then calculate the sample expectation over a number of trials. As the number of trials used becomes arbitrarily large, the Monte Carlo estimate of the price converges to the theoretical value.

One way to think of the risk-neutral measure is to consider it a representation of the probability distribution of underlying security prices if all investors were "risk-neutral" or indifferent to risk.

Risk-neutral scenarios are Monte Carlo draws from the risk-neutral probability distribution of the underlying security prices on which the payouts of a derivative are dependent. A risk-neutral scenario generator is structured so that the stochastic processes for the underlying state variables or security prices have expected growth rates consistent with the risk-neutral measure in each and every time period.

We often use the term "arbitrage-free" to refer to risk-neutral scenarios, as the principle of no arbitrage is the foundation for risk neutrality in the correct pricing of derivatives. In this book, the terms "market-consistent" and "risk-neutral" are used somewhat interchangeably, because one of the purposes of risk-neutral scenarios is to reproduce observable market prices as well as to price exotic or complex derivatives consistently with observed market prices.

Uses

Risk-neutral scenarios are typically used by practitioners to answer the following types of questions:

- **What is the market-consistent value or fair value of an insurance liability?**
- **What is the expected hedging cost of an insurance guarantee with an embedded derivative?**
- **What is the price or fair value of an exotic derivative?**
- **How much would a market participant demand to assume liability cash flows?**

All of these questions effectively ask: What is a set of cash flows worth in the market? As a result, they cover a much narrower scope than questions addressed by real-world scenarios of possible outcomes. Typically, only the mean present value of cash flows from a set of risk-neutral scenarios has significance; other features of the distribution are not relevant.

---

[3] For the purposes of this non-technical discussion, we consider measure and probability distribution to be equivalent.

Use of risk-neutral scenarios for pricing purposes involves discounting cash flows to obtain an expected present value. Typically, these scenarios are generated by assuming cash flows will be discounted under risk neutrality; that is, the scenarios use discounted factors appropriate for valuing bonds with no cash flow uncertainty.

Calibration and parameterization

A risk-neutral ESG is typically parameterized to observed market prices of relevant instruments. For instance, a simple lognormal equity model with two constant parameters (equity drift rate and return volatility) can be calibrated to be consistent with prices of two instruments – a single zero-coupon bond (or swap) and a single equity option of a given maturity and strike price. A lognormal equity model with time-dependent drifts and volatility can be calibrated to replicate market prices of a zero-coupon bond and an equity option of every maturity within the projection horizon.

The calibration process becomes increasingly complicated with the complexity of a model. With stochastic equity volatility or stochastic interest rate models, the goal of the calibration might be to fit a large sample of market prices of options or swaptions. When there are more instruments to fit than there are parameters in the model, optimization may be used to find the combination of parameters that constitutes the best fit to the overall set of market prices.

When calibrating a model of stochastic interest rates and equity returns to observed market prices of equity options, the modeler should be careful to define the equity return volatilities being used as excess-return volatilities, rather than total-return volatilities, and then adjust the market inputs accordingly. Excess return refers to the additional return that equities earn above the risk-free rate of return.

Market prices of options and swaptions may themselves be quite volatile from day to day, resulting in parameter instability. When the risk-neutral ESG is used for the management of an ongoing hedging program, practitioners may choose to adjust their parameterization process to sacrifice fit to observed market prices in favour of parameter stability.

Risk-neutral ESGs should be tested by using the generator to calculate prices of instruments (calculating the expected present value of the cash flows) and to confirm they are consistent (within Monte Carlo error) with the observed market prices to which the model has been calibrated. In addition, the user may also gain insight by pricing derivatives outside of the calibration set to test for reasonableness.

Technical discussion on calibration of specific models is covered in other sections of this book.

Other considerations

Sometimes risk-neutral ESGs will have a limited number of observable market inputs for calibration. One example is a situation in which the longest available traded option has a 10-year maturity, but the ESG is required to produce scenarios that extend 30 years. In this case, judgment regarding assumptions in the non-traded space is needed; the solution is often a calibration that blends market prices with historical data. In other situations, market prices may be available but unreliable because of illiquidity or for other reasons. The practitioner will have to apply judgment on which prices to use and which ones to bypass.

When there are more instruments to fit than there are parameters in the model, optimization may be used to find the combination of parameters that constitutes the best fit to the overall set of market prices.

I.B.2 Real-world Scenarios

Background

In contrast to risk-neutral scenarios, which use an unrealistic assumption about risk premiums for purposes of calculating derivative prices under the no-arbitrage assumption, real-world scenarios take into account investor risk preferences. The compensation required by investors to take on riskier portfolios is either implicitly or explicitly used in the construction of these scenarios. By definition, real-world scenarios seek to avoid the unrealistic assumptions of the risk-free world.

The goal of real-world scenarios is to produce a realistic pattern of underlying market prices or parameters that will ultimately be used to generate realistic distributions of outcomes. Because the past is often viewed as a good basis for future expectations, real-world scenarios are often developed to maintain consistency with observed historical market experience. But they can also be vulnerable to a considerable amount of subjectivity. Different modelers might have different views about the course of future market movement, the reasonableness of certain scenarios, and the relationship between assumed parameters and results.

Real-world scenarios seek to maintain consistency with stylized facts observed in the actual evolution of market prices. These include the following:

- Risk premiums above the risk-free rate that equities tend to earn over the long term.

- Term premiums that investors in longer-term bonds require over the yields of shorter-term bonds.

- Credit spreads in excess of long-term default costs that compensate the holders of credit risk.

- Implied volatilities reflected in option prices that are in excess of realized return volatility exhibited by equities. Implied volatilities are commonly measured using market-observed prices and a pricing model such as the Black-Scholes equation. For example, the modeler enters values for all variables in the pricing model, including market-observed price, but excluding volatility. The modeler then solves for the volatility in the pricing model that would produce the market-observed price.

Note that none of the above are reflected in the development of risk-neutral scenarios. Specific features of different models are discussed in other sections.

> **The goal of real-world scenarios is to produce a realistic pattern of underlying market prices or parameters that will ultimately be used to generate realistic distributions of outcomes.**

Uses

Real-world scenarios are used to answer what can be broadly classified as "what-if" questions such as:

- What does the distribution of present value earnings look like?

- How much capital does the company need to support worst-case scenarios?

- What level of pricing is required to earn a target return at least X% of the time without assuming excessive downside risk?

- What kind of earnings volatility could a block of business generate?

- How does the distribution of final capital change with changes in investment strategy?

- How much residual risk remains from alternative hedging or risk management strategies?

In a sense, each of these questions asks, "What outcome might we expect if market prices behave as we might realistically expect?" The answers allow managers to see the implications of what might happen given a particular evolution in market prices, rates, or parameters, and thereby guide their understanding of possible outcomes.

I.B.3 Techniques

In this section, we will discuss the various projection techniques, including Monte Carlo simulations, lattice methods, and regime-switch models, that can be used for financial reporting and capital assessment.

I.B.3.a Monte Carlo Simulation

The Monte Carlo (MC) method is one of the most efficient numerical methods in finance, particularly as it applies to risk analysis, stress testing of portfolios, and the valuation of securities. Since this method was first developed, its efficiency has been substantially increased. Its development is, indeed, fortuitous in view of the fact that, as global markets become more efficient, more complex stochastic modeling is needed.

In modern financial theory, the prices of financial instruments are often modeled by continuous-time stochastic processes. Assuming no arbitrage, the price of a derivative security is the expectation of its discounted payoff under the risk-neutral measure. Here, the expectation is truly an integral of the payoff function with respect to the risk-neutral measure. The dimension of the integral is the number of observations. The models should choose an efficient numerical valuation method that can approximate the actual solution as closely as possible in a fairly rapid manner, unless a closed-form solution does not exist.

In order to evaluate the expectation, an MC method draws upon random samples and approximates them with an average of all the outcomes. In general, the modeler will need to:

- Generate sample paths of the underlying asset price or interest rate over a certain time period under the risk-neutral measure.

- Calculate the discounted cash flows of the sample paths.

- Average the discounted cash flows of a security on a sample path.

For example, suppose a stock price follows a lognormal distribution, i.e., the natural logarithm of the stock return is normally distributed, where S_t is a stock price at time t. To simulate the stock price at time t, the algorithm of MC simulation would be as follows.

Algorithm I.B-1

1.   Generate $\varepsilon \sim N(0,1)$

2. $S_t = \exp\left[\mu^* + \sigma^* \, \varepsilon\right]$

where $N(0,1)$ denotes a standard normal distribution.

We now consider a European call option on a non-dividend-paying stock satisfying the following process:

$$dS = \mu S\, dt + \sigma S\, dz, \tag{I.B-1}$$

where S is a stock price, μ is the expected rate of return, σ is the volatility of the underlying asset, and dz is a Wiener process. From Itô's lemma, a stock price at a future time T is lognormally distributed. That is, with risk-free interest rate r,

$$\ln S_T \sim N(\ln S_0 + (r - \sigma^2/2)T, \sigma\sqrt{T}). \tag{I.B-2}$$

Here, the stock price can be simulated by Algorithm I.B-1 by replacing

$$\begin{aligned} \mu^* &= \ln S_0 + (r - \sigma^2/2)T \\ \sigma^* &= \sigma\sqrt{T} \end{aligned} \tag{I.B-3}$$

Therefore, the MC estimate of the call option price is obtained by calculating the following algorithm as indicated:

Algorithm I.B-2

1. Draw random sample $\varepsilon_i \sim N(0,1)$

2. Simulate the stock price $S_T^{(i)} = S_0 \exp[(r - \sigma^2/2)T + \sigma\varepsilon_i\sqrt{T}]$

3. Compute the discounted payoff of the call option that corresponds to the simulated
$S_T^{(i)}$, i.e., $c_i = e^{-rT}\max(S_T^{(i)} - K, 0)$

4. Repeat Steps 1-3 until $i = N$

5. Compute the estimated call option price by

$$\hat{c} = \frac{1}{N}\sum_{i=1}^{N} c_i, \tag{I.B-4}$$

where $\hat{c}$ is the MC estimate of the call option price.

The estimate in Equation I.B-4) asymptotically converges to the Black-Scholes price with a sufficiently large number of N. The Black-Scholes price of a European call option is

$$c = S_0 N(d_1) - Ke^{-rT}N(d_2), \tag{I.B-5}$$

where

$$\begin{aligned} d_1 &= \frac{\ln(S_0/K) + (r + \sigma^2/2)T}{\sigma\sqrt{T}} \\ d_2 &= d_1 - \sigma\sqrt{T} \end{aligned} \tag{I.B-6}$$

where S_0 is an initial stock price, K is a strike price, r is a risk-free interest rate, and T is a time to maturity. $N(\cdot)$ denotes a standard normal cumulative distribution function.

The accuracy of an MC estimate can be measured by its sampling standard error. The MC sampling standard error of the estimated call option price is defined by

$$\text{MC sampling error} = \frac{1}{\sqrt{N}} Stdev(c_i),$$
(I.B-7)

Where c_i is the call option price obtained by the ith simulated stock price of $S_T^{(i)}$ at time T and $Stdev(c_i)$ is the standard deviation of c_i.

As an illustration, consider a plain vanilla call option on a non-dividend-paying stock. We assume that the stock price is 100, the strike price is 100, a risk-free rate is 10%, the stock price volatility is 20%, and time to maturity is one year. That is,

$$S_0 = 100, \quad K = 100, \quad r = 10\%, \quad \sigma = 20\%, \quad \text{and} \quad T = 1$$

Monte Carlo simulation is attractive because the convergence rate is independent of the dimension of the integral, which makes multi-integration feasible.

Using MC simulation, the estimated price of this call option is 13.28 and its standard error is 0.20, based on 2,000 scenarios. This can be reconciled with the Black-Scholes price of 13.27. In comparison with other numerical methods of integration, MC simulation is attractive because the convergence rate is independent of the dimension of the integral, which makes multi-integration feasible. Also, it is flexible and easy to accommodate complex models, such as the payoff functions of the derivatives that depend on multiple underlying assets. In particular, MC simulation accommodates the situation when the underlying asset is not only path-dependent, but also path-independent in option pricing.

On the other hand, one drawback of MC simulation is a relatively slow convergence rate. Thus, to obtain a certain degree of accuracy, it requires a sufficiently large number of iterations. Another disadvantage of MC simulation is that it might not be useful to value American-style options.

The number of runs necessary depends on the accuracy required. According to the MC standard error given in Equation I.B-7, the accuracy is inversely proportional to the square root of the number of runs. This means that the number of runs should be increased by the power of an accuracy factor. For instance, to increase the accuracy by a factor of 100, the number of runs should be increased by 100^2, or 10,000.

Variance reduction

Despite MC simulation's straightforward and relatively intuitive implementation, a large number of often computationally intensive iterations is required to achieve a certain degree of accuracy. To minimize iterating the algorithm, variance-reduction methods are typically incorporated into account in MC simulations. This practice can dramatically increase the accuracy of our estimate, while substantially saving computing time. Four variance-reduction methods are most frequently used.

Antithetic-variable technique

The antithetic-variable technique uses an antithetic random number, as well as a random number originally used in MC simulation. Suppose that $f(u)$ is a target function to be estimated and u is a uniform random variable. In the antithetic-variable procedure, we first generate $u_1 \sim U[0,1]$, where $U[0,1]$ denotes a uniform distribution on $[0,1]$ and calculate $f(u_1)$ and $f(u_2)$, where u_2 is the opposite sign of u_1. Then the estimator of $f(u)$ is

$$\tilde{f} = \frac{1}{2}(f(u_1) + f(u_2)) \tag{I.B-8}$$

and the final estimate of this estimator is the average of $\tilde{f}$. The corresponding standard error of the estimate is

$$\frac{1}{\sqrt{N}} Stdev(\tilde{f}) \tag{I.B-9}$$

where N is the number of runs. This is smaller than the standard error of the crude MC estimate, because $Stdev(\tilde{f}) < Stdev(f(u))$, provided f is monotone.

Despite Monte Carlo simulation's straightforward and relatively intuitive implementation, a large number of often computationally intensive iterations is required to achieve a certain degree of accuracy. To minimize iterating the algorithm, variance-reduction methods are typically incorporated into account in Monte Carlo simulations.

Control variate technique

Instead of using a given function $f(u)$, a control variate technique calls on the modeler to choose another function of $g(u)$ that resembles $f(u)$ but is simpler than a given function, where the calculation of $g(u)$ is feasible. Suppose that $f(u)$ is an option price to be estimated, but its analytical solution is not available. To simulate $f(u)$ by the control variate technique, we consider a similar option with a price $g(u)$ that has an analytical solution. The first step is to calculate the estimates of $f(u)$ and $g(u)$ based on the same set of random numbers. The second step is to obtain the price of $g(u)$ from the closed-form solution. Thus, the final estimate of $f(u)$ equals

$$f*(u) - g*(u) + g(u) \tag{I.B-10}$$

where $f*$ and $g*$ are the estimates obtained from the first step. If such a similar derivative does not exist, we can define a function $g(u)$ using a linear regression to approximate $f(u)$. The standard error of the control variate estimator is

$$\frac{1}{\sqrt{N}} Stdev(f(u) - g(u)) \tag{I.B-11}$$

which is smaller than the standard error of the crude MC estimate.

Stratified sampling

Stratified sampling divides the distribution of a market variable into homogeneous subgroups or "stratum". Each stratum is then sampled individually according to its probability. Typically, strata are either intervals or regions that are uncorrelated with one another. The weight (or probability) attached to a given stratum is proportional to the length of the interval or the volume of the region. The optimal sample size in each stratum is proportional to the size of the stratum (e.g., the length of the interval), and the standard deviation of the stratum. In general, the algorithm of stratified sampling is arrived at by:

1. Determining an interval $[x_i, x_{i+1}]$, $i = 1, ..., m$

2. Sampling n_i number of $v_i \sim U[x_i, x_{i+1}]$, $i = 1, ..., m$

3. Evaluating the function f at n_i random points, uniformly distributed over stratum i and its average, given by

$$h_i = \frac{1}{n_i} \sum_{j=1}^{N} f(v_i^{(j)}) \qquad \text{(I.B-12)}$$

4. Computing the weighted average of the stratum mean, where the weight is proportional to the length of the interval, given by

$$\hat{f} = \sum_{i=1}^{k} (x_{i+1} - x_i) h_i \qquad \text{(I.B-13)}$$

Then the standard error of the estimate in Equation I.B-13 is given by

$$\sum_{i=1}^{n_i} (x_{i+1} - x_i) \frac{Stdev(h_i^{(j)})}{\sqrt{n_i}} \qquad \text{(I.B-14)}$$

This is smaller than the standard error of the estimate calculated by the crude MC simulation.

Importance sampling

Importance sampling is based on the concept of weighting observations in different parts of the sample space differently. The goal is to increase the accuracy of the estimator, perhaps dramatically, by drawing samples from the spaces with a larger weight.

Importance sampling is based on the concept of weighting observations in different parts of the sample space differently. The goal is to increase the accuracy of the estimator, perhaps dramatically, by drawing samples from the spaces with a larger weight. To this end, importance sampling generates samples under the heavy loads and adjusts the results for the difference. For example, consider a plain vanilla call option that is priced deep out-of-the-money. Based on the sample paths generated by crude MC simulation, most of the payoff will be zero, because the option starts deep out-of-the-money. But the use of the importance-sampling technique allows us to choose only "important" paths in which the stock price is greater than the strike price.

Let p be a weight of a sample path and f a probability-density function of a stock price. In the importance-sampling technique, a sample is drawn from a probability-density function of $g = f/p$. A function of g is referred to as an importance function. Then the final estimate of the option price is the average of discounted payoff multiplied by p. That is, the estimate of the option price is given by

$$\frac{1}{N} \sum_{i=1}^{N} \frac{f(z_i)}{g(z_i)} \qquad \text{(I.B-15)}$$

and the corresponding standard error of this estimate is given by

$$\sum_{i=1}^{N} Stdev\left(\frac{f(z_i)}{g(z_i)}\right), \qquad \text{(I.B-16)}$$

where z_i is drawn from a probability-density function of g.

I.B.3.b Lattices

Unlike MC simulation, a lattice method is a powerful way to value certain derivatives that allow an early exercise before the maturity. The lattice model is intuitive and relatively simple to use. Moreover, it is useful in valuing both American- and European-style derivatives. The lattice method, however, can be difficult to apply in situations where the payoff depends on the past history as well as the current value; when the derivatives depend on multiple underlying assets, it can be computationally intensive. The binomial is the simplest lattice method. The trinomial adds an additional layer of complexity.

Binomial lattice simulations

The simplest lattice method is a binomial tree or lattice, which uses the construction of different possible paths of a stock price over time to price a derivative. A stock price is assumed to move only up or down with intensities u and d, respectively, within the time period of length Δt.

One-step binomial tree

A one-step binomial tree can be illustrated by movements of a plain vanilla call option on a non-dividend-paying stock with only two possible outcomes for the stock price over the interval of time, Δt. The stock prices in the time interval Δt are either $S_0 u$ or $S_0 d$, where S_0 is an initial stock price, $u > 1$, and $d < 1$. The corresponding payoff of the call option when a stock price moves up to $S_0 u$ is denoted by $C_u = \max(S_0 u - K, 0)$, and the payoff of the call option in the downward movement of the stock price is denoted by $C_d = \max(S_0 d - K, 0)$. K denotes a strike price. Figure I.B-1 illustrates the call-option price with the movement of the stock price in the short time interval of length Δt.

■ **Figure I.B-1**

Call-option price with a non-dividend-paying stock price movement in the time interval under a one-step binomial lattice model.

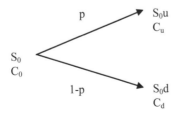

Under the risk-neutral valuation, all the assets are assumed to earn the risk-free rate of interest, and the current stock price is assumed to equal the expected value of the stock price discounted at the risk-free rate. In the risk-neutral, binomial tree world, the approach to valuing the option price is to determine the probabilities of up and down movement in the stock price that sets the discounted expected value of the stock equal to the current stock price.

Let us denote the probability of an upward movement in the stock price in a risk-neutral world by p, and a risk-free rate by r. Hence, the stock price at time 0 in the risk-neutral world is given by

$$S_0 = e^{-r\Delta t}[pS_0u + (1-p)S_0d]$$

(I.B-17)

Solving Equation I.B-17 for p, we obtain the following condition for p:

$$p = \frac{e^{r\Delta t} - d}{u - d}$$

(I.B-18)

This can imply the corresponding u and d, given by

$$u = e^{\sigma\sqrt{\Delta t}}, \quad \text{and} \quad d = u^{-1}$$

(I.B-19)

where σ is a volatility of the stock. Thus, the payoff of the call option at time 0 is

$$C_0 = e^{-r\Delta t}[pC_u + (1-p)C_d]$$

(I.B-20)

Multi-step binomial trees

A multi-step binominal tree typically involves a large number of time steps that are used to value the price of a derivative. This approach can be illustrated by extending the previous example of a one-step binomial tree to a large number of time steps, Δt, which are intended to reflect the movement of the option. A stock price at time $m\Delta t$ is given by

A multi-step binominal tree typically involves a large number of time steps that are used to value the price of a derivative.

$$S_m = S_0u^nd^{m-n}, \qquad m = 0, 1, \ldots, n$$

(I.B-21)

where u and d still satisfy the relationship in Equation I.B-19.

Hence, the call-option price is evaluated moving backward from the end of the tree, time T, the point at which the price of T is known. The complete multi-step binomial tree is illustrated in Figure I.B-2.

■ Figure I.B-2

Call-option price with a non-dividend-paying stock price movement in the time interval under a multi-step binomial lattice model.

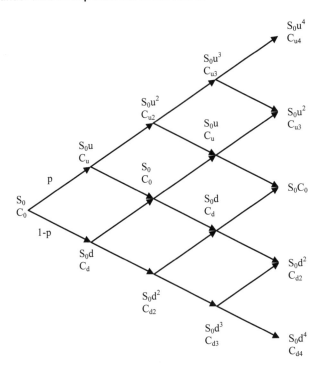

For a dividend-paying stock, let us assume that there is a single dividend and the dividend yield is defined as a percentage of the stock price. If η denotes a dividend yield, then the ex-dividend stock price at each time step is given by

$$S_m = S_0(1-\eta)\, u^n d^{m-n}, \qquad m = 0, 1, \ldots, n \qquad \text{(I.B-22)}$$

Figure 3 shows the complete binomial tree of a stock paying a dividend at a dividend yield when the dividend is paid between Time 1 and 2.

Figure I.B-3

Call-option price with a dividend-paying stock price movement in the time interval under a multi-step binomial lattice model.

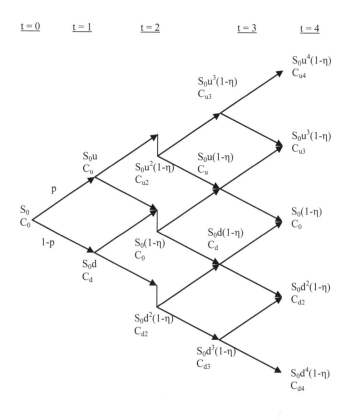

Trinomial lattice simulation

The trinomial lattice is an alternative model to the binomial lattice model. In a trinomial tree model, it is assumed that the movement of a stock price has three possible outcomes such as down, middle, and up. Let us denote probabilities of down, middle, and up by p_-, p_0, and p_+, respectively. Figure I.B-4 illustrates a single-step trinomial lattice model for a non-dividend-paying stock.

The trinomial lattice is an alternative model to the binomial lattice model. In a trinomial tree model, it is assumed that the movement of a stock price has three possible outcomes such as down, middle, and up.

Figure I.B-4

A non-dividend-paying stock price movement in the time interval under a one-step trinomial lattice model.

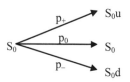

Under the risk-neutral valuation, the probabilities and parameters satisfy the following relationships:

$$p_- = -\sqrt{\frac{\Delta t}{12\sigma^2}}\left(r - \frac{1}{2}\sigma^2\right) + \frac{1}{6}, \quad p_0 = \frac{2}{3}, \quad \text{and} \quad p_+ = -p_- + 2/6,$$

(I.B-23)

$$u = e^{\sigma\sqrt{3\Delta t}}, \quad \text{and} \quad d = u^{-1}.$$

I.B.3.c Regime-switching Models

In the traditional models of stock returns, it is common to assume a geometric Brownian motion in which a stock return is lognormally distributed and the returns over any discrete time interval are independent, providing there is no overlapping period. A log of stock returns over the period $[r, t]$ follows normal distribution as shown below:

$$\log\left(\frac{S_t}{S_r}\right) \sim N\left(\mu(t-r), \sigma^2(t-r)\right)$$

(I.B-24)

for a mean μ and volatility σ, both of which are constant.

This model is called independent lognormal (ILN), or simply, lognormal. Because ILN is simple and reasonably fits to short-term intervals, it is widely used in the area of finance. The Black-Scholes formula, a standard option-pricing model, is a typical example. However, empirical studies indicate that ILN sometimes fails to capture extreme price movement and the fluctuation of volatility. This is mainly due to the fact that ILN assumes constant volatility. Also, actual movement of stock return has some autocorrelation, which ILN does not assume.

While several time-series models have been developed to capture volatility fluctuation, one of the simple ways is to assume that volatility takes K discrete values and randomly switches among them. This is called a regime-switching model. When ILN is assumed in each regime, the model is called regime-switching lognormal (RSLN). The RSLN model captures price movement more accurately than ILN, while maintaining the simplicity of the ILN model. The probability of changing regime depends only on the current regime and not on the history of a process. This feature is called Markov process.

In particular, when the number of regimes $K=2$, the interpretation of RSLN is that the market switches randomly between two states, or regimes. One is a stable, low-volatility regime representing good economic condition, and the other is a bad economy under which volatility is higher.

The regime-switching model was first introduced in the area of econometrics to explain the movement of an economic cycle by modeling GDP growth rate; several regime-switching models were tested with a varying number of regimes (Hamilton 1989; Hamilton and Susmel 1994). In the area of life insurance, Hardy (1999, 2001) applied the idea of regime switching to evaluate the minimum guarantee risk of segregated funds in Canada.

While several time-series models have been developed to capture volatility fluctuation, one of the simple ways is to assume that volatility takes *K* discrete values and randomly switches among them. This is called a regime-switching model.

Following Hardy's great work, here is an abstract of RSLN and an explanation of its parameter estimation.

In a general form of RSLN with K regimes, let μ_i denote the mean and $\sigma^2 i$ the variance in regime i, respectively. In a discrete time series (e.g., monthly), let $\rho(t)$ be an integer between 1 and K and represent the regime applying in the interval $(t, t+1)$. Then RSLN follows the process:

$$\log\left(\frac{S_{t+1}}{S_t}\right)\bigg| \rho(t) \sim N\left(\mu_{\rho(t)}, \sigma^2{}_{\rho(t)}\right) \tag{I.B-25}$$

where $|\rho(t)$ means the condition of current regime.

The transition matrix $P = (p_{ij})$ denotes the probability of moving regimes.

$$p_{ij} = \Pr\left(\rho(y+1) = j \big| \rho(t) = i\right), \; i = 1, 2, ..., K, \quad j = 1, 2, ..., K \tag{I.B-26}$$

In the case of two regimes, there are six parameters:

μ_1 : mean parameter for regime 1

μ_2 : mean parameter for regime 2

σ_1 : standard deviation parameter for regime 1

σ_2 : standard deviation parameter for regime 2

p_{12} : transition probability from regime 1 to regime 2

p_{21} : transition probability from regime 2 to regime 1

In particular, when the number of regimes K=2, the interpretation of Regime Switching Lognormal is that the market switches randomly between two states, or regimes. One is a stable, low-volatility regime representing good economic condition, and the other is a bad economy under which volatility is higher.

Figure I.B-5 illustrates the process of generating scenarios of a two-regime RSLN model. Here, ε_t is a random number that follows standard normal distribution.

▌ Figure I.B-5

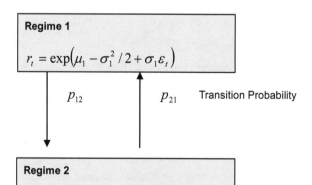

One of the techniques to estimate the parameters of RSLN is to maximize the likelihood function. Given the observations of returns $y = (y_1, y_2, \ldots, y_n)$, the likelihood for the set of parameters $\Theta = \{\mu_1, \mu_2, \sigma_1, \sigma_2, p_{12}, p_{21}\}$ is defined as

$$L(\Theta) = f(y_1 | \Theta) f(y_2 | \Theta, y_1) f(y_3 | \Theta, y_1, y_2) \cdots f(y_n | \Theta, y_1, y_2, \cdots, y_{n-1}) \qquad \text{(I.B-27)}$$

where f is the probability density function for the distribution y.

$f(y_t | \Theta, y_1, y_2, \cdots, y_{t-1})$, a contribution of one of the observations y_t, is the sum of four possible values:

$$f(\rho(t), \rho(t-1), y_t | \Theta, y_1, y_2, \cdots, y_{t-1}) \ \text{for} \ \rho(t) = 1, 2 \ \text{and} \ \rho(t-1) = 1, 2 \qquad \text{(I.B-28)}$$

Each $f(\rho(t), \rho(t-1), y_t | \Theta, y_1, y_2, \cdots, y_{t-1})$ is written as the product of three components:

    1) probability of being regime ρ $(t-1)$ (invariant probability)

$$\pi_{i,t-1} \equiv p(\rho(t-1) = i | \Theta, y_1, y_2, \cdots, y_{t-1}) \qquad \text{(I.B-29)}$$

    2) transition probability from ρ $(t-1)$ to ρ (t)

$$p_{ij} \equiv p(\rho(t) = j | \rho(t-1) = i, \Theta) \qquad \text{(I.B-30)}$$

    3) standard normal distribution of y

$$g_{j,t} = f(y_t | \rho(t) = j, \Theta) = \Phi((y_t - \mu_j)/\sigma_j) = \frac{1}{\sigma_j \sqrt{2\pi}} \exp\left(-\frac{1}{2}\left(\frac{y_t - \mu_j}{\sigma_j}\right)^2\right) \qquad \text{(I.B-31)}$$

That is,

$$f(y_t | \Theta, y_1, y_2, \cdots, y_{t-1}) = \sum_{j=1}^{2} \sum_{i=1}^{2} \pi_{i,t-1} \times p_{ij} \times g_{j,t}$$

$$\pi_{i,t} \equiv p(\rho(t) = i | \Theta, y_1, y_2, \cdots, y_t)$$

can be calculated recursively by the following equation:

$$\pi_{i,t} = \sum_{k=1}^{2} f\left(\rho(t-1) = k \middle| \Theta, y_1, y_2, \cdots, y_t\right) \times p_{ki}$$

$$= \frac{\displaystyle\sum_{k=1}^{2} f\left(\rho(t-1) = k, y_t \middle| \Theta, y_1, y_2, \cdots, y_{t-1}\right) \times p_{ki}}{f\left(y_t \middle| \Theta, y_1, y_2, \cdots, y_{t-1}\right)} \tag{I.B-32}$$

$$= \frac{\displaystyle\sum_{k=1}^{2} \pi_{k,t-1} \times p_{ki} \times g_{i,t}}{\displaystyle\sum_{j=1}^{2}\sum_{i=1}^{2} \pi_{i,t-1} \times p_{ij} \times g_{j,t}}$$

In order to complete the calculation, we need to determine the initial regime. $\pi = (\pi_{1,0}, \pi_{2,0})$ is calculated as the stationary probabilities:

$$\pi_{1,0} = \frac{p_{21}}{p_{12} + p_{21}}, \pi_{2,0} = \frac{p_{12}}{p_{12} + p_{21}} \tag{I.B-33}$$

Therefore, the first recursion for a given parameter set $\Theta = \{\mu_1, \mu_2, \sigma_1, \sigma_2, p_{12}, p_{21}\}$ is,

$$f(y_1 | \Theta) = f(\rho(0) = 1, y_1 | \Theta) + f(\rho(0) = 2, y_1 | \Theta)$$
$$= \pi_{1,0} \Phi\left(\frac{y_1 - \mu_1}{\sigma_1}\right) + \pi_{2,0} \Phi\left(\frac{y_1 - \mu_2}{\sigma_2}\right) \tag{I.B-34}$$

In maximizing $L(\Theta)$, standard search method is used by changing the six variables $\Theta = \{\mu_1, \mu_2, \sigma_1, \sigma_2, p_{12}, p_{21}\}$ with appropriate constraints. The Society of Actuaries provides an Excel tool originally created by Mary Hardy to estimate the parameters.

Hardy (2001) compared RSLN with other models such as ILN, autoregressive conditional heteroskedasticity (ARCH), and generalized ARCH (GARCH) by using the monthly historical data of the Toronto Stock Exchange (TSE300) from 1956 to 1999. Figure I.B-6 shows a summary of the estimated parameters of two-regime RSLN. The estimated parameters of ILN with the same data are $\mu = 9.8\%$ and $\sigma = 15.6\%$.

▌ Figure I.B-6

	Mean (Annualized)	Volatility (Annualized)	Transition Probability	Invariant Probability
Regime 1	$\mu_1 = 14.8\%$	$\sigma_1 = 12.0\%$	$p_{12} = 3.7\%$	$\pi_1 = 84.9\%$
Regime 2	$\mu_2 = -18.9\%$	$\sigma_2 = 26.9\%$	$p_{21} = 21.1\%$	$\pi_2 = 15.1\%$

As expected, Regime 1 (a good economy) has a higher mean and lower volatility than Regime 2. Invariant probability shows that the economy in Regime 1 was at the probability of 84.9%. The chart in Figure I.B-7 shows the probability of being Regime 1 in each year.

▌ Figure I.B-7

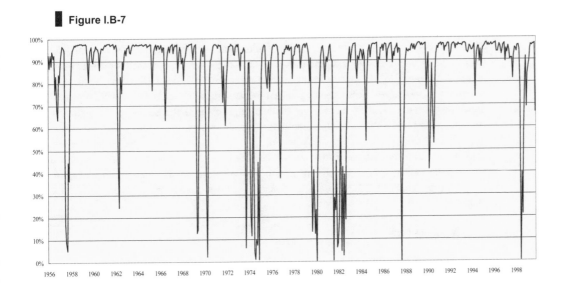

Hardy (2001) compared major statistics of fitness such as Bayesian information criterion (BIC) and Akaike information criterion (AIC) with other models, and found that for the historical data of TSE300 from 1956 to 1999, RSLN with two regimes (RSLN-2) provides the best fit to the data (see Figure I.B-8).

▌ Figure I.B-8

Model	Parameters	Log Likelihood	BIC	AIC
ILN	2	885.6	879.4	883.6
GARCH	4	896.0	883.5	892.0
RSLN-2	6	922.7	**903.9**	**917.7**
RSLN-3	8	925.9	888.3	913.9

The RSLN model is widely used, especially in North America in the area of liability valuation and capital requirement. For example, the Canadian Institute of Actuaries (2002) used it together with other models in determining the calibration criteria of the scenarios to evaluate the minimum guarantee risk of segregated funds (variable products). RSLN is also used in the pricing of products when the tail risk of stock and other assets significantly affects the profitability.

The Regime Switching Lognormal model is widely used, especially in North America in the area of liability valuation and capital requirement.

To generate the scenario of RSLN:

1) Determine the first regime by generating a random number following uniform distribution over the interval [0,1]. If the random number is smaller than the invariant probability of the first regime, then the first regime is 1. Otherwise, the first regime is 2.

2) Generate lognormal returns in the current regime. This requires the generation of a random number following standard normal distribution.

3) Generate a random number following uniform distribution to determine whether the regime is switched or not.

Then steps 2 and 3 are repeated.

While RSLN is a convenient model to capture the tail behaviour of stock returns, several difficulties exist when using it. Depending on the initial numbers of the search process, parameter estimation may not converge to the unique solution. In some cases, the search process ends at a local maximum. In this regard, it is important to test multiple initial numbers. In addition to a maximum likelihood estimate, there are more robust techniques, such as Gibb's sampling. Interested readers can refer to Kim and Nelson (1999) for more detailed information.

Also, some historical data can show odd results. For example, the Institute of Actuaries of Japan (2003) tested the fitness of various models to the Japanese equity index (TOPIX). Figure I.B-9 shows the summary of RSLN parameters based on the historical data between April 1953 and March 2003.

■ Figure I.B-9

	Mean (Annualized)	Volatility (Annualized)	Transition Probability	Invariant Probability
Regime 1	$\mu_1 = 16.3\%$	$\sigma_1 = 9.7\%$	$p_{12} = 6.5\%$	$\pi_1 = 33.9\%$
Regime 2	$\mu_2 = 1.2\%$	$\sigma_2 = 20.4\%$	$p_{21} = 3.3\%$	$\pi_2 = 66.1\%$

Regime 1 shows a higher mean and lower volatility than Regime 2 as expected, but the invariant probability of Regime 1 is lower than that of Regime 2. This may be due to the long-standing recession that followed the collapse of Japan's so-called bubble economy in 1989. Also, if only the historical data between April 1983 and March 2003 are used, different initial values lead to different parameters with almost the same likelihood.

I.B.4 Nested Stochastic Projections

Nested stochastic projections, also referred to as "stochastic on stochastic" projections, are an increasingly important consideration in developing actuarial models to meet the needs of the insurance industry. Such projections introduce the notion of probability into a result for future time periods.

In an insurance model, stochastic projections are derived from values projected over time using a set of randomly generated economic scenarios. The purpose is to measure the sensitivity of key model results relative to the economic variation introduced by the randomly generated scenarios. This information cannot be obtained when a variable is projected along any one of the random scenarios. In such cases, the development of the future economic environment is based on a single deterministic scenario. For a stochastically derived variable, this information is insufficient. We require an additional set of randomly generated economic paths in order to re-determine its value. The purpose of the nested stochastic projection is to generate this additional information.

Nested stochastic projections, also referred to as "stochastic on stochastic" projections, are an increasingly important consideration in developing actuarial models to meet the needs of the insurance industry.

One might regard a nested stochastic projection as a way to introduce another layer of economic scenario dimensionality to the stochastic projection model. Within each stochastic "outer scenario," one or more sets of nested "inner paths" is embedded. Each path is a newly generated economic outlook extending forward from a select time point in the projection, continuing the pre-path economic outlook modeled via a particular scenario. We define the point in time at which the inner paths begin as a "node." Note that the assumptions or methodology underlying random generation of the nested path may not necessarily be the same as that used to generate each outer scenario. We use the expressions "outer scenario" and "inner path" to indicate their relationship in the overall projection. The chart in Figure I.B-10 conceptualizes the structure of a nested stochastic projection.

■ **Figure I.B-10**

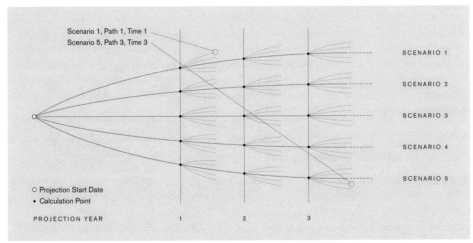

Excerpted from "The Future of Capital Modeling," by Pat Renzi, Milliman Insight, Issue 2, 2006.

In most nested stochastic projections, the inner paths are only generated when a stochastically determined variable is needed for interim projection results. In other words, once the results of the nested paths at a given point of time are computed, only a single result (i.e., a liability, capital requirement, fair value, option cost, etc.) is retained. The result obtained satisfies a key result determined at the time the inner paths began projecting forward. Once obtained, the projection resets and then continues forward along the original outer scenario until such time as a new set of generated nested paths is required.

Nested stochastic solutions to practical applications

Such an approach might be required in simulating dynamic hedge performance for a variable annuity product with underlying guarantees. Such guarantees are designed to assure a policyholder of a sufficient benefit payment, regardless of account value performance on the premium deposits. In such a case, the fund returns and interest rates driving the fixed and variable account balances of the policy might be generated with a set of real-world outer-scenario assumptions calibrated to recent historical fund performance. In this manner the future exposure of the company to the risk behind these guarantees is estimated.

For variable annuity (VA) products with underlying guarantees, it may be desirable for a company to establish a hedge to offset cash flows associated with the underlying guarantees. In order to

In particular, when the number of regimes K=2, the interpretation of Regime Switching Lognormal is that the market switches randomly between two states, or regimes. One is a stable, low-volatility regime representing good economic condition, and the other is a bad economy under which volatility is higher.

simulate the performance of such hedges, the fair-market value of liabilities under market-consistent risk-neutral inner paths must be determined at selected periods. Various shocks to individual components of the inner-path economic assumption set may also be introduced in order to determine the inherent values for Delta, Rho, Vega, and other "Greeks." The purpose of incorporating such Greeks into the construction of the hedge instrument is to optimize hedge effectiveness. By improving hedge effectiveness, the cash flows of the hedge instrument are more finely tuned to offset the guaranteed cash flows under a larger set of economic conditions. For each outer scenario projected in the proposed model, the Greeks and hedge positions must be re-determined at regular intervals. The simulated asset allocation for the appropriate hedge is based on the unique risk profile of the underlying guarantee at that time.

Therefore, when a hedge position is required for a particular outer scenario's projected result, the state of the model at that time is saved into memory. Future cash flows associated with the guarantee are then projected along shocked and non-shocked sets of stochastic risk-neutral paths. Greeks are produced by discounting these cash flows back along each path and averaging the results across each set of paths. The hedge position is finally estimated from the resulting Greeks and saved into memory. The model is then allowed to proceed back along the outer scenario, and it continues until the next hedge position calculation is required, at which time the nested stochastic process is repeated.

Nested stochastic modeling and the principles-based approach

The example described above is only one case in which nested stochastic projections are required for a real-world application. Developments in the insurance industry are creating the demand for integrated nested stochastic models that can meet the day-to-day requirements of even the smallest insurance operation. In the United States, for instance, a principles-based approach to liability and capital requirements is driving change, especially in life insurance companies because of the longer-term risk exposure involved in their products.

U.S. life insurance regulators have stipulated minimum capital requirements for most insurance companies as a formulated set of risk-based capital (RBC) elements. Over time, some elements of the RBC measure have adopted stochastic testing requirements to a limited number of interest rate sensitive product types (generally annuities and universal life products). These stochastic requirements have been adopted in phases over time, beginning with C-3 Phase I (relating to interest rate risk), C-3 Phase II (relating to market risk tied to underlying product guarantees in variable products), and ultimately C-3 Phase III (applicable to a majority of life insurance products). This principles-based approach to capital determination seeks to tie all the procedures together into a single method and form.

In a similar manner, U.S. life insurance liabilities have traditionally been formula-driven, but with the adoption of the Variable Annuity Commissioners' Annuity Reserve Valuation Method (VACARVM) for variable annuity products, the U.S. life insurance industry has witnessed the advent of stochastically determined liability requirements. The principles-based approach will ultimately include a methodology for stochastic liability determination for all life insurance products in the marketplace.

Although none of the new evaluation methods explicitly require nested stochastic projection when reporting minimum requirements at select valuation dates, there are many occasions when nested

Developments in the insurance industry are creating the demand for integrated nested stochastic models that can meet the day-to-day requirements of even the smallest insurance operation.

stochastic projections become vital in the performance of future projections subject to the principles-based approach:

- **When pricing new products**
- **When developing pro forma statements for planning purposes**
- **In the performance of capital budgeting for one or more product lines**
- **When conducting an actuarial appraisal of business value**
- **In the process of analyzing or pricing a reinsurance agreement**
- **Or, more generally, in any case where it is necessary to determine the required liability and/or capital amounts in one or more future projection periods**

Nested stochastic modeling and other international accounting standards

Similar to the principles-based approach, a stochastic valuation and reporting methodology will apply or has already applied to other financial reporting standards in other parts of the world.

In Europe, the convergence of financial reporting standards and the desire to better reflect insurance risk has led to the introduction of the Solvency II regulation. This proposal applies a stochastic approach to solvency testing and capital determination. Companies determining future capital needs that are subject to this regulation will need to employ nested stochastic modeling in much the same way United States companies need to employ the principles-based approach.

European Embedded Value (EEV) is another standardized reporting method being developed in Europe. It is expected to be performed on either a real-world or market-consistent (risk-neutral) basis using stochastic scenarios. Pro forma statements of embedded value may very well be developed by nested stochastic calculations.

As of March 2006, the Financial Services Agency of Japan requires domestic insurance companies to establish stochastically tested liabilities to measure the risk on variable annuity products with underlying minimum guarantees. This process is performed using assumptions specified by the agency for expected returns and volatilities that are not necessarily tied to expected market returns. Given a sophisticated pricing model incorporating various scenarios, a nested stochastic process (either deterministically defined or stochastically projected according to company expectations of market behaviour) may be used to re-project the Financial Services Agency's stochastic paths to determine future liability requirements along each scenario.

Managing the nested stochastic modeling process

First, assume a normal stochastic projection using a reasonably sized model of 10,000 model points – a model point is a unique policy or modeled "cell" requiring specific assumptions in the projection. A typical stochastic liability or capital determination model should generally include, at a minimum, 1,000 outer scenarios. Also assume that a majority of the business in-force is expected to run off in 30 projection years, the established projection period. Using annual time steps in the projection, 300 million individually calculated cellular cycles are required to perform a complete analysis. A typical single-processor machine (circa 2008) might complete the total stochastic projection in a 24-hour period. But the same model with 1,000 nested stochastic inner paths across

A typical single-processor machine (circa 2008) might complete the total stochastic projection in a 24-hour period. But the same model with 1,000 nested stochastic inner paths across each future annual time step, and scenarios with each path extending another 30 years, would take another 8.7 trillion calculation cycles, thereby consuming machine time for another 79 years!

each future annual time step, and scenarios with each path extending another 30 years, would take another 8.7 trillion calculation cycles, thereby consuming machine time for another 79 years! Practically speaking, the above model is unnecessarily robust for most purposes. Clearly we need methods that complete the projection in a reasonable amount of time and that would not unduly distort the key results. Generally speaking, these approaches would use either brute force, finesse, or a combination of the two.

The brute-force approach is the simplest and most expedient, but it is an expensive luxury. As an alternative, the software industry offers solutions computed via distributed processing. Distributed processing is an algorithm utilizing the spare processing potential of multiple desktop machines linked together to a common server. Grid processing is yet another solution that involves a dedicated and expandable server consisting of many grid "engines" (with one engine equivalent to a single processor). Manufacturers have begun to recognize the need for increased computing power and now include multi-core processors in a single chip, essentially turning each desktop into its own grid server.

> **The brute-force approach is the simplest and most expedient, but it is an expensive luxury.**
>
> **The software industry offers solutions computed via distributed processing.**
>
> **The finesse approach is ultimately more effective, but requires considerable actuarial judgment and continuous vigilance.**

The finesse approach is ultimately more effective, but requires considerable actuarial judgment and continuous vigilance. Given the above example, we have four potential methods by which to attack the run-time problem.

Reducing the number of model points

There are many model reduction techniques employed by actuaries, ranging from simple issue age grouping to more sophisticated automatic cluster modeling. A seriatim projection processes each policy individually, an exercise that is both impractical and unnecessary in the stochastic requirement framework. Deferred annuities and traditional whole-life policies might be subject to high levels of compression without serious loss of result significance, while other plan types, such as structured settlements, are not as easily managed. Understanding the product features is, therefore, the first key step of the compression process; repeated testing of compression success (i.e., closeness of result fit between the seriatim and compressed model) is an ongoing process that must be managed with care.

Reducing the number of outer scenarios

While regulatory requirements typically stipulate the minimum number of scenarios to apply for liability valuation and capital determination purposes, the projection of future amounts is not subject to the same minimum, and we could choose a representative subset of scenarios when projecting values into the future. There are various techniques that have been developed in the financial engineering world to reduce scenarios in a scientific way, such as antithetic, control variate, and Brownian bridge. Reducing the number of outer scenarios via cluster modeling is still another possible solution. Cluster modeling is an algorithmic process that maps the results of various scenarios together under a set of conditions establishing the "closeness of fit."

Reducing the number of inner paths

Where inner-path results are determined at a CTE level greater than 0%, we might also pre-establish which paths generally fall below the percentile cut-off, and omit them in the re-projection from all nodes. For example, under proposed standards for VACARVM in the United States, only the scenarios driving the conditional tail expectation at the 70th percentile (CTE70) of the worst present value of capital results contribute to the stochastic result. Assuming that the bottom 30% of "worst case" paths driving valuation results will continue to drive the worst-case results in the future, we might exclude the projected nested stochastic paths that have no impact on the derived results (i.e., the remaining 70% of paths). We must use careful actuarial judgment when making such decisions, because the selected paths driving a CTE result for any particular projection scenario or node may not necessarily be the same.

Reducing the number of nodes

It is not always necessary to re-project inner paths at each and every time step in the model. In fact, the further out the node in the projection, the less credible the results may be. One reason is that, while the assumptions underlying the random economic generator are constant for each new set of future inner paths, these assumptions are, themselves, subject to change from fluctuations in the projected economic environment. Another solution for reducing run-time would, therefore, be to reduce the node durations to projection years 1-5, 10, 15, 20, and 30, and then interpolate the results established by each inner-path projection along each year projected in the outer scenario.

I.B.5 Deflators

Introduction

Previous sections have already discussed real-world and risk-neutral stochastic scenarios, the circumstances under which each is appropriate, and techniques for generating each type of stochastic scenario. Yet we have not fully explored the way in which these two stochastic scenarios are related to one another and the tools available for connecting or, more specifically, translating between risk-neutral and real-world scenarios. Deflators serve as this link.

Yet we have not fully explored the way in which these two stochastic scenarios are related to one another and the tools available for connecting or, more specifically, translating between risk-neutral and real-world scenarios. Deflators serve as this link.

Mathematical definition

As suggested above, a deflator is a stochastic discount factor through which a set of realistic scenarios may be filtered to produce a market-consistent valuation. The mathematical concept used in this conversion is discussed below.

In risk-neutral stochastic projection, the expected present value of future cash flows (Vo) is calculated as follows:

$$Vo = \sum \left(Ct,i * qi * (1+r)^\wedge(-t) \right)$$

(I.B-35)

where Ct,i is the cash flow at time t in scenario i, qi is the probability of scenario i under the risk-neutral probability measure (or Martingale), and r is the risk-free interest rate. Similarly, the expected present value of future cash flows in a real-world setting is calculated using the following formula:

$$Vo = \sum \left(Ct,i * pi * Dt,i \right)$$

(I.B-36)

where $C_{t,i}$ is the cash flow at time t in scenario i, p_i is the probability of scenario i under the real-world probability measure, and $D_{t,i}$ is the risk-adjusted discount factor or deflator. Equating the two expressions for V_0 above and performing some simple algebraic manipulation, we obtain the following (not necessarily unique) solution:

$$D_{t,i} = (q_i / p_i) * (1 + r)^\wedge(-t) \qquad\qquad\text{(I.B-37)}$$

By solving for the discount factor that equates the two expressions of V_0, we are explicitly finding a set of real-world interest rates that give the same, market-consistent valuation as the risk-neutral equation. In this way, deflators are little more than "back-in" numbers, which force the real-world scenarios to be consistent with the risk-neutral scenarios (and, therefore, with observed market conditions).

Properties

Deflators are scenario-specific. That is, the stochastic deflator function, $D_{t,i}$, is defined for each scenario, i. Unlike the risk-free rate used for risk-neutral valuation, the stochastic deflator need not be (and, in fact, usually is not) the same for each scenario. In fact, separate stochastic deflators are associated with each real-world scenario.

It is important to keep in mind which assumptions in a model represent reality (or, at least, an expectation of future reality) and which assumptions are theoretical constructs with no real basis in reality. For example, risk-neutral valuations use the risk-neutral (or risk-free) interest rate based on observed market conditions, such as government bonds. The rate is based on reality, but the associated probability of the risk-free rate, known as the Martingale measure, is an artificial construct, which does not represent the real-world likelihood that a modeler would assign to any future state or event. Rather, the probability measure (the q_i in the formulas above) is forced, so that the model produces the correct market-observed price for the calibrating instrument.

In a real-world valuation, however, the modeler is free to select a probability measure that is grounded in reality, meaning the p_i should reflect the modeler's true expectations regarding future states or outcomes. But it is clear from our mathematical development that the $D_{t,i}$ are completely determined by the other variables: the risk-free rate, the Martingale measure, and the real-world probability measure.

These concepts are further explored in the example that concludes this section.

Applications

Deflators can be used whenever a market-consistent valuation is desired. Although it is commonly believed that only risk-neutral valuations are market-consistent, this is not the case. As noted previously, deflators are the stochastic interest rates, which, along with a set of real-world probabilities, replicate observed market prices. In other words, deflators make real-world valuations market-consistent.

Deflators are scenario-specific.

Market-consistent valuations are becoming increasingly important in the insurance industry. Common applications of market-consistent valuation (and, therefore, potentially deflators) in the insurance industry include:

- **The hedging of insurance liabilities such as embedded options/guarantees in variable annuity or variable universal life products**

- **Performing mark-to market valuation of insurance options and guarantees**

- **Complying with insurance industry regulations that require market-consistent valuations, such as:**

    □ International Financial Reporting Standards (IFRS)

    □ UK Peak-2 and ICA

    □ Swiss Solvency Test

    □ EEV, which is increasingly interpreted as Market-consistent Embedded Value (MCEV)

The examples above are a small subset of the potential uses of deflators. In general, deflators can be used anytime a market-consistent valuation is desired.

Practical considerations

Although deflators are an attractive option because they can be used in concert with a real-world probability measure, the potential user should consider the following:

- **Deflators tend to be numerically unstable as the growth rate and risk-free rate are simulated simultaneously.**

- **Deflators tend to require more simulations for convergence than risk-neutral valuation.**

- **Deflators require additional sophistication of the economic scenario generator because of:**

    □ The need to find a different set of deflators for each real-world parameterization

    □ The need to find a different set of deflators for each asset modeled

    □ The need to explore further complications for items, such as stochastic volatility

- **Deflators tend to be less transparent than risk-free rates.**

- **Because of incomplete markets:**

    □ It is not possible to replicate the value of some assets

    □ There is often more than one possible risk-neutral measure

    □ Risk-neutral and deflator models can give different, arbitrage-free results

    □ For path-dependent options, further pricing differences can occur compared to risk-neutral valuations

> Deflators are the stochastic interest rates, which, along with a set of real-world probabilities, replicate observed market prices. In other words, deflators make real-world valuations market-consistent. Market-consistent valuations are becoming increasingly important in the insurance industry.

Illustrative example

Consider an asset that has the (undiscounted) values in various future states shown in Figure I.B-11.

■ **Figure I.B-11**

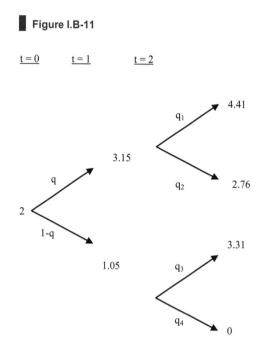

First we solve for the Martingale measure (or risk-neutral probabilities), assuming a risk-free rate, r, of 5.0%. In the tree above, q represents the risk-neutral probability of an up-move at $t = 0$; the q_i represent the risk-neutral probabilities of the indicated move at $t = 1$. To get the conditional probabilities at $t = 1$, given what occurred at $t = 0$, we need to divide the q_i by q or $1-q$, as appropriate. For example, q_1/q is the probability of an up-move to a security price of 4.41 given that we are currently at a security price of 3.15.

We can solve for q from the following:

$$3.15\left(\frac{1}{1+r}\right)q + 1.05\left(\frac{1}{1.05}\right)\left(1-q\right) = 2$$

$$q = \tfrac{1}{2}$$

and so

$$1\text{-}q = \tfrac{1}{2}$$

as well, because with probability = 1, we must either move up or down from the mode at $t = 0$.

Now we can solve for the risk-neutral probabilities at the $t = 1$ nodes. At the "up" node, we have the following equation:

$$4.41 \left(\frac{1}{1+r} \right)^2 \left(\frac{q_1}{q} \right) + 2.76 \left(\frac{1}{1.05} \right)^2 \left(\frac{q_2}{q} \right) = 3.15 \left(\frac{1}{1+r} \right)$$

And

$$q_1 + q_2 = q = \frac{1}{2}$$

Solving this system of equations yields:

$$q_1 = 1/6 \qquad \text{and} \qquad q_2 = 1/3$$

In a similar fashion, we can solve for q_3 and q_4, and find:

$$q_3 = 1/6 \qquad \text{and} \qquad q_4 = 1/3$$

At this point, we have completely parameterized the risk-neutral model. That is, we know the risk-free rates and the risk-neutral probabilities that apply to every scenario and every step within each scenario.

Now we explore how deflators can be used to produce a mathematically equivalent real-world model. We begin by setting the real-world probability measure, which is based on the modeler's expectations and is determined from first principles.

The real-world probabilities are illustrated on the tree in Figure I.B-12.

■ Figure I.B-12

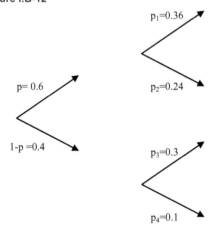

$p_1 = 0.36$

$p = 0.6$

$p_2 = 0.24$

$1-p = 0.4$

$p_3 = 0.3$

$p_4 = 0.1$

We can now see that we do, in fact, reproduce the market-observed price using the stochastic deflators we developed.

Using Equation I.B-37 we can calculate the stochastic deflator for each path:

$$D_2, up, up = \left(\frac{q_1}{p_1} \right) \left(\frac{1}{1+r} \right)^2 = 0.4199$$

$$D_2, up, up = \left(\frac{q_1}{p_1}\right)\left(\frac{1}{1+r}\right)^2 = 0.4199$$

$$D_2, up, down = \left(\frac{q_2}{p_2}\right)\left(\frac{1}{1+r}\right)^2 = 1.2598$$

$$D_2, down, up = \left(\frac{q_3}{p_3}\right)\left(\frac{1}{1+r}\right)^2 = 0.5039$$

$$D_2, down, down = \left(\frac{q_4}{p_4}\right)\left(\frac{1}{1+r}\right)^2 = 3.0234$$

Finally, we can check that the real-world model is market consistent.

The security price at $t = 0$ should be:

4.41 $(p_1)(D_2, up, up)$ + 2.76 $(p_2)(D_2, up, down)$

+3.31$(p_3)(D_2, down, up)$ + 0 $(p_4)(D_2, down, down)$

= 4.41(0.36)(0.4199) + 2.76(0.24)(1.2598) + 3.31(0.3)(0.5039)

= 2.00

We can now see that we do, in fact, reproduce the market-observed price using the stochastic deflators we developed.

I.B.5.a Copulas

Sklar's theorem allows for separating a multivariate joint distribution function into components: one representing the marginal distributions, and the other a copula that describes the multivariate dependency structure.

A copula[4] is a joint distribution function in which all of the marginal distributions are uniform on [0, 1]. It is highly useful in stochastic modeling because of Sklar's theorem, which holds that, given a joint distribution function $F_{X_1,...,X_n}(x_1,...,x_n)$, there exists a copula $C_{U_1,...,U_n}(u_1,...,u_n)$ such that

$$F_{X_1,...,X_n}(x_1,...,x_n) = C_{U_1,...,U_n}\left(F_{X_1}(x_1),...,F_{X_n}(x_n)\right).$$

Sklar's theorem allows for separating a multi-variate joint distribution function into components: one representing the marginal distributions, and the other a copula that describes the multivariate dependency structure. Furthermore, apart from regularity conditions, there are no restrictions on the form of the marginal distributions. This is convenient, because we often have considerable information on the marginal distributions (e.g., stock returns, interest rates, exchange rates, frequency distributions, and severity distributions), but only imperfect information on their dependency structure (perhaps only an approximate correlation matrix). If the joint distribution happens to be multivariate normal, then it is completely specified by the mean vector and variance-covariance matrix. In general, however, this is not true. There can be multiple joint distributions, each with the same correlation matrix and marginal distributions. The use of a copula, therefore, allows more control over the dependency structure, not only to specify the correlation, but also to specify precisely where the marginal distributions may be correlated.

---

[4] This section includes advanced statistical topics and requires a thorough knowledge of statistical concepts. This section may be skipped without loss of continuity.

Examples of copulas include:

Minimum copula: $C_{U_1,\ldots,U_n}(u_1,\ldots,u_n) = \max\{0, u_2 + \cdots + u_n - (n-1)\}$

Maximum copula: $C_{U_1,\ldots,U_n}(u_1,\ldots,u_n) = \min\{u_1,\ldots,u_n\}$.

Independent (product) copula: $C_{U_1,\ldots,U_n}(u_1,\ldots,u_n) = \prod_{i=1}^{n} u_i$

Normal (Gaussian) copula: $C_{U_1,\ldots,U_n}(u_1,\ldots,u_n) = \Phi_{X_1,\ldots,X_n}\left(\Phi_{X_1}^{-1}(u_1),\ldots,\Phi_{X_n}^{-1}(u_n)\right)$,

where Φ is the normal distribution function.

Archimedean family: $C_{U_1,\ldots,U_n}(u_1,\ldots,u_n) = \varphi^{-1}\left[\varphi(u_1),\ldots,\varphi(u_n)\right]$, where φ is called the "generator" function, and satisfies:

$$\varphi(1) = 0$$

$\varphi'(t) < 0, \forall t \in (0,1)$ i.e., φ is strictly decreasing; and

$\varphi''(t) \geq 0, \forall t \in (0,1)$ i.e., φ is convex

The minimum and maximum copulas are sometimes called the Fréchet-Hoeffding bounds.

Bivariate Archimedean copulas include:

Independent copula $\varphi(t) = -\ln t$, $C(u,v) = uv$

Gumbel copula: $\varphi(t) = (-\ln t)^{\theta}, \theta \geq 1, C(u,v) = e^{-\left[(-\ln u)^{\theta} + (-\ln v)^{\theta}\right]^{\frac{1}{\theta}}}$

Clayton copula: $\varphi(t) = t^{-\theta} - 1, \theta < 0, C(u,v) = e^{-\left[(-\ln u)^{\theta} + (-\ln v)^{\theta}\right]^{\frac{1}{\theta}}}$

Frank copula: $\varphi(t) = -\ln \dfrac{e^{-\theta t} - 1}{e^{-\theta} - 1}$, $C(u,v) = -\dfrac{1}{\theta}\ln\left(1 + \dfrac{(e^{-\theta u} - 1)(e^{-\theta v} - 1)}{e^{-\theta} - 1}\right)$

Remember that positive monotonic transformations of a random variable cannot change the random variable's rank, and that the proportion of concordant and discordant pairs depends only on a random variables rank.

Because of Sklar's theorem, we can evaluate a joint distribution with arbitrary marginal distributions simply by evaluating its copula with each of the uniforms u_i replaced by the marginal distributions evaluated at x_i. Any multivariate joint distribution will have the same Kendall's τ and Spearman's ρ as its associated copula.[5] This is generally not true with Pearson's correlation. Remember that positive monotonic transformations of a random variable cannot change the random variable's rank, and that the proportion of concordant and discordant pairs depends only on a random variables rank. Consequently, both Kendall's τ and Spearman's ρ are unaffected by positive monotonic transformations of a random variable. Since all valid marginal distribution functions are monotonic, this implies that all multivariate distributions and their associated copulas have the same Kendall's τ and Spearman's ρ. Given this property, Kendall's τ and Spearman's ρ are often considered more robust measures of correlation and are often preferred for evaluating the correlation of the distributions typically encountered in practice.

---

[5] Kendall's τ and Spearman's ρ are non-parametric measures of the strength of the relationship between two variables. For more details, see Kruskal (1958), pp. 814-861.

Fitting copulas

There are several methods available for fitting copulas. Since a copula is just a multivariate joint distribution, any of the methods used to fit a distribution to data can be used. Maximum likelihood is the most common. Before a copula can be fit, however, the best copula must be selected.

There are several methods available for fitting copulas. Since a copula is just a multivariate joint distribution, any of the methods used to fit a distribution to data can be used. Maximum likelihood is the most common.

One way to test which copula is the best is to fit a number of different copulas and compare the values of a penalized likelihood statistic, such as Akaike's information criterion (AIC) or the Bayesian information criterion (BIC). These comparisons will be only approximate, however, because the various copulas tested will not usually be nested models. Other alternatives are to compare the empirical and fitted copulas using statistics similar to Q-Q plots.

In deciding which copula to select, Venter (2003) recommends plotting tail concentration ratios. These can be evaluated both theoretically using a copula, and empirically using data. Comparing the theoretical to the empirical helps ascertain which copula fits best, particularly in the tails.

The upper-tail concentration ratio is defined as:

$$R(z) = \Pr(U > z | V > z) = \frac{\Pr(U > z, V > z)}{\Pr(V > z)} = \frac{\Pr(U > z, V > z)}{1 - z}, \text{ for } z \in (0,1) \quad \text{(I.B-38)}$$

In terms of the copula, we can evaluate

$$R(z) = \frac{1 - 2z + C(z,z)}{1 - z} \quad \text{(I.B-39)}$$

at the limit as $z \to 1$, $R(z) = R$, the upper-tail dependence parameter.

Similarly, the lower-tail concentration ratio is defined as

$$L(z) = \Pr(U < z | V < z) = \frac{\Pr(U < z, V < z)}{\Pr(V < z)} = \frac{\Pr(U < z, V < z)}{z}, \text{ for } z \in (0,1) \quad \text{(I.B-40)}$$

In terms of the copula, we can evaluate

$$L(z) = \frac{C(z,z)}{z} \quad \text{(I.B-41)}$$

at the limit as $z \to 0$, $L(z) = L$, the lower-tail dependence parameter.

Once a copula is selected, it can be fit. As mentioned above, maximum likelihood is the most common method. Both the parameters of the copula and the parameters of the marginal distributions can be estimated simultaneously.[6] Alternatively, one could first estimate the marginal distributions individually, then estimate the copula as a second step. Parametric or non-parametric estimators of the marginals can be used. It is usually difficult to calculate a closed-form solution to the likelihood equations, particularly in higher dimensions. Yet it is fairly straightforward to evaluate

---

[6]   See for example the R package "copula." Please see www.r-project.org for further detail and explanation.

the likelihood for individual points numerically, which is the reason numerical optimization is typically used.

We gave several examples of bivariate Archimedean copulas above. In the bivariate case, there is a simple relationship between the generator function of the bivariate Archimedean copula and Kendall's τ.

$$\tau = 1 + 4 \int_0^1 \frac{\varphi(t)}{\varphi'(t)} dt \qquad \text{(I.B-42)}$$

Independence: $\tau = 0$

Clayton: $\tau = \dfrac{\theta}{\theta - 2}$

Frank: $\tau = 1 - \dfrac{4}{\theta}\{D_1(-\theta) - 1\}$

where $D1$ is the Debye function $D_1(x) = \dfrac{1}{x} \int_0^x \dfrac{t}{e^t - 1} dt$ for positive x and

$D_1(x) = D_1(-x) - \dfrac{x}{2}$ for negative x.

Gumbel: $\tau = 1 - \theta^{-1}$

Because of the limitations on the parameter θ, as noted by Frees and Valdez (1998), it can be readily observed that Gumbel and Clayton only allow non-negative values of τ, whereas Frank allows both positive and negative values. One simple method for fitting these bivariate copulas is to calculate the traditional non-parametric estimator for τ and to invert the above formulas to solve for θ. Such a method can also be used to obtain starting values for numerical maximum likelihood returns.

While they do have extensions to the general multivariate case, Archimedean copulas often prove too restrictive because symmetry causes all pairs of variables to have the same dependency parameter θ.[7]

A disadvantage of the normal copula in many insurance and financial situations, however, is that both the upper- and lower-tail dependency parameter for the normal copula is zero.

The normal copula can be more flexible in this regard, because it allows specification of the correlation matrix as a parameter (in addition to the parameters associated with the marginals). A disadvantage of the normal copula in many insurance and financial situations, however, is that both the upper- and lower-tail dependency parameter for the normal copula is zero.

We can substitute the Student's t distribution for the normal distribution to obtain the Student's t copula with the addition of just one more parameter: degrees of freedom. With the Student's t copula, the lower the degrees of freedom, the higher the degree of dependency in the tails. With the Student's t copula, however, only one parameter controls the tail dependency among all pairs.

Other options that allow for more control include nesting Archimedean copulas.[8]

---

[7] In multivariate cases, this is often called the exchangeable Archimedean copula (EAC).
[8] See, for example, Cavu and Trede (2006).

Simulating from copulas

Many software products, such as R, S, or Matlab (and similar products), allow direct generation of correlated multivariate quantiles. Even without that type of software, it is often easy to simulate random draws from a multivariate joint distribution by first drawing n uniforms from the copula, then inverting each of the marginal distributions evaluated at the uniforms:

1. Randomly draw $u_1, ..., u_n$ from the inverse of the copula $C_{U_1,...,U_n}^{(-1)}\left(u_1,...,u_n\right)$.

2. Compute $x_1, ..., x_n$ as $F_{X_1}^{-1}(u_1), ..., F_{X_n}^{-1}(u_n)$.

A simple variation of this exists when all random variables are drawn simultaneously.[9]

1. Randomly draw k tuples $u_1, ..., u_n$ from the inverse of the copula $C_{U_1,...,U_n}^{(-1)}\left(u_1,...,u_n\right)$, and arrange as a $(k \times n)$ matrix U.

2. Randomly sample k values independently from each of the n marginal distributions, and arrange as a $(k \times n)$ matrix X.

3. Sort each column of X so the values have the same order as the corresponding column of U.

There are different ways of drawing the uniforms from the inverse of the copula based on the form of the copula. We illustrate one algorithm with the normal copula below:

1. Randomly draw a vector of n independent uniform $(0,1)$ quantiles, $u_1, ..., u_n$. Most software products provide an easy way to do this.

2. Transform these to independent normal $(0,1)$ quantiles by inverting the standard normal cumulative distribution function $z = z_1, ..., z_n = \Phi^{-1}(u_1), ..., \Phi^{-1}(u_n)$.

3. Transform these to correlated normal $(0,R)$ quantiles by left multiplying z by the Cholesky factorization of the desired correlation matrix $R : z' = Cz$. Note that many software products such as R, S, or Matlab allow you to directly generate correlated multivariate quantiles. If this is the case, you can just start here.

4. Transform the correlated normal $(0,R)$ quantiles to correlated uniform quantiles using the normal $(0,1)$ cumulative distribution function: $u' = u'_1, ..., u'_n = \Phi(z'_1), ..., \Phi(z'_n)$.

In order to obtain draws from the Student's t distribution with n degrees of freedom, you would divide each of the normal tuples z' in Step 3 by $(y/n)^{0.5}$, where y is drawn from a χ^2 distribution with n degrees of freedom, and evaluate the Student's t distribution in place of the normal distribution in Step 4.

Various methods also exist for the Archimedean copulas, depending upon the form of the copula. One method is to consider the generator function of an Archimedean copula that is itself the inverse of the Laplace transform of a common latent variable y. Following Frees and Valdez (1998), assume that $X_1, X_2, ..., X_p$ are conditionally given y, independent with marginal distributions $H_i(x)^y$. Then the multivariate distribution is given by the copula form with the generator being the inverse of

---

[9] This is similar to the Iman-Conover Method. For more information on this method, see Middlehall (2005).

the Laplace transform of the latent variable γ. The following algorithm can be used to generate random variables from this copula:

1. Generate the latent random variable γ having Laplace transform τ.

2. Independently of Step 1, generate U_1, U_2, ..., U_p independent random (0,1) random numbers.

3. For $k=1,...,p$, calculate $X_k = F_k^{-1}(U_{*k})$ where $U_{*k} = \tau\left(-\gamma^{-1}\ln U_k\right)$.

A method that works with any copula is the conditional distribution function method. Nelsen (2005) provides an algorithm using this method for bivariate Archimedean copulas:

1. Generate two independent uniform (0,1) variates u and t;

2. Set $w = \phi'^{(-1)}\left(\dfrac{\phi'(u)}{t}\right)$

3. Set $v = \phi^{(-1)}\left(\phi(w) - \phi(u)\right)$

The random variable v is based on the function $v = c_u^{(-1)}(t)$ for $c_u(t) = \dfrac{\partial C(u,v)}{\partial u} = P\left[V \leq v \mid U = u\right]$, i.e., the conditional distribution of v given $U = u$. This method is readily extendable to higher dimensions, provided the conditional distribution function is invertible.

References for Section I.B

Canadian Institute of Actuaries (2002). *2002 report from the CIA Task Force on segregated fund investments*. Canadian Institute of Actuaries.

Casualty Actuarial Society (CAS), Dynamic Risk Modeling Handbook Working Party. *Dynamic risk modeling handbook*.

Casualty Actuarial Society (CAS), Enterprise Risk Management Committee (May 2003). Overview of enterprise risk management." *CAS Forum*: 99-163. Retrieved September 8, 2009, from http://www.casact.org/pubs/forum/03sforum/03sf099.pdf.

Cavu, C. & Trede. M. (January 2006). Hierarchical Archimedean copulas. Retrieved September 8, 2009, from http://www.uni-konstanz.de/micfinma/conference/Files/Papers/Savu_Trede.pdf.

Coutts & Devitt (1989). The assessment of the financial strength of insurance companies - generalized cash flow model. *Financial Models of Insurance Solvency*, eds. Cummins, J.D. & Derrig, R.A. United Kingdom: Kluwer Academic Publishers.

Daykin, et al. (1989). The solvency of a general insurance company in terms of emerging costs. *Financial Models of Insurance Solvency*, eds. Cummins, J.D. & Derrig, R.A. United Kingdom: Kluwer Academic Publishers.

Daykin, Pentikainen, and Pesonen (1994). *Practical risk theory for actuaries*. Chapman & Hall.

Feller, William (1968) *An introduction to probability theory and its uses.* Volume 1, Third edition. New York: John Wiley & Sons.

Forrester, Jay W. (1961). *Industrial dynamics.* MIT Press.

Frees, E. W. & Valdez, E. A. (1998). Understanding relationships using copulas. *North American Actuarial Journal* Vol. 2: 1-25.

Hamilton, J.D. (1989). A new approach to the economic analysis of non-stationary time series. *Econometrica* 57: 357-84.

Hamilton, J.D. & Susmel, R. (1994). Autoregressive conditional heteroskedasticity and changes in regime. *Journal of Econometrics* 64: 307-33.

Hardy, M.R. (1999). Stock return models for segregated fund guarantees. Segregated Funds Symposium Proceedings, Canadian Institute of Actuaries.

Hardy, M.R. (2001). A regime-switching model of long-term stock returns. *North American Actuarial Journal* 5-2: 42-53.

Hardy, M.R. (2003). *Investment guarantees: Modeling and risk management for equity-linked life insurance.* John Wiley & Sons Inc.

Institute of Actuaries of Japan, Task Force on the Minimum Guarantee of Variable Annuities (2003). Report on the reserve for the minimum guarantee risk of variable annuities.

Kim, C.J. & Nelson, C. R. (1999). *State-space models with regime switching.* MIT Press.

Kruskal, W. (1958). Ordinal measures of association. *Journal of the American Statistical Association* 53.

Mildenhall, Stephen J. (Winter 2006). Correlation and aggregate loss distributions with an emphasis on the Iman-Conover Method. CAS Forum.

Nelsen, R., B. (2005). *Dependence modeling with Archimedean copulas.* Retrieved September 8, 2009, from http://www.lclark.edu/~mathsci/brazil2.pdf.

Pentikainen (1988). On the solvency of insurers. *Classical Insurance Solvency Theory,* eds. Cummins, J.D. & Derrig, R.A. Finland: Kluwer Academic Publishers: 1-49.

Venter, Gary G. (2003). *Fit to a t – estimation, application and limitations of the t-copula.* ASTIN Colloquium, Berlin. Retrieved September 8, 2009, from www.actuaries.org/ASTIN/Colloquia/Berlin/venter1.pdf.

Many of the tools presented in this section are powerful and flexible and have applications beyond those limited to the space of this book. As with any powerful tool, it is important to know when its use is appropriate and when it is not.

I.C   Distributions and Fitting

Books have been written on the subject of loss distributions and estimating parameters of stochastic models. A single section in a larger book, therefore, cannot do justice to such a multifaceted topic. But a brief discussion will serve our purposes for examining the potential of stochastic models.

Many of the tools presented in this section are powerful and flexible and have applications beyond those limited to the space of this book. As with any powerful tool, it is important to know when its use is appropriate and when it is not. To this end, we will provide some explicit assumptions for each of the tools discussed in this section. If the assumptions are valid, then the particular tool will be useful; if not, then it may lead to incorrect conclusions.

The flexibility of many of the tools discussed here also makes it impossible to address all their various applications. For this reason, derivations of the various formulas are provided to be used as a roadmap for cases the reader may encounter in the future. If not of immediate interest, these deviations can be skipped without sacrificing an understanding of the topics covered.

I.C.1 Stochastic Models

As simplifications of complex or partially understood processes, stochastic models attempt to capture particular key features of underlying uncertainty by means of making assumptions about the outcome distributions and certain characteristics of them. Because of these assumptions, the distribution of outcomes is influenced by at least three features:

- **Process uncertainty:** Even if a process is completely understood, its results might be subject to uncertainty because of random chance. For example, the rolling of a fair die is completely understood, but the outcome of any given roll cannot be determined before rolling.

- **Parameter uncertainty:** Stochastic models often depend on a limited number of key values, often termed parameters. Just as the event to be forecast must be estimated, the model's parameters often must also be estimated. Parameter uncertainty reflects the uncertainty inherent in the estimate of parameters, even when there is certainty that the particular statistical model being used is appropriate. In the die example, parameter uncertainty addresses the question of whether the die itself is fair and, if not, precisely what the likelihoods are of observing each side.

- **Model uncertainty:** To the extent that stochastic models are abstractions of a complex, sometimes poorly understood process, some models may be better at capturing the critical characteristics of the process than others. Unless the process itself is known, uncertainty arises regarding the model's ability to generate a representative distribution of the outcomes of concern. In the case of the die example, model uncertainty takes the form of whether the numbers of interest arise from the roll of a die (whether fair or not) or from some other phenomenon.

Any one of these three sources of uncertainty can cause distortions in the distribution of outcomes.

In this book, a stochastic model is viewed as a statement about the likelihoods of the various possible values for an item of interest, x. The likelihoods depend on the value of a parameter θ that does not depend on x. Both x and θ can be real numbers or vectors. Though this statement can be quite simple, for instance "x follows a Poisson model with expected value 5," it can also be quite complex and involve the use of multiple statistical models combined in sophisticated ways. Typically, stochastic models are most useful when we can express them in functional form. In such cases, the function is sometimes called the probability density function (pdf) and is written as in Equation I.C-1.

Even if a process is completely understood, its results might be subject to uncertainty because of random chance. For example, the rolling of a fair die is completely understood, but the outcome of any given roll cannot be determined before rolling.

$$\text{likelihood} = f\left(x|\theta\right) \qquad \text{(I.C-1)}$$

If x can take on only discrete values, then this function gives the probability of the value of x being a particular amount, and the function f is usually called the distribution function of x. If x can take on a range of real values, then the function f is often called the pdf of x, and for any subset S of the range of possible values of x, the probability that the value of x is in the subset is given by Equation I.C-2.

$$\Pr\left(X \in S|\theta\right) = \int_S f\left(x|\theta\right)dx \qquad \text{(I.C-2)}$$

It is important to stress that, in the context of this discussion, a stochastic model of a variable of interest x makes a statement about the likelihood of x depending on a parameter θ that does not depend on x.

Although not always recognized, a large portion of analysis related to life insurance and pensions already assumes a stochastic model as implied by the mortality table used in a particular calculation. In this case, a mortality table can be used to estimate the probability that an individual of a particular age will die in any given future year. This stochastic model can then be used to estimate various quantities, such as the present value today at 5% of $1 paid at the end of each year that the individual lives (for an annuity or pension), or the present value today at 5% of $1 paid to the individual's beneficiary on the death of that individual (for a life insurance policy). Here the parameter may not explicitly enter into the calculation of the stochastic model itself, but rather, the parameter may refer to which table in a library of mortality tables is being used.

A significant movement toward stochastic modeling of unpaid claims has also been made in non-life actuarial circles. Unpaid claim estimation methods, which have traditionally relied on aggregate historical data assembled in triangles, can be easily recast into a stochastic framework, if future expectations are defined not as deterministic statements, but rather as stochastic statements dependent on a number of key parameters.

An example of such a statement is "the payments for claims occurring in year i that are made j years after i will have an over-dispersed Poisson model with mean $\alpha_i \beta_j$ and variance proportional to $(\alpha_i \beta_j)^2$ with the constant of proportionality uniform for all cells." This statement highlights the point made earlier regarding the likelihood of a value of interest (payments in a particular cell), depending on parameters that do not depend on the value of interest. It seems reasonable, therefore, that models and techniques applicable to one problem may also be helpful in solving other problems.

These examples point out that the key in using stochastic models lies in estimating the parameter θ, which can be estimated using techniques discussed in this section.

I.C.2 Empirical vs. Model Distributions

If there is concern about the likelihood of an event, one obvious approach would be to record a number of observations of the phenomenon of interest, say n, and then see how often various values occur. A very simple way of answering the question of what the distribution of amounts looks like is to calculate the proportion of amounts that are no more than an amount x. The proportion at the smallest value is k_1/n, if there are k_1 instances of the smallest value. Similarly, the proportion at the second-smallest value is $(k_1 + k_2)/n$ if there are k_2 instances of the second-

---

Although not always recognized, a large portion of analysis related to life insurance and pensions already assumes a stochastic model as implied by the mortality table used in a particular calculation.

smallest value, and so forth. This construction gives us the empirical cumulative density function of the underlying phenomenon. It is clear that this is a step function that remains constant among members of the population. That is, $F(x_1) = F(x_2)$ if both x_1 and x_2 are between k_i and k_{i+1}.

If we have a complete enumeration of the phenomenon of interest, then this gives all possible information about the likelihood of various values; however, in practice, a complete enumeration will seldom be available. Rather, we often have only a sample of observations from an underlying process and are usually most interested in areas where observations are particularly sparse. For this reason we turn to models or simplifications of reality.

I.C.3 A Simple Approach – Matching of Moments

A number of stochastic models can be conveniently stated in a closed form and are dependent on a relatively small number of parameters. Klugman et al. (1998)[10] present a taxonomy of such models, often known as distributions. One such model defined using only non-negative integers is the Poisson, whose model is shown in Equation I.C-3.

$$f\left(x|\theta\right)=\frac{e^{-\theta}\theta^{x}}{x!} \tag{I.C-3}$$

It happens that the expected value of X, defined in Equation I.C-4 is simply θ.

$$E\left(X\right)=\sum_{x=0}^{\infty}x f\left(x|\theta\right) \tag{I.C-4}$$

We notice in this case that the model is completely described by only one parameter; thus, estimating the parameter, or "fitting" the model, boils down to estimating one value, which in this case happens to be equal to the mean or average value for the distribution. If we knew we had a sample of several items, x_1, x_2, ..., x_n, randomly drawn from the same Poisson model, then they should have the same expected value. It would therefore seem reasonable that their average would approximate the value of the unknown parameter θ.

This observation is the root of the approach called "matching of moments." The name is derived by the fact that the kth moment of a model is given by Equation I.C-5 for the model of a continuous variable, with the integral being replaced by the appropriate sum for discrete variables.

$$E\left(X^{k}\right)=\int x^{k}\,f\left(x|\theta\right)dx \tag{I.C-5}$$

Sometimes it is more convenient to talk about moments around the mean as defined in Equation I.C-6.

$$E\left(\left(X-E\left(X\right)\right)^{k}\right)=\int\left(x-E\left(X\right)\right)^{k}f\left(x|\theta\right)dx \tag{I.C-6}$$

We often have only a sample of observations from an underlying process and are usually most interested in areas where observations are particularly sparse. For this reason we turn to models or simplifications of reality.

---

[10] Klugman et al., 1998, Appendices A and B.

Again, if x is a discrete variable, then we replace the integral with a sum. If k is 2 in Equation I.C-6, we have the formula for the variance, a very common statistic that gives a sense of how "tightly" values are packed around the mean. Functions of higher moments exist that also give information about the shape of a model. Examples include the coefficient of skewness in Equation I.C-7 and the coefficient of kurtosis shown in Equation I.C-8.

$$\text{skewness} = \frac{E\left(\left(X-E(X)\right)^3\right)}{E\left(\left(X-E(X)\right)^2\right)^{\frac{3}{2}}} \tag{I.C-7}$$

$$\text{kurtosis} = \frac{E\left(\left(X-E(X)\right)^4\right)}{E\left(\left(X-E(X)\right)^2\right)^2} \tag{I.C-8}$$

Skewness gives a sense of whether a model is symmetric, and if not, which side would appear to have a longer "tail." Kurtosis gives a sense of how distinct a model's peak is.

As with the Poisson model, many of the more common models have expressions for their moments in terms of their parameters. Consider, for example, the normal (or sometimes called normal) model with pdf shown in Equation (I.C-9). It has two parameters, referred to here as using the customary μ and σ^2.

$$f\left(x\mid\mu,\sigma^2\right) = \frac{1}{\sqrt{2\pi\sigma^2}} e^{-\frac{(x-\mu)^2}{2\sigma^2}} \tag{I.C-9}$$

With this parameterization the mean and variance are equal to μ and σ^2 respectively. Because it has exactly two parameters, the normal model is often said to be completely determined by its mean and variance.

Customary parameterizations are not always this convenient. Consider the lognormal model, which is also a two-parameter model, but is defined only for *positive* real numbers, as opposed to the normal, which is defined for *all* real numbers. A random variable X has a lognormal model if and only if the random variable $ln(X)$ has a normal or normal model. A very common parameterization of the pdf for the lognormal model is given in Equation I.C-10.

$$f\left(x\mid\mu,\sigma^2\right) = \frac{1}{x\sqrt{2\pi\sigma^2}} e^{-\frac{(\ln(x)-\mu)^2}{2\sigma^2}} \tag{I.C-10}$$

The use of the parameter representations of μ and σ^2 is not accidental; they represent the parameters of the related normal model of $ln(X)$. In this case, the mean and variance of the lognormal, though able to be expressed solely in terms of the two parameters, have more complicated representations as shown in Equations I.C-11 and I.C-12.

$$E(X) = e^{\mu+\frac{1}{2}\sigma^2} \tag{I.C-11}$$

$$Var(X) = E\left((X - E(X))^2\right) = e^{2\mu + \sigma^2}\left(e^{\sigma^2} - 1\right) \qquad \text{(I.C-12)}$$

Given a random sample drawn from a model with more than one parameter, matching of moments entails the solving of a series of simultaneous equations, typically one for each parameter, matching the various moments of the sample with corresponding moments of the model.

Two examples, both based on an independent and random draw of the following amounts from the same model – 8, 10, 25, 3, 6, 9, and 5 – will illustrate this point. If we were to assume the model is normal, the sample mean and sample variance can be calculated using Equations I.C-5 and I.C-6, assuming, because all seven values are randomly picked, that $f(x|\theta) = 1/7$ for each of the seven sample values, and 0 otherwise. Since this is a discrete model, we would use sums instead of integrals in these formulas. The sample mean of these numbers is 9.4 and the sample variance is 45.4, which are our matching-of-moments estimates for the parameters of the normal model.

If we were to assume a lognormal model, however, with the parameterization given in Equation I.C-10, the problem becomes somewhat more complicated. From Equations I.C-11 and I.C-12 we see that the sample coefficient of variation, i.e., the ratio of the sample standard deviation (square root of the sample variance) to the sample mean, is a function of only one parameter. In particular we have the relationship shown in Equation I.C-13 for a lognormal model.

$$cv(X) \equiv \frac{\sqrt{Var(X)}}{E(X)}$$

$$= \frac{\sqrt{e^{2\mu + \sigma^2}\left(e^{\sigma^2} - 1\right)}}{e^{\mu + \frac{1}{2}\sigma^2}}$$

$$= \frac{e^{\mu + \frac{1}{2}\sigma^2}\sqrt{e^{\sigma^2} - 1}}{e^{\mu + \frac{1}{2}\sigma^2}} \qquad \text{(I.C-13)}$$

$$= \sqrt{e^{\sigma^2} - 1}$$

The cv of our sample is 0.71. We use this value to solve Equation I.C-13 for σ^2 and obtain an estimate of 0.41. We then note, from Equation I.C-11, that we have the relationship in Equation I.C-14.

$$\mu = \ln(E(X)) - \frac{1}{2}\sigma^2 \qquad \text{(I.C-14)}$$

Substituting the sample mean and our estimate for the parameter σ^2 into Equation I.C-14 gives an estimate of 2.038 for the parameter μ.

Thus, matching of moments does provide estimates of the parameters of a model, but provides no additional information of how close those estimates are to the true underlying parameters of the model.

Although it would seem this method might work in almost all situations, its limitations quickly become apparent in situations where the true underlying stochastic models are not well behaved.

In particular, there is no requirement that a stochastic model have finite moments. However, the moments calculated from a finite sample drawn from any stochastic model must, by their nature, be finite. It is thus impossible to derive any model with infinite moments using the method of matching of moments.

One such model that is frequently used for estimating the size of insurance claims is the two-parameter Pareto model, whose pdf is given by Equation I.C-15.

$$f_x(x|\theta,\alpha) = \frac{\alpha\theta^\alpha}{(x+\theta)^{\alpha+1}} \tag{I.C-15}$$

This happens to be a rather heavy-tailed model – that is, the chances for relatively large claims are noticeable. In fact, the kth moment of this model is not finite if $k \geq \alpha$. So if α is less than 1, the expected value is not finite, although the model is well-defined over all positive real values of x.

In this and other situations in which the data are limited, the concept of limited expected value is useful. In general, the limited expected value of a random variable X at limit l is defined to be the expected value of the smaller of X and M. A continuous real-valued random variable is given by Equation I.C-16 with sums replacing integrals for discrete variables.

$$\begin{aligned}E\left(X \wedge M|\theta\right) &= \int_{-\infty}^{M} x f\left(x|\theta\right) dx + M \int_{M}^{\infty} f\left(x|\theta\right) dx \\ &= \int_{-\infty}^{M} x f\left(x|\theta\right) dx + M\left(1 - F\left(M|\theta\right)\right)\end{aligned} \tag{I.C-16}$$

Here F represents the cumulative density function for the random variable X and is the probability that the value of X is less than or equal to M. Higher moments have similar representation, as given in Equation I.C-17.

$$\begin{aligned}E\left((X \wedge M)^k|\theta\right) &= \int_{-\infty}^{M} x^k f\left(x|\theta\right) dx + M^k \int_{M}^{\infty} f\left(x|\theta\right) dx \\ &= \int_{-\infty}^{M} x^k f\left(x|\theta\right) dx + M^k\left(1 - F\left(M|\theta\right)\right)\end{aligned} \tag{I.C-17}$$

Thus, even if one or more moments of the original model are infinite, these limited moments are finite, and the matching-of-moments method can be used to estimate parameters for the model. In the case of the two-parameter Pareto, Equations I.C-18 and I.C-19 give the various limited moments.

$$E\left(X \wedge M|\theta,\alpha\right) = \begin{cases} \dfrac{\theta}{\alpha-1}\left(1 - \left(\dfrac{\theta}{M+\theta}\right)^{\alpha-1}\right), & \text{if } \alpha \neq 1 \\[2ex] -\theta\ln\left(\dfrac{\theta}{M+\theta}\right), & \text{if } \alpha = 1 \end{cases} \tag{I.C-18}$$

$$E\left((X \wedge M)^k|\theta,\alpha\right) = \frac{\theta^k \Gamma(k+1)\Gamma(\alpha-k)}{\Gamma(\alpha)} F_B\left(\frac{M}{M+\theta}\Big|k+1,\alpha-k\right) + M^k\left(\frac{\theta}{M+\theta}\right)^\alpha \tag{I.C-19}$$

In this formulation, Γ represents the gamma function, sometimes called the generalized factorial, and F_B, the cumulative density function for the beta model.

Although the matching-of-moments method does not provide estimates about the likelihood that the model's true parameters are actually close to the model's estimated parameters, the parameter estimates themselves are often quite useful. In many cases the resulting estimates are the same as those from other, more sophisticated methods. In addition, they can be used as starting values for some numerical estimation methods.

I.C.4 A Richer Approach – Maximum Likelihood

Let us start with an observation in which we know a model and its parameters. In this case, we can assess the likelihood that a model will give rise to a certain value or set of values. In fact, the function $f(x|^{\theta})$ does precisely that job for a single observation x. If we have a number of independent observations from the same model, then the likelihood they will all appear is simply the product of the likelihoods that each will appear. This value – the likelihood – is written as shown in Equation I.C-20.

$$L\left(x_1, x_2, \ldots, x_n \middle| \theta\right) = \prod_{i=1}^{n} f\left(x_i \middle| \theta\right) \qquad \text{(I.C-20)}$$

A fixed sample from the model will then have different likelihoods for different allowable values of the parameter. The maximum likelihood estimator (MLE) is the value of the parameter for which the model has the highest chance of producing the values observed in the sample. The MLE has a number of very useful and very powerful properties under fairly weak regularity conditions on the model. If one assumes that the sample is actually drawn from the assumed model, then the MLE has the following three quite useful properties:

> The maximum likelihood estimator is the value of the parameter for which the model has the highest chance of producing the values observed in the sample. The maximum likelihood estimator has a number of very useful and very powerful properties under fairly weak regularity conditions on the model.

- **Asymptotically unbiased**

As the number of random observations n becomes large, the expected value of the MLE approaches the value of the parameter. Hence, for large values of n, the MLE can be expected to be close to the true parameter.

- **Asymptotically efficient**

As the number of random observations n becomes large, the average squared error of the MLE compared to the parameter nears the Cramér-Rao lower bound for that error, and thus, no other unbiased estimator has a lower average squared error. Hence, for large values of n, the MLE is at least as accurate (small average squared error) as any other unbiased estimator for the parameter.

- **Asymptotically normal**

As the number of random observations n becomes large, the model for the MLE will tend to be close to a normal model. Furthermore, the parameters of that normal model can be determined from the MLE and the observed sample. This last property is probably one of the most useful and powerful traits of the MLE. Consequently, the MLE can be used to provide not only an estimate of the parameter, but also a sense of how uncertain the estimate may be.

These properties hold not just for models with simple closed-form representations, such as the Poisson, normal, and lognormal examples above, but they also hold for complex models, such as the more general non-life estimation problems described in other parts of this book. This point is important enough to bear repeating – maximum likelihood is a powerful and robust method for estimating the parameters of complex statistical models as well as simpler models, *if one is willing to assume that the underlying data come from a specific stochastic model.*

For a more complete discussion of MLE, including examples for normal and lognormal models, censored and truncated data, loss forecast models, evaluation of models, exponential fit and generalized linear models, mixed models, and Bayesian models, see Appendix 1.

References for Section I.C

Klugman, S.A, Panjer, H.H., & Willmot, G.E. (1998). *Loss models: From data to decisions*, First Edition. Wiley.

I.D   Random Number Generation

Most dictionaries define the word "simulation" with an implied sense of negativity. For example:

> Simulate: to give or assume the appearance or effect of often with the intent to deceive.
>
> (Merriam-Webster's Online Dictionary)

The Concise Oxford English Dictionary also includes imitation of conditions with models within its definition:

> Feign, … pretend to be, act like, resemble, wear the guise of, mimic, … imitate conditions of, (situation, etc.) with model, …   (Concise Oxford Dictionary)

It is the positive application of simulation through modeling that we will focus on within this book. Physicists and academics may use simulation in experiments to gain insights into physical systems for the purpose of education and training. Pilots use flight simulations to learn their skills without risking lives before they have sufficient experience. Biologists simulate cancer cell growths to take early actions in preventing potential damages.

Physicists and academics may use simulation in experiments to gain insights into physical systems for the purpose of education and training. Pilots use flight simulations to learn their skills without risking lives before they have sufficient experience. Biologists simulate cancer cell growths to take early actions in preventing potential damages.

In the world of finance, assets and key instruments are modeled and simulated to project future financial outcomes in order to understand the potential impacts of the risks associated with a portfolio. Methods and tools of risk containments and reductions, such as hedging, can be thus devised. This book aims to provide readers with a review of simulation tools that are currently applied in the finance and insurance industry.

The expression "Monte Carlo" is actually different from "simulation." According to Hubbard (2007), the term "Monte Carlo" was coined by the early pioneers of mathematical simulations, Stanislaw Ulam, Enrico Fermi, John von Neumann, and Nicholas Metropolis. It is used as a reference to a casino, where repetitions in games of chance are analogous to the nature of Monte Carlo simulation. But where the former can leave a dent in one's bank account, the latter would have projected and forewarned the inherent bias within the games, even perhaps prevented the ruin of the gambler. Monte Carlo simulation introduces randomness into simulations using a stochastic model for a deterministic system, such as random sampling from a probability distribution for a process that would otherwise be deterministic. This is sometimes referred to as Monte Carlo integration or Monte Carlo testing.

It can be seen, however, that Monte Carlo experiments involve doing something stochastic with simulation – that is, using a stochastic model for a deterministic system or time series. This in turn involves using stochastic simulation, which is really about sampling from stochastic models.

Ripley (1987) points out that too much emphasis is placed within the literature on producing the samples, and too little on what is done with these samples. In this book, we aim to redress this lack of balance, focusing on how to sample as well as on the financial and actuarial applications.

I.D.1 True and Pseudo Random Number Generators

The first element for a stochastic simulation is a source of randomness.

Because the actual simulations are done in computers, the stream of randomness should be either produced by or able to interface with computers. This is what random number generators aim to achieve. We consider separately the concepts of true random number generators (TRNGs) and pseudo random number generators (PRNGs).

True random number generators make use of naturally occurring events as the source of inputs for randomness, which can be fed into computers. This can range from something as simple as the length of time between keystrokes to things as complex as the delay between occurrences of radioactive decay or the variations of the amplitude in atmospheric noise detected by radios. The main feature for TRNGs is to generate random numbers by identifying and detecting small and unpredictable changes in the data. A good overview of TRNGs can be found in Haahr (2009).

Pseudo random number generators are mathematical algorithms that produce sequences of numbers that seem to be random. As a next number in the sequences normally depends on previous number(s), the sequences themselves are deterministic. These sequences are finite in nature, such that at some point a number will repeat itself, say in the form of X_i and X_{i+k}. This then leads to periodicity being introduced into many of these sequences, so that $(X_i, \ldots, X_{i+k-1})$ is the same as $(X_{i+k}, \ldots, X_{i+2k-1})$, where k is the *period* of the generator.

It is more desirable to use PRNGs than TRNGs when one is doing stochastic simulations, even though the latter is considered to be a better source of randomness. PRNGs are much more *efficient*, meaning that the amount of time required for them to generate large sets of numbers is small compared to TRNGs. Often we need to check the correctness of a piece of programming code in the simulations and want to compare how two or more different policies can affect the underlying model. As remarked in Dagpunar (2007, p. 17), by using the same set of random number streams for the experiments, one would hope that there is a reduction in the variance of the estimator for the differences in response among the policies. These simulation procedures require the random numbers to be *reproducible*, which is a key characteristic for PRNGs as they are

It is more desirable to use pseudo random number generators than true random number generators when one is doing stochastic simulations, even though the latter is considered to be a better source of randomness.

deterministic, but is not the case for TRNGs. It is mainly their efficient and deterministic natures that make PRNGs most suitable for stochastic simulations.

Ripley (1987) notes that many users of simulation tools are content to remain ignorant of how random numbers are produced, merely calling standard functions to produce them. Such attitudes are dangerous, however, because random numbers are in fact in the foundation of the simulation model. With this in mind, we now explore pseudo random number generators more in-depth, looking into different classes of PRNGs that are being used in today's simulation world.

I.D.2 Linear Congruential Generators

Pseudo random number generators sample numbers from a uniform distribution, $U(0, 1)$. The numbers produced are assumed to be independent. They are then used as a basis to further sample numbers from various underlying statistical distributions that the stochastic models are based on. Ways to do this will be addressed in the next chapter.

Linear congruential generators (LCG) are the earliest and perhaps the best known class of PRNGs. They were first introduced in Lehmer (1951). The general form of linear congruential generators, which produce non-negative integers, is defined by the sequence of numbers:

$$X_i = (aX_{i-1} + c) \bmod M \qquad\qquad (\text{I.D-1})$$

The parameters are: $a(> 0)$ the *multiplier*, $c(\geq 0)$ the *shift* or the *increment*, and M the *modulus*. It is initialized with a *seed*, X_0. The parameters a and c are in the interval $[0, ..., M - 1]$. As the modulo M process returns remainders after divisions, the stream of X_i also belongs in the same interval as the multiplier and the increment. Now the pseudo uniformly random sequence (U_i) is obtained by setting $U_i = X_i / M$. We call the subset of LCG with $c = 0$ *multiplicative* and the rest *mixed*. It is clear that, with such generators, at least one value in the set of $M + 1$ values of $(X_0, ... X_M)$ must repeat as, say, X_i and X_{i+k}. It follows that as future observations of X_i are predictable from its current value, the cycle $(X_i, ... X_{i+k-1})$ is repeated in $(X_{i+k}, ... X_{i+2k-1})$, $(X_{i+2k}, ... X_{i+3k-1})$, and so on. We say that the sequence X_i is periodic with a *period* $k \leq M$. The use of modulo operator makes this class of generators *congruential*.

There are a number of properties and theorems regarding the periods of LCG, which are useful in constructing streams of pseudo random numbers, as longer lengths of periods are desirable. It can be noted trivially that the full period, $k = M$, can always be achieved by setting $a = c = 1$ and for those are multiplicative; the maximum period they can achieve is $M - 1$. The following results from number theory assist in the choosing of the parameters to achieve full or maximal periods:

Theorem I.D-1

A linear congruential generator has full period M if and only if:

$$\gcd(c, M) = 1,$$
$$a \equiv 1 \bmod p \text{ for each prime factor } p \text{ of } M,$$
$$a \equiv 1 \bmod 4, \text{ if } 4 \text{ divides } M,$$

where $gcd(c, M)$ denotes the greatest common divisor between the two parameters.

Theorem I.D-2

A multiplicative congruential generator has the maximal period of $M - 1$ only if M is prime. Suppose M is a prime number, then the period divides $M - 1$, and is the maximal period of $M - 1$ if and only if a is a primitive root of M, which requires $a \neq 0$ and $a^{(M-1)/p} \neq 1 \bmod M$ for each prime factor p of $M - 1$.

Proofs for these theorems are available in Ripley (1987, p. 46)

Because most stochastic simulations are done on computers, it is not surprising that different compilers have implemented various forms of LCG. A short list of these LCGs is shown in the table in Figure 1.D-1, including both mixed and multiplicative generators. It is worth noting that for the mixed generators, the moduli, M, are in the form of 2^b. This is an efficient choice for computer simulation as modulo operations can be reduced by ignoring the binary calculations beyond b bits, as noted in Dagpunar (2007, page 21-22). Interested readers can check whether these generators satisfy the conditions required to gain either full periods or maximal periods.

█ Figure I.D-1

List of LCGs for Different Compilers

Source	M	a	c
'RND( )', MS Visual Basic 6.0[11]	2^{32}	1140671485	12820163
'Gsl_rug_rand' Unix[12]	2^{31}	1103515245	12345
'rand( )', Maple[13]	$10^{12}-11$	427419669081	0
"Congruential", Mathematica[14]	$a^{48}-a^{8}+1$	2^{31}	0

The properties of LCGs are often analyzed through studies of the lattice structures associated with them. This is done by first using the generator of period k to produce the entire sequence of numbers. Then we can plot overlapping pairs of consecutive numbers (U_0,U_1), ..., (U_{k-1},U_0) to review the lattice structure. If the sequence is truly sampled with independent $U(0,1)$ random variables, the pair of consecutive numbers is necessarily independent from each other. This implies that the pairs should be distributed uniformly over $[0,1)^2$, the unit plane.

The lattice structures of the LCG with $a = 5$, $c = 1$, and $M = 256$ and $a = 9$, $c = 1$, and $M = 256$ are plotted in Figures I.D-2 and I.D-3. The most striking feature of the graphs is that the points can be covered by parallel lines. This detraction from $U[0,1)^2$ is unavoidable for all LCGs. Marsaglia (1968) points out that this is also true in general such that n multituples of consecutive numbers in the $[0,1)^n$ hypercube lie in finite numbers of hyperplanes. It is due simply to the linear nature of the LCG algorithms. This is the main reason for avoiding LCGs in stochastic simulations that require very large sets of numbers, despite their ease of implementation and fast generations of numbers.

The lattice structures in Figures I.D-2 and I.D-3 also show that the second LCG requires more lines to cover the points, and that the ratio of the length between the longer vector and the shorter vector that

The linear nature of the Linear Congruential Generator algorithms is the main reason for avoiding Linear Congruential Generators in stochastic simulations that require very large sets of numbers, despite their ease of implementation and fast generations of numbers.

---

[11]   At http://support.microsoft.com/kb/231847/en-us

[12]   At http://www.gnu.org/software/gsl/manual/html_node/Unix-random-number-generators.html

[13]   Entacher, K. (2000)

[14]   At http://www.fourmilab.ch/hotbits/

construct the individual lattice cells is also smaller than the first LCG. This is an indication that the second LCG has a more uniform density within its lattice than the first one; therefore it is more desirable.

Figure I.D-2

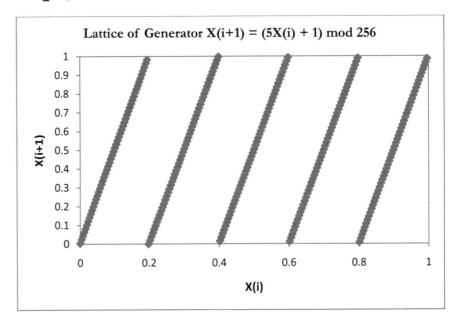

Lattice of Generator X(i+1) = (5X(i) + 1) mod 256

Figure I.D-3

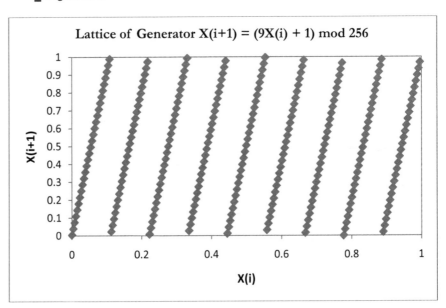

Lattice of Generator X(i+1) = (9X(i) + 1) mod 256

I.D.3 Non-linear PRNGs

The other class of pseudo random number generators are non-linear, which have little or no lattice structure. They are often divided into sub-classes referred to as inversive congruential generators (ICGs) and shift register generators (SRGs).

I.D.3.a Inversive Congruential Generators

These were first introduced in Eichenauer and Lehn (1986) and are defined by the following integer sequence:

$$x_{n+1} = (a\widetilde{x}_n + b) \bmod p, \ n \geq 0, \tag{I.D-2}$$

where $\widetilde{x}_n = x_n^{-1}$ if $x_n \neq 0$, otherwise $\widetilde{x}_n = 0$.

The sequence is then normalized by dividing p to get the pseudo uniform sequence, $u_n = x_n / p$. The modulus p is taken to be a prime number as it allows the absence of any lattice structure. In Figure I.D-4, this feature is demonstrated with a plot of the "non-overlapping" consecutive pairs (u_{2n}, u_{2n+1}) of the ICG with $p = 2^{31}$-1, $a = 1288490188$, and $b = 1$, in a region that is close to (0.5,0.5). For interested readers, please refer to Hellekalek (1997) for more in-depth discussion on ICGs.

The other class of pseudo random number generators are non-linear, which have little or no lattice structure. They are often divided into sub-classes referred to as inversive congruential generators and shift register generators.

█ **Figure I.D-4**

Absence of Lattice Structure in an ICG with p = 231-1, a = 1288490188, and b = 1

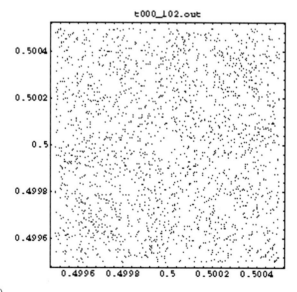

Source: Hellekalek (1997)

I.D.3.b Binary Shift Register Generators

Binary shift register generators are defined with

$$b_i = (a_1 b_{i-1} + \cdots + a_d b_{i-d}) \bmod 2 \tag{I.D-3}$$

This is easy to implement in a so-called shift register, hence the name. Each b_i is determined by $(b_{i-1}, \ldots, b_{i-d})$, which has at most 2^d possible values. As addition of modulo 2 is equivalent to the "exclusive-or" function (XOR), the sequence of numbers is equivalent to:

$$b_i = b_{i-j_1} XOR\, b_{i-j_2} \cdots b_{i-j_k} \tag{I.D-4}$$

where $a_{j_1} = \cdots = a_{j_k} = 1$ and all other $a_j = 0$.

Example I.D-1

A simple 4-bit shift register generator, $X_k = (b_{k4}\ b_{k3}\ b_{k2}\ b_{k1})$, has the following algorithm:

1. $b_{k+1,1} = b_{k3}\, XOR\, b_{k4}$
2. $b_{k+1,i} = b_{k,i-1}$ for $i = 2, \ldots, 4$ (shift register)

The first five outputs from the generator with $X_0 = 0001$ are:

0001, 0010, 0100, 1001, 0011

This generator achieves the maximal period of $2^4 - 1 = 15$.

The analysis of SRGs involves applying the mathematical branches of binary logic and Galois Field algebra, and in particular factorizing polynomials over finite fields. These are beyond the scope of this book. For interested readers, please refer to Ripley (1987).

Masumoto and Nishimura (1998) present the Mersenne twister as a generalized feedback shift register generator. The authors proved that it has a period of $2^{19937} - 1$ and has passed the high-dimensional k-distribution test, which is designed to test absence from uniformity. It is perhaps the most popular choice, at present, for generating numbers in Monte Carlo simulations. The algorithm and C codes are provided at the authors' Web site.

I.D.4 Empirical Tests for Random Numbers

There are various statistical tests that can be used for assessing PRNGs. This section provides a selection of them.

I.D.4.a Kolmogorov-Smirnov Test

As a first step, assessing the effectiveness of a particular PRNG involves checking the goodness-of-fit to uniform distribution for the set of numbers produced. The classical χ^2 test, as described in

Roussas (1973, p. 373) and Kanji (2006, p. 79) is typically used to test the goodness-of-fit to statistical distributions for data with a finite number of categories. This is not effective for random numbers, however, which are assumed to have infinitely numerous values. A similar but more powerful goodness-of-fit test, the Kolmogorov-Smirnov is more often used for testing uniformity of the proposed set of random numbers. This is done by conducting tests on the greatest deviation between the empirical distribution of the random numbers and the uniform distribution. Supposing that we have obtained the sequence of n random numbers, $U_1, ..., U_n$, the empirical distribution function $F_n(x)$ is defined as

$$F_n(x) = \frac{\text{Number of } U_i \leq x}{n} \tag{I.D-5}$$

The test now seeks a statistic, K_n, that is related to the maximum deviation between the empirical distribution and the fitted distribution. We have K_n defined as

$$K_n = \sqrt{n} \max_x |F_n(x) - F(x)| \tag{I.D-6}$$

where $F(x)$ is the cumulative distribution function (CDF) of the fitted distribution.

The fitted distribution for the random number is uniform, which implies that $F(x) = x$. The procedure for testing the uniformity of random numbers is thus:

1. Generate and sort the uniform-random in an ascending order sequence to $U_1, ..., U_n$.

2. Find the statistics:

$$K_n = \sqrt{n} \max_i \left| \frac{i}{n} - U_i \right| \tag{I.D-7}$$

3. Compare K_n to a statistical table, such as Lindley and Scott (1995, p. 70).

I.D.4.b Poker Test (partition test)

This form of test divides the random integer sequence into n sets of five consecutive numbers, in the form of $(X_{5i}, X_{5i+1}, ..., X_{5i+4})$ for $0 \leq i \leq n$. It then assesses the frequency of occurrence of the different partitions. The patterns that can be observed within a set are:

- *abcde* (all different)

- *aabcd* (one pair)

- *aabbc* (two pairs)

- *aaabc* (three of a kind)

- *aaabb* (full house)

- *aaaab* (four of a kind)

- *aaaaa* (five of a kind)

Butcher (1961) describes a simplified version of this test, such that the partitions are $C_1, ..., C_5$, where C_r denotes the partition with exactly r different numbers. Once the numbers of observations in the different partitions are realized, we can apply χ^2 test to assess the generated sequence. For the test, we require the probability P_r, so that the partition C_r will be observed in a single trial. It is not hard to see that

$$P_r = \frac{M(M-1)...(M-r+1)}{M^5}\binom{5}{r} \qquad \text{(I.D-8)}$$

where M is the largest possible number of the random sequence and $\binom{5}{r}$ denotes the combinatorial describing the number of ways to have exactly r different numbers in a group of five. The procedure for the Poker test is thus:

1. Generate and group the integer random number into $(X_{5i}, X_{5i+1}, ..., X_{5i+4})$ for $0 \leq i \leq n$.

2. Observe the number of occurrence, $m_1, ..., m_5$ for the partitions $C_1, ..., C_5$.

3. Find the statistics for χ^2 test, such that

$$\chi^2 = \sum_{r=1}^{5} \frac{(m_r - nP_r)^2}{nP_r} \qquad \text{(I.D-9)}$$

4. Compare χ^2 value, which has 5-1 degrees of freedom, to a statistical table, such as Lindley and Scott (1995, p. 40).

I.D.4.c Permutation Test

Knuth (1981) describes this test as one for assessing the relative ordering within the groups that the random sequence is divided into. Similar to the Poker test, the sequence is divided into n groups of k numbers, obtaining $(U_{ik}, U_{ik+1}, ..., U_{ik+k-1})$ for $0 \leq i < n$, where $U_0 > U_1 < U_2 > U_4$ could be one of the orderings for a grouping of four. There can be a total of $k!$ relative orderings within each group. As it is equally likely for each ordering to be observed during one trial, each of them must have the probability of $P = 1/(k!)$. We can now perform χ^2 test with $k!-1$ degrees of freedom to assess the random sequence in a process similar to the Poker test.

The Diehard Battery of Tests of Randomness was devised by Marsaglia. It consists of many of the empirical tests that are similar to the three reviewed.

The Diehard Battery of Tests of Randomness was devised by Marsaglia and published on a CD-ROM that is also available on the Web[15]. It consists of many of the empirical tests that are similar to the three reviewed above. Because of its stringent nature, the Diehard is viewed as a good set of tests for PRNGs. Many generators, especially LCGs, pass very few tests included in the Diehard. A PRNG that passes most of the Diehard tests is considered to be effective in generating random numbers. One of the main reasons for the popularity of the Mersenne twister is its ability to pass this severe series of test, as noted on its author's Web site.

---

[15] See http://stat.fsu.edu/pub/diehard/.

I.D.5 Methods of Sampling Non-uniform Distributions

In the previous chapter, we have seen how to produce streams of pseudo random uniform numbers using different generators. As most of the stochastic simulations do not sample just from $U(0, 1)$ distribution, it is crucial to learn how to use the uniform sequence to produce the sequence of desired distribution. In this chapter, we consider six main techniques for this purpose. They are:

- **Inversion**
- **Acceptance/rejection and "squeeze"**
- **Composition**
- **Switching**
- **Ratio of uniforms**
- **Tabular**

Useful examples of applying these techniques for sampling different distributions are provided for each.

Note: In this chapter, we use U with or without subscripts to denote $Uniform\ (0,1)$ random numbers generated via PRNGs, unless it is stated otherwise.

As most of the stochastic simulations do not sample just from U(0, 1) distribution, it is crucial to learn how to use the uniform sequence to produce the sequence of desired distribution.

I.D.5.a Inversion Method

Let X be a continuous random variable, whose cumulative distribution function (CDF) is $F_x(x)$. Suppose now that $U \sim Uniform\ (0,1)$, then $F_X^{-1}(U)$ has the same CDF as X. This is because of the following observation:

$$\Pr(F_X^{-1}(U) < x) = \Pr(R < F_X(x)) = F_X(x),\qquad\text{(I.D-10)}$$

where the second equality is due to R being uniformly distributed. Therefore, we can obtain sample points for X by using $X = F_X^{-1}(U)$, provided that the inverse function exists. In practice, if u is a sample point from $Uniform\ (0,1)$ produced by one of the PRNGs, then $x = F_X^{-1}(u)$ is taken to be a sample point from X. Notice that it is important for the initial samples, u, not to detract significantly from uniform distribution because that is one of the main underlying assumptions.

Example I.D-2 [Exponential: $X \sim Exponential\ (\lambda)$]

Then $F_X(x) = 1 - e^{-\lambda x}, x \geq 0$

And $F_X^{-1}(u) = -\dfrac{1}{\lambda}\ln(1-u), u < 1$

Example I.D-3 [Cauchy: $X \sim Cauchy\ (m,\gamma)$]

$$\text{Then } F_X(x) = \frac{1}{2} + \frac{1}{\pi}\arctan(\frac{x-m}{\gamma})$$

$$\text{And } F_X^{-1}(u) = m + \gamma\tan(\pi(u - \frac{1}{2}))$$

For discrete distributions, or those where a closed formula for the inverse CDF is not available, we define

$$f_k = \Pr(X = k)$$

$$F_k = \Pr(X \le k)$$

$$F_k^{-1} = \min(k : \text{such that } F_k \ge u)$$

The method for inversion then involves searching a table of F_k for a suitable index k. An algorithm for this would be:

1. Generate U and set $k = 1$.

2. While $F_k \le U$, set $k = k + 1$.

3. Return $X = k$.

Ripley (1987) and Chen and Asau (1974) provide alternative, more efficient search algorithms.

Example I.D-4 [Binomial: $X \sim Binomial\ (N, p)$]

For small N,

1. Set $X = 0$

2. For $i = 1$ to N

   Generate U; if $U < p$ then $X = X + 1$.

3. Return X.

For large N, it is costly to sample in such way. Relles (1972) suggests a way to reduce the cost, based on j-th element in an ordered set of uniformly random variates that follows $Beta(j, N - j + 1)$, which is proven in Kendall and Stuart (1958). Knuth (1998, p. 136) presents the following algorithm:

1. Set $X = 0$.

2. Loop

   $$i = \text{int}[1 + Np]$$

   Generate $B \sim Beta\ (i, N + 1 - i)$

   If $B \ge p$ then $p = p / B, N = i - 1$

   Else $X = X + i,\ p = p(p - B)(1 - B),\ N = N - i$

until N is efficiently small, such that the previous algorithm can be continued with Step 1 skipped. We discuss later how beta distribution can be sampled in Example I.D-5.

I.D.5.b Acceptance/rejection Method

Suppose we wish to sample from a probability density function $f(x)$, which does not have a closed form for its inverse function. It is easy, however, to sample from another pdf $g(x)$, such that $f(x) / g(x) \leq M < \infty$ for all x, where M is a constant. Ripley (1987, p. 60) suggests the following general acceptance/rejection method:

1. Loop

$$\text{Generate } Y \text{ from } g \text{ and } U \text{ from } Uniform\ (0,1)$$

Until $MU \leq f(Y)/g(Y)$

2. Return $X = Y$.

The returned variable, X, has the desired pdf f because

$$\Pr\left(Y \leq x \text{ and } Y \text{ is accepted}\right) = \int_{-\infty}^{x} h(y)g(y)dy,$$

Where $h(y) = f(y)/(g(y) \cdot M)$. This implies that

$$\Pr\left(Y \text{ is accepted}\right) = \int_{-\infty}^{\infty} h(y)g(y)dy,$$

and

$$
\begin{aligned}
\Pr(Y \leq x \mid Y \text{ is accepted}) \quad &= \quad \left.\int_{-\infty}^{x} h(y)g(y)dy \middle/ \int_{-\infty}^{\infty} h(y)g(y)dy\right. \\
&= \quad \left.\int_{-\infty}^{x} f(y)dy \middle/ \int_{-\infty}^{\infty} f(y)dy\right. \\
&= \quad \int_{-\infty}^{x} f(y)dy \\
\text{p.d.f. of } X \quad &= \quad f(x).
\end{aligned}
$$

The test $MU \leq f(Y)/g(Y)$ accepts Y with the required probability. The number of trials before a Y is accepted has a geometric distribution with mean M, so the algorithm works best if M is small. It is not necessary to know $f(x)$, but only of $f(x)_1 \propto f(x)$ and a bound on $f_1(x)/g(x)$.

Example I.D-5 [Beta Distribution: $X \sim Beta\ (\ , \beta)$]

Jöhnk (1964) proposes the following algorithm for beta distribution:

1. Loop:

$$\text{Generate independent } \quad U_1, U_2 \sim Uniform\ (0,1)$$

$$\text{let } V_1 = U_1^{1/\alpha}, \; V_2 = U_2^{1/\beta}$$

until $Z = V_1 + V_2 \leq 1$.

2. Return $X = V_1 / Z$.

Note: The algorithm is slow if $\alpha + \beta$ is large (because of low acceptance rates).

Example I.D-6 [Standard Normal: $X \sim Normal(0,1)$]

Marsaglia and Bray (1964) apply the acceptance/rejection method to sample from normal distribution, using the following algorithm:

1. Loop

    Generate independent $U_1, U_2 \sim Uniform$ (-1,1)

    until $Z = U_1^2 + U_2^2 \leq 1$.

2. Let $C = -2 \ln Z$.

3. Return $X = \left(CZ^{-1}\right)^{1/2} U_1$, $Y = \left(CZ^{-1}\right)^{1/2} U_2$.

Step 1 from the algorithm crucially generates, by the acceptance/rejection method, a point (U_1, U_2) that is uniformly distributed in a unit disc. As the variate Z is now uniformly distributed in the interval $[0,1]$, Step 2 of the algorithm inverse transforms Z into an exponentially distributed variate that is the sum of the squares of two normally distributed variates in a fashion similar to Example I.D-2. The final step simply recovers those normal variates and standardizes them into $Normal$ $(0,1)$ variates. A more detailed discussion is in the original paper or in Kloeden and Platen (2000, p. 13).

The boundary condition $MU \leq f(x) / g(x)$ can sometimes be implemented more practically using the so-called "squeeze" method, as suggested in Marsaglia (1977). With this approach, we need to find functions $a(x)$ and $b(x)$ with $a(x) \leq f(x) / g(x) \leq b(x)$ for all x. Then $MU \leq a(Y)$ means we can accept Y, and $MU > b(Y)$ means we reject Y, where the explicit evaluation of $f(x)/g(x)$ is not needed. This method can speed up the process of sampling if $a(x)$ and $b(x)$ fit well to $f(x)$.

I.D.5.c Composition Method

Under the Composition Method the density f (x) is said to be a compound of other distributions. One trick is to split the range of X into intervals.

Suppose we have $f(x) = \sum_1^r p_i(x) f_i(x)$.

The density $f(x)$ is said to be a compound of other distributions. One trick is to split the range of X into intervals.

Example I.D-7 [Exponential]

Suppose $f_i(x)$ is the pdf for standard exponential distribution, conditional on $i - 1 \leq x < i$. Then $p_i(x) = \Pr(i - 1 \leq x < i) = e^{-(i-1)} - e^{-i} = e^{-(i-1)}\left(1 - e^{-1}\right)$, so $\{p_i\}$ is a geometric distribution on 1,2,3,... and $f_i(x) = e^{-[x-(i-1)]}/\left(1 - e^{-1}\right)$ on $[i - 1, i)$. This leads to the following algorithm, which is discussed in Luc Devroye (1986):

1. Let $I = 0$.

2. Generate U_1, set $T = U_1$.

3. Generate U_2. If $U_1 \leq U_2$ return $X = I + T$.

4. Else regenerate U_1. If $U_1 < U_2$ go to 3.

5. Else, $I = I + 1$, go to 2.

Walker (1974, 1977) provides a technique for applying this to discrete distributions. This can be useful for compound Poisson applications in non-life insurance applications where we are interested in the distribution S of multiple N claims on a risk variable X, i.e.,

$$S = \sum_{i=1}^{N} X_i \text{ where } N \sim Poisson(\lambda).$$

Walker provides a method for splitting the range into intervals that can be useful for compound Poisson applications in non-life insurance applications where we are interested in the distribution *S* of multiple *N* claims on a risk variable *X*.

I.D.5.d Switching Method

Atkinson and Whittaker (1976) label the technique of using the acceptance method in conjunction with splitting the range of X as the method of switching.

Example I.D-8 [Beta: $X \sim Beta\ (\alpha, \beta)$]

Consider the special case $\alpha = \beta < 1$. We divide the interval $(0,1)$ into $(0,0.5)$ and $(0.5,1)$, using envelope $g_1(x) \propto x^{\alpha-1}$ on $(0,0.5)$ and $g_2(x) \propto (1-x)^{\beta-1}$ on $(0.5,1)$. The envelope is sampled by:

1. Generate U_1 and let $Y = U_1^{1/\alpha} / 2$.

2. Generate U_2. If $U_2 > 0.5$, set $Y = 1 - Y$.

By using the symmetry of the density, the whole algorithm becomes:

1. Loop

   Generate U_1, U_2, let $Y = U_1^{1/\alpha} / 2$.

   until $U_2 \leq \left[2(1 - Y)\right]^{\alpha-1}$

2. Generate U_3. If $U_3 > 0.5$, set $Y = 1 - Y$.

3. Return $X = Y$.

Atkinson and Whittaker (1976) also give a fuller version for $\alpha \neq \beta$.

I.D.5.e Ratio of Uniforms Method

Suppose (U_1, U_2) is a uniformly distributed point within the unit disc. Ripley (1987, p. 66) points out that U_1 / U_2 has the distribution of the ratio of two independent normal variates. This is also the Cauchy distribution, see Hinkley (1969).

Example I.D-9 [Cauchy]

Kinderman and Monahan (1977) sets out the Synthetic Tangent algorithm as follows:

1. Loop

   Generate U_1, U_2,

   Set $V = 2U_2 - 1$

   until $U_1^2 + V^2 \leq 1$.

2. Return $X = V/U_1$.

The ratio of uniforms method is based on the Theorem I.D-3.

Theorem I.D-3

Let $h(x)$ be any non-negative function with $\int_{-\infty}^{\infty} h(x)dx < \infty$.

Let $C_h = \left\{(u_1, u_2) : 0 < u_1 \leq \sqrt{h(u_2/u_1)}\right\}$. Suppose (U_1, U_2) is uniformly distributed over C_h and let $X = U_2/U_1$. Then the pdf of X is $h(x) \Big/ \int_{-\infty}^{\infty} h(x)dx$.

This result leads directly to sampling distributions with density proportional to $h(x)$.

Example I.D-10 [Standard Normal]

Knuth (1981) sets $a = e^{\frac{1}{4}}$, $b = e^{-1.35} \approx 0.259$ (other parameters are discussed in Ripley [1987]).

1. Generate U_1 and U_2.

2. Let $X = \sqrt{8/e} \, (U_2 - 0.5)/U_1$ and set $Y = X^2$. $[\sqrt{(8/e)} \approx 1.72]$

3. If $Y \leq 5 - 4aU_1$, go to 6.

4. If $Y \geq 4b / U_1 + 1.4$, go to 1.

5. If $Y > -\ln U_1$, go to 1.

6. Return X.

It is noted in Ripley (1987) that this algorithm is as simple as the acceptance/rejection method. It returns one normal deviate at a time and is comparable in speed. There is little to choose among the Box-Muller (see Kloeden and Platen [2000, p. 12]), Marsaglia's acceptance/rejection, and the ratio of uniforms methods for sensitivity to pseudo random number generators.

Example I.D-11 [Gamma: $X \sim Gamma\,(\alpha)$]

For $\alpha > 1$, Cheng and Feast (1979) give two main types of algorithms derived from the ratio of uniforms method. Overall, they propose that $h(x) = x^{\alpha-1}e^{-x}$ in the theorem. Therefore the region C_h from the theorem is

$$\{(u_1,u_2)\,|\,u_1,u_2 \ge 0, u_1^2 \le (u_2/u_1)^{\alpha-1}e^{-u_2/u_1}\} \subset [0,a]\times[0,b] \qquad \text{(I.D-11)}$$

where $a = [(\alpha-1)/e]^{(\alpha-1)/2}$ and $b = [(\alpha+1)/e]^{(\alpha+1)/2}$. The region C_h now lies within a rectangle. This is the basis for the following algorithm:

1. Loop

   Generate independent U_1 and U_2;

   Set $W = dU_1/U_2$, for any $d \ge b/(a\,(\alpha-1))$

   Until $c\ln U_1 - \ln W + W \le 1$ where $c = 2/(\alpha-1)$.

2. Return $X = (\alpha-1)W$

As α increases, the acceptance region shrinks toward the diagonal $U_1 = U_2$. In response, Cheng and Feast (1979) replace C_h by a parallelogram that bounds C_h. They suggest, for $\alpha > 2.5$, that Step 1 of the above algorithm should be altered with an inner loop to:

1. Loop (outer)

   Loop (inner)

   Generate U_1 and U_2;

   Set $U_2 = U_1 + \alpha^{-0.5}(1 - 1.86U_2)$

   until (inner) $0 < U_2 < 1$

   Set $W = dU_1/U_2$, for any $d \ge b/(a\,(\alpha-1))$

   until (outer) $c\ln U_1 - \ln W + W \le 1$ where $c = 2/(\alpha-1)$.

The first algorithm uses a rectangle to enclose C_h for $1 < \alpha \le 2.5$, and the second a parallelogram for $\alpha > 2.5$ to give a fairly constant computing speed as α is varied.

I.D.5.f Tabular Method

Section I.D.5.a describes how applying the method of inversion to discrete distributions involves indexed or tabular searches. More efficient tab searches are available from Chen and Asau (1974), Marsaglia (1963), Norman and Cannon (1972), and Ripley (1987).

I.D.5.g Sampling Without Replacement

Often we may need to sample discrete distributions without replacement.

Often we may need to sample discrete distributions without replacement. This occurs in disarranging surveys and randomizing experiments. This could be done by sampling the population and rejecting those that have already been selected until the required number of different samples has been found. This method is time-consuming, especially if the required number is comparable to the population total. It is more efficient to sort the population first. For example, after generating $U_1, ..., U_N$, we can sort (U_i, i) on U_i as described in Page (1967). Sampling without replacement can then be done by selecting n smallest U_i, which is a sequential process.

A simpler version of this method inspects the samples individually and is referred as the Conditional Distribution Function approach in Fan et al. (1962). A form of this algorithm for selecting n items from a population of N is:

1. Set $i = 0$ and $j = 0$.
2. Loop

    Generate U.

    If $\dfrac{(n - j)}{(N - i)} > U$ then $X_j - U$ and $j = j + 1$.

    Set $i = i + 1$

    Until $j = n$.

3. Return the list $\{X_j\}$.

This terminates when n samples are chosen, often before the whole population is sampled. At first glance, we might be concerned that maybe more than N items are required for inspection to generate n samples and the selected items are thus chosen with bias. But observe, first, that the "sampling probability" ≥ 1 when there are $n - j$ or fewer individuals left, which ensures that n will be selected after N are inspected. Second, the probability that elements $i_1 < i_2 < ... < i_n$ are picked is $\prod_{i=1}^{N} P_i / (N - i + 1)$ where $P_{i_j} = n - j + 1$ and $P_i = (N - i + 1) - (n - j)$ for $i_j < i < i_{j+1}$. The denominator is $N!$ and the numerator contains $n, n - 1, ..., 1$ for $i_1, ..., i_j$ and $N - n, ..., 1$ for the remaining elements. Thus the probability is $n!(N - n)!/N!$ independent of which elements are specified. See also Vitter (1984), who samples $i_{j+1} - i_j$ directly.

Other techniques are available in Knuth (1981) and in McLeod and Bellhouse (1983).

I.D.5.h Other Techniques and Special Cases

Gamma distribution

Because of its versatility, the gamma distribution is also one of the most widely applied (and analyzed) distributions.

The pdf of the gamma is $f(x) = x^{k-1} \dfrac{e^{-k/\theta}}{\theta^k \Gamma(k)}$ and $\Gamma(k) = \int_0^\infty t^{k-1} e^{-s} \, ds$.

Consider the case where $\theta = 1$, the following algorithm from Ahrens and Dieter (1974) is very practical and popular.

Example I.D-12 [Gamma]

1. Generate U_1, U_2.

2. If $U_1 > e/(k+e)$, go to 4.

3. Let $X = \{(k+e)U_1/e\}^{1/k}$. If $U_2 > e^{-X}$ go to 1, else go to 5.

4. Let $X = -\ln\{(k+e)(1-U_1)/ke\}$. If $U_2 > X^{\alpha-1}$ go to 1.

5. Return X.

This partitions $(0, \infty)$ into $(0,1)$ and $(1, \infty)$ and uses separate envelopes on each. Section 3.5 sets out the ratio of uniforms method from Cheng and Feast (1979).

Other algorithms are available in Ahrens and Dieter (1974), Atkinson and Pearce (1976), Jöhnk (1964), and Tadikamalla and Johnson (1981).

Stable distributions

A random variable X is said to be stable, or to have a stable distribution, if:

1. for every positive integer n; and
2. for every set of independent and identically distributed random variables $\{X_1, X_2, ..., X_n\}$ with the same distribution as X;

there exist constants $a_n > 0$ and b_n such that the sum $X_1 + X_2 + ... + X_n$ has the same distribution as $a_n X + b_n$.

Finkelstein (1997) points out that there are infinitely many distributions that fall into the class. Except for three cases (the normal, the Cauchy, and the inverse chi-squared), the probability density function of the stable distributions cannot be written in closed form. However, the characteristic function can be written in closed form. Lévy (1925) showed that the stable distributions all have a characteristic function, which takes the form:

$$\Psi(t) = E\left[e^{itZ}\right]$$

(I.D-12)

$$= \begin{cases} \exp(i\delta t) - \left|\gamma t\right|^{\alpha}(1 + i\beta\,\text{sgn}(t)\tan(\pi\alpha/2)), & \text{if } \alpha \neq 1 \\ \exp(i\delta t) - \left|\gamma t\right|^{\alpha}(1 + i\beta\dfrac{2}{\pi}\text{sgn}(t)\ln\left|t\right|), & \text{if } \alpha = 1 \end{cases}$$

where :

$\text{sgn}(t) = 1$ if t is positive, -1 if t is negative and 0 otherwise.

Except for three cases (the normal, the Cauchy, and the inverse chi-squared), the probability density function of the stable distributions cannot be written in closed form. However, the characteristic function can be written in closed form.

This leads to a useful parameterization for the stable family, with δ being the location parameter, γ the scale parameter, $\beta \in [-1,1]$ measuring the skewness of the distribution, and $\alpha \in (0,2]$ determining kurtosis and tail thickness.

It is often believed that an important factor affecting the widespread use of the normal distribution is the fact that this distribution has a domain of attraction stemming from the central limit theorem. In fact, all the stable distributions have a domain of attraction. The generalized central limit theorem (see Feller [1966]), states that, if a sum of independent and identically distributed random variables from *any* distribution with finite or infinite variance has a limiting distribution, then the limiting distribution will be a member of the stable class.

If the summands have finite variance, then the central limit theorem applies, and the limiting distribution is the normal distribution. If the summands have infinite variance, then the generalized central limit theorem applies, with the limiting distribution being stable but non-normal.

Finkelstein (1997) notes that a number of techniques for simulating from stable distribution are available, but the method of Chambers et al. (1976) is the most practical. Chambers et al. (1976) show that if $V \sim Uniform \left(-\frac{\pi}{2},\frac{\pi}{2}\right)$ and $W \sim Exponential$, then

It is often believed that an important factor affecting the widespread use of the normal distribution is the fact that this distribution has a domain of attraction stemming from the central limit theorem. In fact, all the stable distributions have a domain of attraction.

$$\delta + \gamma \frac{\sin(\alpha V)}{[\cos(V)]^{1/\alpha}} \left[\frac{\cos\{1-\alpha\}V}{W} \right]^{\frac{1-\alpha}{\alpha}} \tag{I.D-13}$$

simulates the stable distribution.

More generally, one can consider infinitely divisible distributions, of which stable distributions are a subclass. Bondesson (1982) uses an approximation composition method, letting X be a sum of random variables with randomly chosen distributions. For the stable distributions this reduces to the method of Bartels (1978).

Special cases/examples of this distribution are:

- $\alpha = 2, \beta = 0$: $Normal (\delta, \gamma^2)$

- $\alpha = 1, \beta = 0$: $Cauchy (\delta, \gamma)$.

It follows that the above methods can be used for sampling from either of these distributions. More generally, if we are interested in sampling from the average or some other function of the sum of a particular random variable (regardless of whether it has finite or infinite variance), then one approximation technique involves estimating the stable distribution in whose domain of attraction it resides, and then using the above technique(s) for sampling from the relevant stable distribution. This method is discussed extensively in Bartels (1978) and Koutrouvelis (1980). An example of this is the binomial distribution, which, for large N, is asymptotically normal.

Substitution method

Some distributions can be seen to be expressed in terms of, or established by, other distributions, which are the special cases from above.

- **An example is Student's *t* distribution, which is $\frac{Normal}{\chi_v^2 / v}$, where χ_v^2 is a special case of a gamma distribution.**

- Other examples are the normal and Cauchy distributions, which are in fact special cases of the stable distribution family as discussed in 3.8.2 above.

- The beta distribution is also related to the gamma distribution:
  If $X \sim Gamma\,(\alpha)$ and $Y \sim Gamma\,(\beta)$, therefore $\dfrac{X}{X+Y} \sim Beta(\alpha,\beta)$.

- For large N, the binomial distribution behaves like a normal.

I.D.6 Summary

We can summarize the different methods available for the distributions.

Normal	Accept/Reject	I.D-6
	Ratio of Uniforms	I.D-10
	Substitution	Section titled "Substitution Method"
Exponential	Inversion	I.D-2
	Composition	I.D-7
Cauchy	Inversion	I.D-3
	Ratio of Uniforms	I.D-9
	Substitution	Section titled "Substitution Method"
Stable	Chambers et al.	Section titled "Stable Distributions"
Student's t	Substitution	Section titled "Substitution Method"
Gamma	Ratio of Uniforms	I.D-11
	Ahrens and Dieter	I.D-12
Beta	Accept/Reject	I.D-5
	Switching	I.D-8
Binomial	Inversion	I.D-4
	Substitution	Section titled "Substitution Method"
Other Discrete	Tabular	Section I.D.5.f
	Sampling with Replacement	Section I.D.5.g

References for Section I.D

Ahrens, J.H. & Dieter, U. (1974). Computer methods for sampling from gamma, beta, poisson and binomial distributions. *Computing* 12, 223-246.

Atkinson, A.C. & Whittaker, J. (1976). A switching algorithm for the generation of beta random variables with at least one parameter less than 1. *Journal of the Royal Statistical Society* A 139, 464-467.

Bartels, R. (1978). Generating non-normal stable variates using limit theorem properties. *Journal of Statistical Computation and Simulation* 7, 199-212.

Bebbington, A.C. (1975). A simple method for drawing a sample without replacement. *Applied Statistics* 24, 136.

Bondesson, L. (1982). On simulation from infinitely divisible distributions. *Advances in Applied Probability* 14, 855-869.

Chambers, J.M., Mallows, C.L. & Stuck, B.W. (1976). A method for simulating stable random variables. *Journal of the American Statistical Association* 71, 340-344.

Chen, N. & Asau, Y. (1974). On generating random variates from an empirical distribution. *American Institute of Industrial Engineers Trans.* 6, 163-166.

Cheng, R.C.H. & Feast, G.M. (1979). Some simple gamma variate generators. *Applied Statistics* 28, 290-295.

Dagpunar, J.S. (2007). *Simulation and Monte Carlo with applications in finance and MCMC.* London: Wilery.

Eichenauer, J. & Lehn, J. (1986). A non-linear congruential pseudo random number generator. *Statististical Papers* 27, 315-326.

Entacher, K. (2000). A collection of classical pseudorandom number generators with linear structures - advanced version. Retrieved May 14, 2009, from http://crypto.mat.sbg.ac.at/results/karl/server/node5.html#SECTION00054000000000000000.

Fan, C. T., Muller, M. E., & Rezucha, I. (1962). Development of sampling plans using sequential (item by item) selection techniques and digital computers. *Journal of the American Statistical Association* 57, 387-402.

Feller, W. (1966). *An introduction to probability theory and its applications*, Vol. 2. New York: John Wiley and Sons.

Finkelstein, G.S. (1997). Maturity guarantees revisited: Allowing for extreme stochastic fluctuations using stable distributions. *British Actuarial Journal* v3, 411-482.

Haahr, Mads (2009). Introduction to randomness and random numbers. RANDOM.ORG Web site. Retrieved September 9, 2009, from http://random.org/randomness/.

Hellekalek, P. (1997). Inversive pseudorandom number generators: Concepts and links. Retrieved May 14, 2009, from http://random.mat.sbg.ac.at/generators/wsc95/inversive/inversive.html.

Hinkley, D.V. (1969). On the ratio of two correlated normal random variables. *Biometrika* 56 (3), 635–639.

Hubbard, D. (2007). *How to measure anything: Finding the value of intangibles in business.* New York: John Wiley & Sons.

Jöhnk, M.D. (1964). Erzeugung von Betaverteilen und Gammaverteilung Zufallszahlen. *Metrika* 8, 5-15.

Jones, T.G. (1962). A note on sampling a tape-file. *Communications of the ACM.* 5, 343.

Kanji, G.K. (2006). *100 statistical tests*, 3rd Edition. Sage Publications Ltd.

Kendall, M.G. & Moran, P. a. P. (1963). *Geometrical probability.* London: Griffin.

Kinderman, A.J., Monahan, J.F., & Ramage, J.G. (1977). Computer methods for sampling from student's t distribution. *Mathematics of Computation* 31, 1009-1018.

Kloeden, P. & Platen, E. (2000). *Numerical solution of stochastic differential equations (stochastic modelling and applied probability).* Berlin: Springer-Verlag.

Knuth, D. (1981). *Art of computer programming, volume 2: Seminumerical algorithms* (2nd Edition). Addison-Wesley.

Koutrouvelis, I.A. (1980). Regression-type estimation of the parameters of stable laws. *Journal of the American Statistical Association* 75, 918-928.

Lehmer, D.H. (1951). Mathematical methods in large-scale computing units. *Proceedings of the 2nd Symposium on Large-Scale Digital Calculating Machinery:* 141-146. Cambridge, Mass.: Harvard University Press.

Lévy, P. (1925). *Calcul des probabilités.* Paris: Gauthier-Villars.

Lindley, D. V. & Scott, W. F. (1995). *New Cambridge statistical tables,* 2nd Edition. Cambridge University Press.

Marsaglia, G. (1963). Generating discrete random variables in a computer. *Communications of the ACM* 6, 37-38.

Marsaglia, G. (1968). Random numbers fall mainly in the planes. *Proceedings of the National Academy of Sciences of the United States of America* 61, 25-28.

Marsaglia, G. (1977). The squeeze method for generating gamma variates. *Computers & Mathematics with Applications* 3, 321-325.

Marsaglia, G. & Bray, T. A. (1964). A convenient method for generating normal variables. *SIAM Review.* 6, 260-264.

Matsumoto, M. & Nishimura, T. (1998). Mersenne twister: A 623-dimensionally equi-distributed uniform pseudo-random number generator. *ACM Transaction on Modeling and Computer Simulation* 8, 3-30. Algorithm and C codes are available at http://www.math.sci.hiroshima-u.ac.jp/~m-mat/MT/emt.html.

McLeod, A.I. & Bellhouse, D. R. (1983). A convenient algorithm for drawing a simple random sample. *Applied Statistics* 2, 363-371.

Norman, J. E. & Cannon, L. E. (1972). A computer program for the generation of random variables from any discrete distribution. *Journal of Statistical Computation and Simulation* 1, 331-348.

Relles, D. A. (1972). A simple algorithm for generating binomial random variables when N is large. *Journal of the American Statistical Association* 67, 612-613.

Ripley, B.D. (1987). Stochastic simulation. New York: John Wiley & Sons.

Roussas, G. G. (1973). *A course in mathematical statistics.* Academic Press.

Walker, A. J. (1974). New fast method for generating discrete random variables with arbitrary frequency distribution. *Electronics Letters* 10, 127-128.

Walker, A. J. (1976). An efficient method for generating discrete random variables with general distributions. *ACM Transactions on Mathematical Software* 3, 253-256.

I.E.   Risk Measures

The measurement of risk is one of the central issues in the risk management of financial institutions. The need to quantify risk may arise from many different sources, but companies tend to be particularly concerned with the distribution of profit and loss. IAA (2004), in its report of the Insurer Solvency Assessment Working Party, defined "risk measure" as a function of the probability distribution of losses. Such a measurement is used to determine either the total capital requirement based on the aggregate distribution of losses, or an indicated capital requirement for a component based on the loss distribution of the component risk only.

The measurement of risk is one of the central issues in the risk management of financial institutions. The need to quantify risk may arise from many different sources, but companies tend to be particularly concerned with the distribution of profit and loss.

There are several approaches to the measurement of losses. A static factor model is based on a linear combination of a static risk factor multiplied by a company-specific amount that can typically be found in the company's financial statements, such as the amount of a specific asset class or premium income.

The other approach is a scenario-based risk measure. Risk is calculated by measuring the impact of specific scenarios on the distribution of loss. These scenarios could cover multiple risk drivers simultaneously. When stochastic scenarios are used, the correlation between risk drivers must be taken into consideration when generating them.

The resulting loss is aggregated across all risk types, leading to its stochastic distribution, and required capital is determined by applying risk measure to the company total losses.

The two risk measures that have generally been used by financial institutions are Value at Risk (VaR) and conditional tail expectation (CTE). CTE is also referred to as Tail Value at Risk (Tail VaR), expected shortfall, and worst conditional expectation (WCE). Other measures, such as the standard deviation of the losses of a company, are also possible. All these measures are based on a view of the possible future loss as a probability distribution.

I.E.1 VaR

The origin of VaR stems from the demand of J.P. Morgan's chairman to see the bank's aggregate risk exposure at 4:15 p.m. every day.

VaR assesses the risk amount as a given quantile α ($0 \leq \alpha < 1$) of the distribution of loss X.

$$VaR_{\alpha}(X) = F_X^{-1}(1-\alpha) \qquad \text{(I.E-1)}$$

Or $\Pr[X \leq VaR_{\alpha}(X)] = \alpha$.

A more formal definition is $VaR_{\alpha}(X) = \inf\{V | \Pr[X \leq V] \geq \alpha\}$.

The origin of VaR stems from the demand of J.P. Morgan's chairman to see the bank's aggregate risk exposure at 4:15 p.m. every day. This 4:15 report was extended to worldwide financial institutions with the introduction of the RiskMetrics system. VaR helps risk managers aggregate their risk amount across business and product lines and to impose risk limit. In the banking industry, $\alpha = 99\%$ is often used for 10-day market risk.

In the area of market risk, there are three common ways to calculate VaR in practice.

I.E.1.a Variance-covariance Method

In the variance-covariance method, VaR is expressed in a linear form such as a multiple of the standard deviation of returns. It is often assumed that the return follows normal or lognormal distribution, and the parameters are estimated by historical data. For example, 10-day VaR at 99% confidence level, $VaR_{99\%}$ is calculated as 2.33 x $\sigma_{day} \sqrt{10}$ by using the standard deviation of daily returns.

While the variance-covariance method offers a simple analytical solution, there are several disadvantages. VaR may not accurately capture the tail risk if a distribution is skewed. Also, linear form cannot adequately express the risk when options or other non-linear instruments are contained in the portfolio. Option Greeks and higher order, such as the quadratic model, need to be incorporated. And when multiple risks inherent are present, it may difficult to find appropriate models for a multivariate distribution.

I.E.1.b Monte Carlo Simulation

This method simulates future portfolio returns by assuming the model of portfolio returns and its parameters. Essentially, there is no restriction on the model, because the analytic form is not necessary. VaR is calculated as a quantile of the simulated loss distribution. While Monte Carlo simulation is more robust than the variance-covariance method, it is time-consuming and may be difficult to apply to large and/or complex portfolios. And as with the variance-covariance method, finding the appropriate multivariate model may be difficult.

I.E.1.c Historical Simulation

Historical simulation resembles Monte Carlo simulation in that it generates a scenario and calculates a quantile of distribution; however, unlike Monte Carlo simulation, historical simulation is a non-parametric approach and does not assume any underlying model or parameters. Instead, historical data is directly used as a histogram of portfolio returns. There is no need to estimate volatility and correlations, as those are already embedded in the historical data. However, the range of outcomes is limited by the historical data, which may not adequately represent the risk for future events. Successful use of this approach greatly depends on the modeler's ability to collect sufficient qualities of relevant data for all risks. Extreme value theory (EVT) may be helpful to provide the estimates of the tail risk.

While VaR provides a convenient tool in normal market conditions over a short timeframe, it also presents several problems. VaR cannot capture the risks that occur with low frequency and high severity. For example, when a loss distribution X follows

$$X = \begin{cases} 0 & with \ probability \ 99\% \\ 10000 & with \ probability \ 1\% \end{cases}$$

the mean loss is 100. However, $VaR_{95\%} = 0$.

VaR is also criticized as a risk measure because of its poor aggregation properties. Arztner et al. (1999) introduced the concept of coherent risk measure that satisfies the following set of consistency rules:

1) Translation invariance

Adding a risk-free asset should not affect the value of the risk measure. For all constant a, $\rho(X + ar) = \rho(X) - a$, with r the return of risk-free asset.

> While the variance-covariance method offers a simple analytical solution, there are several disadvantages. VaR may not accurately capture the tail risk if a distribution is skewed.

2) Subadditivity

The value of the risk measure for two risks combined will not be greater than the risk when treated separately. For all random losses X and Y, $\rho(X + Y) \leq \rho(X) + \rho(Y)$. This property requires that a merger does not create extra risk.

3) Positive homogeneity

The value of the risk measure is independent of scale changes in the unit. For all positive constant b, $\rho(bX) = b\rho(X)$.

4) Monotonicity

If one risk is always equal to or greater than another risk, the risk measure has the same or higher value for the first risk. If $X \leq Y$ for each outcome, then $\rho(X) \leq \rho(Y)$.

It can be shown that VaR does not always satisfy Rule 2, subadditivity. That is, the use of VaR as a risk measure may not properly reflect the diversification effect and may understate concentrated risk.

The use of VaR as a risk measure may not properly reflect the diversification effect and may understate concentrated risk.

Also, while this situation holds for other risk measures currently used, VaR may be misleading in times of market turbulence. Because VaR does not consider the cost of liquidation, other methods such as stress testing and scenario analysis would be necessary to supplement this weakness.

I.E.2 Conditional Tail Expectation [CTE]

Conditional tail expectation (CTE) is the average loss in situations in which the loss exceeds the quantile point α. The CTE applied at a confidence level α (0 α 1) ($0 \leq \alpha < 1$) for a loss distribution X is defined as

$$CTE_\alpha(X) = E\big[X \big| X > VaR_\alpha(X)\big]$$ (I.E-2)

When X is not continuous, the definition of CTE must be modified.

$$CTE_\alpha(X) = VaR_\alpha(X) + \frac{\Pr(X > VaR_\alpha(X))}{1 - \alpha} \times E\big[X - VaR_\alpha(X) \big| X > VaR_\alpha(X)\big]$$ (I.E-3)

CTE at a confidence level α is generally greater than VaR at $\alpha + (100\% - \alpha)/2$. That is, $CTE_{90\%}$ is generally greater than $VaR_{95\%}$.

CTE was made popular by Arztner et al. (1997, 1999) by showing its property of coherence that VaR fails to meet. In the insurance industry, CTE has been adopted by the Canadian Institute of Actuaries in its recommendations with respect to the capital requirement of segregated funds with minimum guarantee. The American Academy of Actuaries followed in its RBC C3 Phase II. In Europe, Swiss regulators adopted CTE 99% to its solvency regulation.

Figure I.E-1 shows standard deviation, VaR (90%), and CTE (90%) in order to illustrate how these metrics differ for a typical skewed distribution. Although VaR is commonly used in the banking industry, the insurance business more commonly involves skewed risk distributions. For this reason, the IAA (2004) has expressed a preference for CTE over VaR. On the other hand, it is often harder to estimate CTE from the same amount of scarce data than VaR, which could lead to increased modeling error.

Figure I.E-1

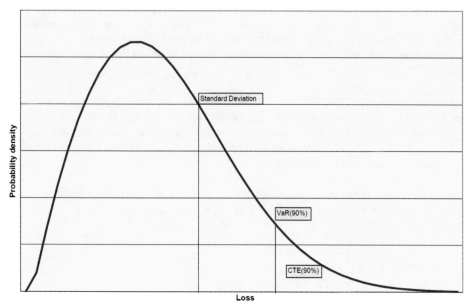

Although VaR is commonly used in the banking industry, the insurance business more commonly involves skewed risk distributions.

I.E.3 Note on the Confidence Level and Time Horizon

While the setting of confidence levels is directly dependent on the risk measure and time horizon, the most common approach is based on the probability of defaulting. The table in Figure I.E-2 shows one-year default rates by credit rating provided by two major credit agencies, Standard & Poor's (S&P) (2005) and Moody's (2005).

Figure I.E-2

Rating	S&P	Moody's
AAA	0.00%	0.00%
AA	0.01%	0.00%
A	0.04%	0.02%
BBB	0.27%	0.16%
BB	1.12%	1.16%
B	5.38%	6.03%
CCC/C	27.02%	23.12%

Sources: *Annual 2005 Global Corporate Default Study and Rating Transition* (S&P); *Default and Recovery Rates of Corporate Bond Issuers, 1920-2004*

If a company targets, for example, AA credit rating using S&P data, the confidence level for one year is 99.99%; however, when the loss is measured with a market-consistent approach, the past default rate may not be useful, because it is accounting-based rather than economic-based. A regulator often targets a confidence level of 99.5% based on BBB credit rating for one year. EU Solvency II projects aim at the confidence level of 99.5% for one-year intervals.

Time horizon is determined as the length of time required for an orderly cancelling out of the risk in question. For example, banking regulation assumes a 10-day holding period for the calculation of market risk in the trading book. This assumption implies that it could take 10 days before all positions are closed out at market prices. Time horizons for illiquid assets such as loans could be longer than for liquid instruments. The appropriate time horizon is not necessarily the same for each risk.

The IAA pointed out that there were likely to be various delays between a solvency assessment and a regulatory action because of the need to prepare the reports, regulatory review, and decisions on appropriate actions. This delay, however, is rarely likely to exceed one year, implying that a one-year horizon for projecting solvency is adequate. Generally, most local regulators appear to be in favour of adopting a one-year time horizon.

While the setting of confidence levels is directly dependent on the risk measure and time horizon, the most common approach is based on the probability of defaulting.

Time horizon is sometimes set at the maturity of the contracts. This approach is called "run-off," and the absence of a regulator's intervention is assumed. RBC C3 Phase II in the United States is a typical example.

I.E.4 Multi-period Risk Measure

The illustrations of risk measure that we have seen in this section so far are *static*, in the sense that they provide the required capital to be held at valuation date taking into consideration only the distribution of future losses. For example, when the risk of insurance liability for the next 20 years is considered, static risk measures focus only on the final value of liability after 20 years. In reality, however, an insurance company may need to increase capital at any point during those 20 years to meet regulatory requirements. On the other hand, if the risk evolves favourably to the company, initially required capital would be excessive.

Multi-period risk measure is winning more attention as the above-mentioned issue emerges for single-period static risk measure. In order to have a better sense of multi-period risk measure, a numerical example of iterated CTE is suggested. For those readers interested in the details, please refer to Hardy and Wirch (2004).

As an example, consider two periods modeled with a binary process, shown in Figure I.E-3.

Figure I.E-3

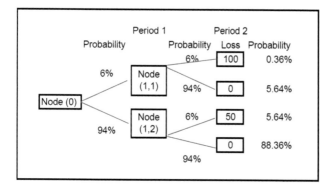

At the end of Period 2, the final value of the liability is 100 with the probability 0.36%, 50 with 5.64%, and 0 with 94%. At Node (0), the required capital at the level of CTE(95%) is calculated as follows:

$$\frac{0.36\% * 100 + (5\% - 0.36\%) * 50}{1 - 95\%} = 53.6 \tag{I.E-4}$$

However, at the end of Period 1, CTE(95%) is either 100 at Node (1,1) or 50 at Node (1,2). In the former case, 53.6 at initial CTE(95%) is not sufficient. Static risk measure completely ignores such possibility of additional capital although it is predictable at Node (0).

Iterated CTE measures risk by a backward process from the final loss through possible paths. From the definition, iterated CTE is 100 at Node (1,1), and 50 at Node (1,2). Iterated CTE at Node (0) is calculated as CTE(95%) of the following distribution of required capital at the end of Period 1.

$$Z = \begin{cases} 100 \text{ at node}(1,1)\text{with probability } 6\% \\ 50 \text{ at node}(1,2)\text{with probability } 94\% \end{cases}$$

That is, iterated CTE is 100 at Node (0). It can be shown that iterated CTE satisfies coherent principles defined in section I.E.1, namely 1) translation invariance, 2) subadditivity, 3) positive homogeneity, and 4) monotonicity. It is also known that iterated CTE is 5) time-consistent, an additional property that is expected for multi-period risk measure.

Time consistency

If a risk measure is the same for two random loss processes X and Y at t for every possible state at t, then the risk measure must also be the same for all earlier dates than t.

In the example of the two-periods binary process, if a risk measure is the same at Nodes (1, 1) and (1, 2), then the risk measure at Node (0) must be same.

The illustrations of risk measure that we have seen in this section so far are static, in the sense that they provide the required capital to be held at valuation date taking into consideration only the distribution of future losses. Multi-period risk measure is winning more attention as the above-mentioned issue emerges for single-period static risk measure.

Another important characteristic of multi-period risk measure is *time step increasing*. That is, multi-period risk measure is expected to be an increasing function of the number of time steps. For example, if a regulator requires annual monitoring of solvency, frequency of risk measure is annual. More frequent monitoring, such as semi-annually, would be more severe than annually, and larger capital would be required if other conditions are the same. According to Hardy and Wirch (2004), while iterated CTE is time step increasing in almost all practical cases, it is possible that iterated CTE is smaller than single CTE in some circumstances.

I.E.5 Note on the Aggregation of Risk

It is widely recognized that risk could be less than the sum of individual risks to the extent that these risks are independent. Typically, however, the risks to which an insurance company is exposed are not independent and have some interaction. Mathematical techniques, such as linear correlation, are used to analyze risk dependencies. But in many cases, there is little historical data to qualify the real relationship among risk factors. It has been pointed out that risk correlations can behave quite differently in extreme scenarios compared with the performance across most of the probability distribution. For example, a severe earthquake or terrorist attack could simultaneously result in mortality and morbidity surges as well as huge drops in asset market price.

> It has been pointed out that risk correlations can behave quite differently in extreme scenarios compared with the performance across most of the probability distribution. For example, a severe earthquake or terrorist attack could simultaneously result in mortality and morbidity surges as well as huge drops in asset market price.

It is therefore necessary to find a method or model to describe dependencies in the absence of reliable source data, especially for extreme events. IAA (2004) recommended copulas as a comprehensive tool to reflect dependencies in a very flexible way. Copulas describe the relationship among the quantiles of distribution of different risks, and they can be selected to recognize tail dependencies in which dependencies occur only in extreme conditions. Interested readers can refer to the appendix of IAA (2004).

I.E.6 Other Risk Measures

Since the introduction of modern portfolio theory by Markowitz, variance or standard deviation has been the dominant risk measure. Although variance is an easily understood concept, it has some drawbacks as a risk measure, because it makes no distinction between positive and negative deviation from the mean. Variance is, in fact, a meaningful risk measure, but only when applied to symmetric distribution, which is often not the case in insurance risk.

Wang (2001) introduced a family of risk measures that use entire distributions of loss rather than the tail of distribution. The risk measure $\rho(x)$ is defined as the mean value under the distorted probability $F^*(X) = g(F(X))$,

$$\rho(X) = E^*(X) = -\int_{-\infty}^{0} g(F(x))dx + \int_{0}^{\infty} [1 - g(F(x))]dx \qquad (\text{I.E-5})$$

VaR corresponds to the discontinuous distortion

$$g(u) = \begin{cases} 0 & when \ u < \alpha \\ 1 & when \ u \geq \alpha \end{cases}$$

CTE corresponds to the distortion

$$g(u) = \begin{cases} 0 & when \ \ u < \alpha \\ \dfrac{u - \alpha}{1 - \alpha} & when \ \ u \geq \alpha \end{cases}$$

The Wang transform method is the special case of such risk measure when the distortion is

$$g(u) = \Phi\left[\Phi^{-1}(u) - \lambda\right] \qquad \text{(I.E-6)}$$

for standard normal cumulative distribution Φ and a constant λ.

Wang transform satisfies the coherence of risk measure. While it has attractive features, Wang transform is more a theoretical concept at this stage, and the practical use is not yet widespread.

References for Section I.E

Artzner P., Delbaen F., Eber J.-M., & Heath, D (1999). Coherent measures of risk. *Mathematical Finance*, 9: 203-228.

Hardy, Mary R. & Wirch, Julia A. (2004). The iterated CTE – a dynamic risk measure. *North American Actuarial Journal* 8.4: 62-75.

International Actuarial Association (2004). *A global framework for insurer solvency assessment.*

Kayes, K. (2005). Risk measurement in insurance, a guide to risk measurement, capital allocation and related decision support issues. Casualty Actuarial Society Discussion Paper Program.

Sanders, D.E.A. (April 2005). *The modeling of extreme events.* Institute of Actuaries.

Wang, S.S. (2001). *A risk measure that goes beyond coherence.* University of Waterloo, Canada.

II. General Applications

II.A Economic Scenario Generators

II.A.1 Interest Rates

This book describes interest rate scenario generation techniques commonly employed to model risks associated with long-term investment products. These include life products, such as variable annuities containing investment guarantees, as well as non-life products.

This section begins a discussion of modeling of realistic yield curve dynamics for short time scales, including issues such as the representation of the yield curve, the shape of the distribution of yield curve changes (normal vs. lognormal), and a principal components picture of yield curve changes.

Calibration of interest rate scenario distribution parameters, key rate analysis of yield curve changes and associated calibration, joint distributions for interest rates and other risk factors, and an expanded discussion of normal versus lognormal dynamics are also explored in this section as part of our discussion of economic scenarios.

Where not explicit, we assume annual rates and annual time steps for convenience of exposition.

Realistic yield curve dynamics

The availability of historical interest rate data provides ample opportunity to develop realistic models that depict yield curve movements observed historically. For example, constant maturity Treasury (CMT) interest rate data over long time periods is readily accessible online from the Federal Reserve (2009). For this reason, it is convenient to use this U.S. rate data for many of the calculations in this book, keeping in mind that the approaches and conclusions are general and apply mainly to developed economies.

Like most government rates, CMT data in the United States is provided in the form of par yield rates,[16] as noted by Hull (2006). However, the data can also be transformed, or "bootstrapped,"[17]

---

[16] For a given bond maturity, the par yield rate is the required coupon rate, so that the bond trades at par. The par yield curve expresses the par yield rate as a function of maturity.

[17] Yield curve information can be represented in terms of either par yield rates, spot rates, or forward rates without loss of information. Transformation between these representations is referred to as bootstrapping.

into continuously compounded spot rates,[18] which have significant theoretical advantages for describing yield curve dynamics. Conversion from par yield to continuously compounded spot rates is calculated using the following formula (with coupons approximated as annual rather than semi annual for convenience):

$$S(0,1) = -\ln\{1/[1+C(0,1)]\}$$
$$S(0,2) = -(1/2)\ln\{[1-C(0,2)\exp(-S(0,1))]/[1+C(0,2)]\}$$
$$S(0,3) = -(1/3)\ln\{[1-C(0,3)\exp(-S(0,1))-C(0,3)\exp(-2S(0,2))]/[1+C(0,3)]\}\text{ etc.}$$

$$(\text{II.A-1})$$

Where $C(0,T)$ is the T-year par yield rate, and $S(0,T)$ is the T-year continuously compounded spot rate.

A key consideration when formulating interest rate scenarios is the assumed shape of the distribution of interest rate changes, typically assumed to be either normal or lognormal. There are, however, disadvantages to each. A purely normal distribution of interest rates produces negative rates in the interest rate scenarios. And a purely lognormal distribution of rates produces very high interest rates with a higher frequency than is realistic. In "real world" applications of distribution of interest rates, it is standard to apply caps and floors to the generated interest rates from either distribution. In option-pricing applications, caps and floors are not applied, because they disrupt the required risk-neutral drift of the scenarios, and because the shape of the tail of the distribution is not critical to the pricing of options, unless the strike differs to a large degree from the value of the underlying security.

A number of considerations can influence the selection of the assumed interest rate distribution.

A number of considerations can influence the selection of the assumed interest rate distribution. Here, we describe results of the maximum likelihood analysis of historical data provided by Klugman (1998). For this purpose, we took 20 years of CMT data for the 1-, 3-, 5-, and 7-year rates (from 1988 to 2009), interpolated intermediate points on the yield curve, and then bootstrapped to spot rates using Equation II.A-1 (for other analyses in this book, 10-year rate data was also used). For both the 3-year and the 7-year spot rates, we assumed that distribution of historical interest rate changes could be generally explained by a process of the constant elasticity of variance (CEV) form

$$\Delta r = \sigma(r/\bar{r})^\gamma \phi \Delta t$$

$$(\text{II.A-2})$$

where drift in the mean is assumed to be small on the time scale of a month, σ and γ are parameters to be determined by a maximum likelihood criteria, $\bar{r}$ is the average rate over the historical period, Δt is the length of the time period, and ϕ is a normal random number. The maximum likelihood parameters obtained are described in the table in Figure II.A-1. A value of γ close to one indicates lognormality, while a value of γ close to zero indicates normality. The maximum likelihood analysis indicates a high degree of normality in rate changes.

▌ **Figure II.A-1**

Rate	Sigma	Gamma
3	0.89%	-0.043
7	0.79%	-0.142

---

[18] For a given bond maturity, the continuously compounded spot rate describes the value of a zero coupon bond relative to par. Specifically, this spot rate is the log ratio of par to the bond value, divided by the maturity. The spot curve expresses the spot rate as a function of maturity.

This likelihood result is just one reason that the authors favour a normal model. Other reasons to favour a normal model include the analytic tractability of the normal model described by Hull (2006), and the natural skew that the normal model produces in swaption[19] prices (which in the authors' experience is more often aligned with the observed skew in recent liquid swaption prices). In the rest of this book, a normal model is assumed unless explicitly stated; however, the analysis readily generalizes to include use of lognormal models. Explicit discussion of this generalization will be introduced where appropriate.

Maximum likelihood analysis can provide reasonable values for the volatility of a given yield curve point, as well as information about the appropriate distribution for the yield curve changes at this point (such as normal or lognormal). Furthermore, a realistic model of yield curve changes must also take into account the correlations among changes in different points on the yield curve. A powerful tool for this purpose is the principal component analysis (PCA) provided by Frye (1997).[20] We have used this tool to analyze spot rate changes from the CMT data, for 3-, 5-, 7-, and 10-year rates. For technical reasons expanded on in the next section, we find it most convenient to perform the PCA analysis on continuously compounded spot rates (where interpolation effects are least pronounced), but then convert these to the forward rates of Hull (2006),[21] where they are most directly applied within a Heath-Jarrow-Morton/Brace-Gatarek-Musiela (HJM/BGM) framework (described in detail in the next section). The tables in Figures II.A-2 and II.A-3 describe results of our PCA analysis for the three most significant factors in yield curve movements, and for spot and forward rates respectively. Consistent with the description in the standard textbook by Hull (2006), our PCA analysis indicates that these factors explain more than 96% of the yield curve variance. We have found that the use of more than three factors is rare in practical applications.

> **Consistent with the description in the standard textbook by Hull (2006), our principal components analysis indicates that these factors explain more than 96% of the yield curve variance.**

Figure II.A-2

Factor \ Maturity	1	2	3	4	5	6	7	8	9	10
1	0.66%	0.77%	0.88%	0.86%	0.85%	0.81%	0.77%	0.75%	0.73%	0.71%
2	-0.39%	-0.26%	-0.12%	-0.05%	0.03%	0.08%	0.13%	0.16%	0.19%	0.22%
3	-0.10%	-0.01%	0.08%	0.07%	0.05%	0.03%	0.00%	-0.03%	-0.06%	-0.08%

Figure II.A-3

Factor \ Maturity	1	2	3	4	5	6	7	8	9	10
1	0.66%	0.87%	1.09%	0.81%	0.79%	0.63%	0.55%	0.60%	0.55%	0.50%
2	-0.39%	-0.13%	0.14%	0.19%	0.36%	0.33%	0.44%	0.34%	0.41%	0.47%
3	-0.10%	0.08%	0.27%	0.03%	0.00%	-0.11%	-0.18%	-0.21%	-0.27%	-0.33%

---

[19] A swaption is an option in which the underlying security has the same value as an interest rate swap.

[20] Principal component analysis is a mathematical tool for transforming a set of correlated variables into a set of uncorrelated variables, where the first variable captures as much of the variance as possible, the second variable captures as much of the remaining variance as possible, and so forth.

[21] When expressed in continuously compounded terms, conversion between forward rates and spot rates is particularly straightforward: the T-year spot rate is a simple average of the forward rates over these T years.

PCA analysis is useful for modeling short time dynamics of yield curves. Subsequent sections address long time yield curve dynamics for applications where either arbitrage-free or realistic scenarios are needed.

HJM/BGM framework for generating arbitrage-free interest rate scenarios

The Heath-Jarrow-Morton / Brace-Gatarek-Musiela (HJM/BGM) framework provides a means for generating risk-neutral interest rate scenarios appropriate for option-pricing exercises.

Having described realistic dynamics for the yield curve on short time scales, we now turn to the more important issue of expected drift in interest rates over longer timeframes. Ignoring drift, and assuming annual rates and time steps, the results from the previous section could be interpreted as prescribing yield curve dynamics of the following form:

$$F_t(t+T) = F_{t-1}(t+T) + \sum_q \Lambda_{q,T+1} \phi_{q,t} \tag{II.A-3}$$

Here, $F_t(t+T)$ is the time t rate T years forward, $F_{t-1}(t+T)$ is the previous rate for this time period, $\phi_{q,t}$ is a normal random number drawn for the q factor at time t, and $\Lambda_{i,j}$ is a matrix element representation of the factors (see Figure II.A-3 for an example).

The HJM/BGM framework provides a means for generating risk-neutral interest rate scenarios appropriate for option-pricing exercises. For a model in which continuously compounded forward interest rates are normally distributed, the HJM/BGM framework prescribes the following form for the generated yield curve changes:

$$F_t(t+T) = F_{t-1}(t+T) + \sum_q \left[\Lambda_{q,T+1} \phi_{q,t} + \Lambda_{q,T+1} \left(-\Lambda_{q,T+1}/2 + \sum_{i=1}^{T+1} \Lambda_{q,i} \right) \right] \tag{II.A-4}$$

This form generates arbitrage-free scenarios consistent with the prices of zero coupon bonds implied by the forward rates in the following sense: if one discounts cash flows path-wise using realized short interest rates and then calculates an expected present value, the price of the zero coupon bond is re-attained. In other words

$$E[\exp(-F_0(0) - F_1(1) - F_2(2) - ... - F_N(N))] = \exp(-F_0(0) - F_0(1) - F_0(2) - ... - F_0(N)) \tag{II.A-5}$$

where $E[...]$ denotes an expected present value over scenarios. This condition is a requirement of arbitrage-free interest rate scenarios used in option valuation applications. Similarly, if a given financial instrument provides a scenario-dependent cash flow CF_N at time N, the contribution to the value of the instrument is

$$PV = E[\exp(-F_0(0) - F_1(1) - F_2(2) - ... - F_N(N))CF_N] \tag{II.A-6}$$

It should be noted that in many option-pricing applications, swap rates are a more appropriate risk-neutral interest rate than Treasury rates. That said, historical data for the swap-to-Treasury spread indicates this quantity is much less volatile than the overall level of rates, and so volatility measures inferred from CMT data are appropriate for modeling swap-rate changes as well.

The HJM/BGM framework describes a general form that arbitrage-free generators must take. As such, popular arbitrage-free generation models that assume a certain form for the interest rate dynamics can be viewed simply as specific examples of HJM/BGM generators that assume a simple parametric form for convenience.

The prescribed drift in HJM/BGM scenarios is appropriate for generating arbitrage-free scenarios, but it may not lead to the kind of realistic scenarios needed for applications such as capital adequacy testing.

Realistic scenarios over longer time scales

For applications such as capital adequacy testing, it may be necessary to use realistic scenarios over longer time scales. For these time scales, neither the drift expression in Equation II.A-3, nor the drift expression in Equation II.A-4 may be particularly realistic, because the expectation values for future interest rates may not exhibit a term structure that is typical in the historical data, and the level of rates may not be consistent with the historical average. A second issue encountered in Equations II.A-3 and II.A-4 is the generation of negative rates, which may be undesirable in applications requiring realistic scenarios.

Specifying a target yield curve ($\{F_\infty(t_{target} + T)\}$) and a time period t_{target} over which the initial curve would tend toward this curve (on an expected basis) could address the first issue. Assuming a constant rate of approach, we obtain an expression of the following form:

$$
\begin{aligned}
F_t(t+T) = F_{t-1}(t+T) + & \left[\sum_q \Lambda_{q,T+1}\varphi_{q,t} \right] + \left[\delta_{t \le t_{target}}(1/t_{target})(F_\infty(t_{target}+T) - F_0(t_{target}+T)) \right] \\
& + \left[(1 - \delta_{t \le t_{target}})(F_\infty(t_{target}+T)) - F_\infty(t_{target}+T+1)) \right]
\end{aligned}
$$

(II.A-7)

where $\delta_{t \le t_{target}}$ is equal to one when $t \le t_{target}$, and equal to zero after that.

Caps and floors can be applied to rates generated by Equation II.A-7. These caps and floors will have some impact on the long-term expected values of the interest rates. If this is a concern for a given application, then the long-term target rates can be adjusted as a calibration exercise to restore long-term targets.

Other features of historical yield curve data may be relevant for given applications, including yield curve inversion frequencies and mean reversion of interest rates. In subsequent sections, we discuss connections among parameters used for scenario generation and features of the generated scenarios, as well as a more general calibration of the scenario generation parameters.

Calibration of the interest rate generator

In addition to the approaches already discussed, a number of other criteria may be used to calibrate the generator to make it consistent with historical distributions of short-term interest rate changes and historical rate averages. A given application will affect which criteria are most important.

In some cases, consistency with prices of liquid options is more important than consistency with statistical features of the historical data. One such case arises when fair valuation accounting requirements require the valuation of financial products to be consistent with market prices. Even in

> For applications such as capital adequacy testing, it may be necessary to use realistic scenarios over longer time scales.

the absence of such requirements, calibration to market prices may be useful to obtain reasonable values for quantities difficult to estimate from historical data, such as anticipated mean reversion rates for the yield curve.

Because of the liquidity of the swaptions market, the prices of these instruments are commonly selected for calibration of interest rate generators. One popular approach, from Hull and White (2000), is to maintain the proportional contribution from the historically calibrated principal component factors, but to scale the overall volatility. In this case, Equation II.A-4 takes the form

$$F_t(t+T) = F_{t-1}(t+T) + k_T \sum_q \left[\Lambda_{q,T+1}\phi_{q,t} + \Lambda_{q,T+1}\left(-\Lambda_{q,T+1}/2 + \sum_{i=1}^{T+1}\Lambda_{q,i} \right) \right] \qquad \text{(II.A-8)}$$

Where k_T describes maturity-dependent scaling factors that bring the scenario-based calculation of swaption prices (see Equation II.A-6) in line with the prices of liquid swaptions. The values of k_T can be reconciled to swaption prices using standard optimization techniques.

In some cases, parametric models have advantages over PCA-based modeling of interest rate scenarios. For example, these models have readily interpreted parameters that can be useful in extrapolating yield curve dynamics to large times, providing a reasonableness check on the unregulated results generated using PCA analysis. One of the simplest parametric models is the one-factor Hull-White (2000) model, in which the factors described in Equation II.A-4 take the following form:

$$\Lambda_{1,j} = \Lambda_{1,1} \exp[-a(j-1)]$$
$$\Lambda_{i>1,j} = 0 \qquad \text{(II.A-9)}$$

In this simple two-parameter model, $\Lambda_{1,1}$ describes the volatility of the short interest rate on small time scales, and a describes the rate at which the short rate tends to revert to the mean. As with the values of k_T in Equation II.A-8, the values of $\Lambda_{1,1}$ and a can be reconciled to swaption prices using standard optimization techniques. The one-factor Hull-White model, however, cannot fit a series of at-the-money[22] swaption prices exactly, so some fit criteria (such as mean squared error) must be used in this case. The one-factor Hull-White model can provide a more easily interpreted physical picture than PCA analysis, and calibration of the Hull-White model helps ensure that the long-time dynamics of the yield curve are transparent and physically reasonable.

Even within PCA analysis, the optimized values of the Hull-White parameters can be useful. For example, if one requires values for the PCA factors beyond provided maturities (nine years in the example provided by Figures II.A-2 and II.A-3), the exponential decay factor described in Equation II.A-9 can be used to create a natural slope for the factor values at high maturities. Market-consistent values for $\Lambda_{1,1}$ and a will depend on the market prices on a given day, but typical recent values have been 1.1% and 5%.

The shape of the Hull-White factors elucidates a more general and fundamental correspondence between the mean reversion rate for interest rates and the decay rate for the interest rate factors. In applications where realistic scenarios are needed, the decay rate of the interest rate factors is an

---

[22] An at-the-money option is an option for which the strike is equal to the value of the underlying.

important feature to calibrate, as one seeks to reproduce relevant statistical properties for the generated scenarios.

In cases where inversion frequencies are important, a multifactor model must be used. The simplest multifactor generalization of the Hull-White model is the two-factor Hull-White model (2000). This model is characterized by a stochastic long-term rate that has its own volatility and mean reversion, independent of (but correlated with) the short rate.

Although analysis using PCA or parametric factors provides a natural description of many equilibrium properties of yield curve scenarios, other descriptions are possible and sometimes useful. In some cases, analysis using so-called key rates can provide a more natural link to statistical properties for the generator.

In some cases, analysis using so-called key rates can provide a more natural link to statistical properties for the generator.

Key rate analysis of yield curve changes and associated calibration

A common approach to modeling yield curve changes is to employ the so-called key rate analysis of Tuckman (2002). This approach assumes that yield curve changes are driven by piecewise linear factors focused around certain important ("key") rates. Assuming a spot key rate model, and key rates of 1, 5, and 10, the key rate factors take the form shown in Figure II.A-4 (for rate volatility assumptions underlying our PCA analysis).

Figure II.A-4

Factor \ Maturity	1	2	3	4	5	6	7	8	9	10
1	0.78%	0.58%	0.39%	0.19%	0.00%	0.00%	0.00%	0.00%	0.00%	0.00%
2	0.00%	0.21%	0.42%	0.64%	0.85%	0.68%	0.51%	0.34%	0.17%	0.00%
3	0.00%	0.00%	0.00%	0.00%	0.00%	0.15%	0.30%	0.45%	0.59%	0.74%

Figure II.A-5

Factor \ Maturity	1	2	3	4	5	6	7	8	9	10
1	0.78%	0.39%	0.00%	-0.39%	-0.78%	0.00%	0.00%	0.00%	0.00%	0.00%
2	0.00%	0.43%	0.85%	1.27%	1.70%	-0.16%	-0.52%	-0.83%	-1.20%	-1.52%
3	0.00%	0.00%	0.00%	0.00%	0.00%	0.89%	1.20%	1.47%	1.79%	2.08%

To use these factors within an HJM/BGM model, the factors should be expressed in terms of forward rates, as shown in Figure II.A-5. Also, HJM/BGM models are most conveniently formulated for factors that are uncorrelated. Correlations among the key rate factors described here can be determined consistently with the PCA analysis; it is then convenient to define uncorrelated factors as follows, using a Cholesky decomposition from Hull (2006):

$$Factor1 = Factor1^{(0)} + \rho_{12}Factor2^{(0)} + \rho_{13}Factor3^{(0)}$$
$$Factor2 = (1-\rho_{12}^2)^{1/2} Factor2^{(0)} + \rho_{23}Factor3^{(0)}$$
$$Factor3 = (1-\rho_{13}^2 - \rho_{23}^2)^{1/2} Factor3^{(0)}$$

(II.A-10)

These uncorrelated factors can be readily used in Equation II.A-4 to create arbitrage-free scenarios.

Use of key rate factors to model changes in the yield curve is advantageous for certain applications. This includes hedging applications where one wants to use a portfolio of simple bonds to match the market sensitivities of a more complex instrument; a key rate analysis can approximately decompose the problem into a set of independent matching problems for different maturities.

A key rate picture is also useful when producing realistic scenarios, particularly if it is coupled with drift adjustments. The parameters in this yield curve modeling approach provide a more intuitive link to features of the historical data, including yield curve inversion frequencies and mean reversion of rates.

Combination of interest rate scenarios with other risk factors

Combining interest rate scenarios with other risk factors is a concern for both risk-neutral scenarios and realistic scenarios. We begin by considering the case of risk-neutral scenarios, in which the considerations are more easily quantified.

When using risk-neutral stochastic interest rate scenarios, the risk-neutral asset is a money market account (or, in discrete set generators, a certificate of deposit account). To be consistent with the valuation framework alluded to in Equation II.A-6, the expected (risk-neutral) growth rate of all assets should match that of the risk-free asset. This would include growth of equities assumed to have a lognormal distribution

$$S_t = S_{t-1} \exp[F_{t-1}(t-1) + \sigma_{t-1}\phi_{t-1}^{(e)} - \sigma_{t-1}^2 / 2]$$ (II.A-11)

Here, S_t is the value of the equity at time t, $F_{t-1}(t-1)$ is the realized short rate at the beginning of the period, σ_{t-1} is the forward equity volatility, and $\phi_{t-1}^{(e)}$ is a normal random number. If interest rate volatility is zero (for example, in the sense of $\Lambda_{1,1} = 0$ in Equation II.A-9), then $F_{t-1}(t-1)$ will be equal to the time-zero forward rate for this forward period, and the traditional "forward measure" distribution underlying the Black-Scholes equation is re-attained, as noted by Hull (2006). However, when there is interest rate volatility, this interest rate volatility becomes a component of the overall equity volatility, and the excess equity volatility parameters σ_{t-1} must be recalibrated for the presence of the stochastic interest rates.

As detailed in Overhaus (2007), correlation among interest rates and the returns on assets, such as equities, introduces yet another source of complexity and affects the calibration of the volatility parameters σ_{t-1}. Figure II.A-6 shows the value of the spot excess equity volatilities that must be used to achieve a cumulative Black-Scholes equity volatility of 20%, given Hull-White parameters $\Lambda_{1,1} = 1\%$ and $a = 0\%$. In general, over long periods, the excess equity volatility must be reduced when stochastic interest rates are present to avoid double-counting the volatility introduced by changes in interest rates. But negative equity rate correlation values can moderate this effect.

In general, over long periods, the excess equity volatility must be reduced when stochastic interest rates are present to avoid double-counting the volatility introduced by changes in interest rates.

█ Figure II.A-6

Maturity	Correlation -20%	0%	20%
1	20.0%	20.0%	20.0%
2	20.1%	20.0%	19.9%
3	20.2%	20.0%	19.7%
4	20.2%	19.9%	19.6%
5	20.3%	19.9%	19.4%
6	20.3%	19.8%	19.3%
7	20.3%	19.7%	19.1%
8	20.3%	19.6%	18.9%
9	20.3%	19.4%	18.7%
10	20.2%	19.3%	18.4%

> ... application of the lognormal Heath-Jarrow-Morton / Brace-Gatarek-Musiela (HJM/BGM) equation presents a number of computational disadvantages.

Lognormally vs. normally distributed interest rate scenarios, revisited

Starting with a discussion of interest rates by describing a number of features of normal versus lognormal interest rate dynamics, we then assumed primarily normal dynamics. But Hull (2006) notes that generalizing results and conclusions for lognormal dynamics is straightforward, as in the example of deriving the lognormal HJM/BGM analog in Equation II.A-4. By contrast, actual application of the lognormal HJM/BGM equation presents a number of computational disadvantages outlined in standard references on the subject such as Hull (2006). Among them are the computation expense associated with applying the required exponentiation operations, and the numerical, rather than analytical, integration requirement for the lognormal approach. Consequently, accuracy for such may require shorter simulation time steps.

In general, the assumed distribution (normal or lognormal) can have consequences for valuation of options. For example, lognormal interest rate models are structurally incapable of generating skew in swaption prices, whereas normal interest rate models generate natural skew. Nevertheless, either model can typically be calibrated to capture features important for a given application.

The authors have outlined a number of advantages associated with normal interest rate models; however, different applications may introduce different considerations, which can affect the model selection decision. The selection can also be influenced by factors such as the economic environment or the current level of interest rates within the economy (country) being considered.

II.A.2 Exchange Rates

With the globalization of the world economies, insurance liabilities and assets are increasingly exposed to foreign exchange components, which should be included in modeling scenarios.

According to interest rate parity (IRP), the foreign exchange (FX) rate movements are determined by the risk-free rate differentials between two economies. For the purpose of discussion, let us use the following notations, assuming only two economies: domestic and foreign.

X(t): exchange rate, at time *t*, between domestic currency and foreign currency expressed as *X(t)* units of foreign currency per one unit of domestic currency.

RFD: domestic nominal continuous risk-free rate.

RFF: foreign nominal continuous risk-free rate.

Then IRP dictates that

$$X(t+1) = X(t) * \exp(RFF\text{-}RFD) \tag{II.A-12}$$

There is much controversy related to the validity of IRP, which is discussed in detail in Solnik and McLeavey (2004; see p. 100). One counterexample to the use of IRP is that of the much lower than presently observed Japanese yen (JPY) to U.S. dollars (USD) ratio. Despite the limitations of IRP, it is still widely used as the cornerstone in generating FX rate scenarios, largely because this relationship can be hedged using current market instruments.

Despite the limitations of IRP (interest rate parity), it is still widely used as the cornerstone in generating FX rate scenarios ...

Because the FX rates are fundamentally driven by the differential between RFF and RFD, the scenario generation processes can be broadly separated into two categories: those using deterministic interest rates, and those using stochastic interest rates.

FX models with deterministic interest rates

The most common FX rate models with deterministic interest rates are lognormal models. The formula for this model is summarized below.

$$X(t+\Delta t) = X(t) * \exp((RFF\text{-}RFD - vol^2 / 2)* \Delta t + \mathrm{sqrt}(\Delta t) *vol * Z) \tag{II.A-13}$$

where *vol* is the assumed volatility, and *RFF* and *RFD* are the deterministic forward risk-free rates. *Z* is a random number from a normal distribution.

This form is very similar to lognormal equity returns with one difference: *RFF-RFD* is substituted for the risk-free rate. The volatility can be determined using two approaches: historical and market.

In the historical volatility approach, the *vol* is the standard deviation of the FX return over certain, though subjective, periods of time. For this reason, this approach can result in substantially different volatilities. Selecting too short a period could jeopardize the credibility of results because of an insufficient number of observations. Conversely, selecting too long a period could introduce data that is no longer relevant. As a rule of thumb, the best observation period is the preceding time period with the same expected life of the business to be modeled. For example, if the scenarios are intended for modeling a block of business with a 10-year expected life from the valuation date of January 1, 2009, then the best observation period would be January 1, 1999, through January 1, 2009. Some practitioners also explicitly add a margin to the historical *vol* for conservatism.

The historical *vol* is constant over time and does not have a term structure. The option values calculated using historical *vol* also do not necessarily conform to the observed market prices of those options.

The historical *vol* approach is often appropriate for companies that take a long-term view and are less concerned with short-term volatility fluctuations.

In the market volatility approach, the *vol* is the implied volatility observed from market quotes. With the observed *RFF* and *RFD*, one should be able to replicate the observed option prices using Monte Carlo simulation based on the scenarios using the Black-Scholes formula with market *vol*.

The market *vol* approach results in a term structure for the volatilities, which is useful if the scenarios are to be used for multiple periods. In the periods where no market quotes are available, the implied forward volatility is graded to a long-term historical amount. The implied spot *vol* is generally not graded to prevent non-sensible results, such as negative implied forward volatility.

The market *vol* approach is often used for companies adopting a market-consistent valuation methodology.

The market *vol* approach results in a term structure for the volatilities, which is useful if the scenarios are to be used for multiple periods.

FX models with stochastic interest rates

In the FX models with stochastic interest rates, the same lognormal formula is used. However, here the *RFF* and *RFD* are both stochastic interest rates. These models are often a by-product of models requiring stochastic interest rates, such as models for guaranteed minimum income benefits (GMIB).

The historical *vol* approach can be used similarly for the FX models with deterministic interest rates.

When using the market *vol* approach, however, the option prices calculated using Monte Carlo simulation would be higher than what the implied *vol* suggests, because the dealer-quoted implied *vols* are based on deterministic interest rates.

In order to calibrate to the observed market price, one has to adjust the implied *vol* down. The adjustment process is an iterative process and must be done for all points on the volatility forward curve. The adjustment can be up to 1% in implied *vol*.

FX model with deterministic interest rates vs. FX model with stochastic interest rates

FX models with stochastic interest rates capture more moving parts in the FX process; therefore, using stochastic interest rates increases the complexity, but does not necessarily increase the accuracy in these FX models. For this reason, many practitioners prefer to use FX models with deterministic interest rates because of their simplicity and shorter run time. The use of deterministic rates is also preferred, since both models need to be calibrated to the same market-observed FX option prices when using implied *vol*. Of course, if stochastic interest rates are already implemented for other reasons, one would be better off using FX models with stochastic interest rates for consistency.

Validating FX models

FX modeling of interest rates and foreign assets is further complicated by the need to validate the model itself. A common approach is to examine the reaction of domestic returns of various assets under given shocks to interest rates.

An upward shock to *RFD* should mean that:

- **Domestic equity returns increase the same as the *RFD* shock.**
- **Domestic bonds experience an immediate loss of value because of its duration.**
- **Domestic bond future returns increase the same as the *RFD* shock.**
- **The FX returns increase the same as the *RFD* shock. Because foreign bonds do not have duration to *RFD*, the returns measured in the domestic currency for both foreign bonds and foreign equity will show an increase the same as the *RFD* shock because of the FX movement.**

If the *RFF* experiences an up shock, then the following should be observed:

- **No change in returns for domestic equity or domestic bonds.**
- **The FX returns decrease the same as the *RFF* shock.**
- **The increase in return measured in foreign currency for foreign equity is negated by the FX return decrease, so the return for foreign equity measured in domestic currency is unchanged. The value of foreign bonds has an immediate drop because of duration, but the future increase in return is negated by the FX return reduction. So the only observable phenomenon in domestic currency is the immediate drop of foreign bonds value.**

II.A.3 Equity Returns

This section describes equity scenario generation techniques commonly employed to model risks associated with long-term investment products, such as variable annuities containing investment guarantees. It begins with an overview of equity scenario generation, and then covers arbitrage-free generation of equity scenarios, stylized facts of equity volatility, extensions to the Black-Scholes framework, realistic equity scenarios, and risk-neutral market calibration of equity models.

An overview of equity scenario generation

Modeling equity scenarios calls for generators that exhibit certain characteristics reflecting properties of equity returns. Given this basic requirement, equity scenario generators must not allow the equity level to drift below zero. This is typically accomplished by assuming that equity levels follow a lognormal distribution.

The most common model for equity returns is geometric Brownian motion (GBM), which uses a stochastic process called a Wiener process, denoted by W_t. The Wiener process starts from zero,

The most common model for equity returns is geometric Brownian motion (GBM), which uses a stochastic process called a Wiener process.

has independent and normally distributed increments, and is continuous in time t as defined by increments of dW_t. The stochastic differential equation (SDE) for GBM is as follows:

$$dS_t = \mu_t S_t dt + \sigma_t S_t dW_t \qquad \text{(II.A-14)}$$

There are two components of this equation. The drift component is the coefficient of dt and the diffusion component is the coefficient of dW_t. Here the drift component μ_t is a deterministic function of t, and the diffusion component σ_t is a deterministic function of t. To remove excess noise from the simulation of S_t, the log transform is applied using Ito's lemma. After applying the log transform the equation is as follows:

$$dS_t = S_t \exp\{(\mu_t - \sigma_t^2/2)dt + \sigma_t dW_t\} \qquad \text{(II.A-15)}$$

From Equation II.A-15 it is clear that the S_t term has been removed from the diffusion coefficient and reduces noise when simulating the process. To generate scenarios, the discrete-time approximation of Equation II.A-15 becomes

$$S_t = S_{t-1} \exp\{(\mu_t - \sigma_t^2/2)dt + \sigma_t \phi_t\} \qquad \text{(II.A-16)}$$

where ϕ_t is a normal random number drawn at time t, S_t is the equity level at time t, μ_t is the drift component at time t, and σ_t is the volatility at time t. Equation II.A-16 represents the most common simulation technique for generating equity scenarios. From this equation we can see that the equity level cannot drift below zero.

The most common extensions of the SDE in Equation II.A-15 are modifications to the diffusion term. Modifications to this term depend on the equity market in consideration, as well as stylistic facts of equity returns, discussed in later sections.

Arbitrage-free equity scenario generation

For equity scenarios to be considered arbitrage-free, a measure change is needed. In Equation II.A-14, the drift component is assumed to be the real-world measure, referred to as measure P. The risk-neutral measure, referred to as the Q measure, provides a way to generate arbitrage-free equity scenarios. Converting P to Q requires a change in the drift term of Equation II.A-14. For equity scenarios to be considered risk-neutral or arbitrage-free, the equity level drift term must be the risk-free rate, which can be calculated from the term structure of interest rates in the economy of interest. Typically in the United States, risk-free rates are bootstrapped from either Treasury rates or the swap curve. Equation II.A-16) changes as follows:

$$S_t = S_{t-1} \exp\{(F_t(t+dt) - \sigma_t^2/2)dt + \sigma_t \phi_t\} \qquad \text{(II.A-17)}$$

The $F_t(T)$ in the drift term is the continuously compounded forward rate at time t for the period from t to T. The forward rates for each period can be derived from the term structure of risk-free rates. Note that the function $F_t(T)$ is a deterministic function of the Treasury rate, or swap rate curve, and is predetermined at time 0.

If the equity pays a dividend, then the continuously compounded dividend yield must be subtracted from the drift term. This adjustment is necessary to preserve risk-neutral scenarios, because the equity level adjusts downward in the presence of a dividend. The expected growth rate of the equity is also lowered.

The dividend-adjusted equation is

$$S_t = S_{t-1} \exp\{(F_t(t+dt) - q - \sigma_t^2 / 2)dt + \sigma_t \phi_t\}$$
(II.A-18)

where q is the continuously compounded dividend yield.

Stylized facts of equity index returns

The geometric Brownian motion is by far the most widely used formula for equity scenario generation. The famous Black-Scholes option-pricing model assumes that the underlying equity price follows a GBM. Therefore, the model inherently assumes that equity returns are incrementally independent and normally distributed. This is contrary to many commonly observed and widely noted behaviours of equity returns, which we will now address.

Implied volatility surface

Arguably the most serious shortcoming of the Black-Scholes option-pricing model is its inability to match options prices over a spectrum of maturities and strikes. These option prices are often represented as an implied volatility surface, which serves as a two-dimensional representation of the prices of options via their implied volatility. Typically the dimensions of the surface are time to maturity and strike. This surface has volatility skew, indicated by the higher implied *vol* of the low strike options compared with high strike options, or vice versa. The surface also has a volatility term structure, represented by different implied volatilities for different maturities. While volatility term structure can be handled with an extension to the Black-Scholes equation, equity volatility skew cannot. Implied volatility skew occurs in the surface of equity options, because low strike puts typically have higher implied volatilities than high strike calls.

▎ Figure II.A-7

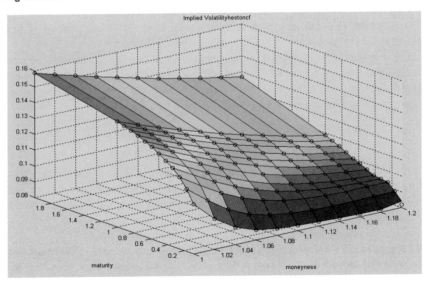

> The famous Black-Scholes option-pricing model assumes that the underlying equity price follows a geometric Brownian motion or GBM.

Since the market crash of 1987, this characteristic has been exhibited by most equity indices volatility surfaces, reflecting, among other things, the market's concern that crash probabilities are much higher than those suggested by the Black-Scholes model. In Figure II.A-7, we provide the implied volatility surface 2005 for the S&P 500 observed on September 30, 2005. The left axis is the maturity of the option and the right axis is the moneyness (strike price/current equity level) of the option. The darker blue areas of the surface are lowest implied volatilities and the red areas are the highest implied volatilities.

Stochastic volatility and the leverage effect

The graph in Figure II.A-8 shows weekly snapshots of the levels of the S&P 500 (black) and the Chicago Board Options Exchange Volatility Index (VIX) (grey) from the start of 2000 to the middle of 2005. The VIX is an index derived from the volatility of short-term at-the-money options on the S&P 500 and can be thought of as a proxy for the market's price for one-month equity volatility.

Two empirical facts emerge from the graph in Figure II.A-8. First, volatility is not constant. In fact, the volatility of the VIX is often greater than sample standard deviation of the S&P 500. Second, VIX movements are inversely correlated to S&P 500 movements. Specifically, note the period from the beginning of 2004 to the end of the sample. This period is marked by a steady *increase* in the S&P 500 and a steady *decrease* in its volatility. This phenomenon, commonly observed in equity return series, is known as the leverage effect and is responsible for the equity volatility skew.

Chicago Board Options Exchange Volatility Index (VIX)

■ **Figure II.A-8**

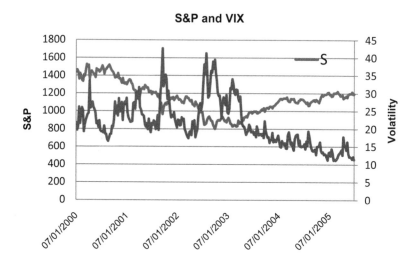

Fat tails

Equity returns are more extreme than a normal distribution would suggest. The graphs in Figure II.A-9 illustrate that the normal approximation is poor in the tails, particularly the lower tail. The graph on the left shows the cumulative density function of the actual observed data (purple) and the closest-fitting normal distribution (red). The graph on the right magnifies the fit in the left tail. Note that the actual observed data is well above the fitted normal, suggesting that actual returns are much more extreme than a normal distribution.

▌ **Figure II.A-9**

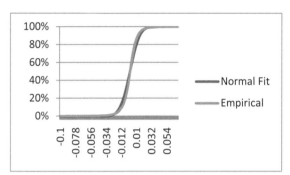
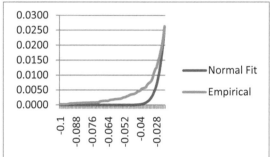

Volatility persistence

While it is debatable whether asset returns have memory, there is no question that the volatility of asset returns has exceptionally long memory. This phenomenon is known as volatility persistence and has strong implications for risk management and hedging strategies. The graph in Figure II.A-10 shows that the volatility of the market at any given time will impact the volatility of the market more than 400 trading days from now. It was derived by taking lagged correlations of the squared normalized daily returns of the S&P 500 from 1986 to 2005. For a time series of this length, any correlation estimate above 1.5% is significant.

▌ **Figure II.A-10**

The volatility of asset returns has exceptionally long memory, known as volatility persistence, and has strong implications for risk management and hedging strategies.

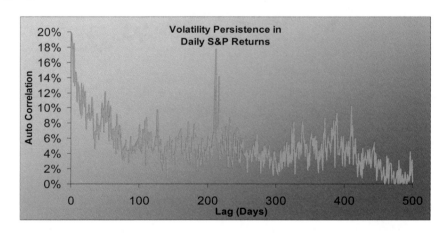

Volatility clustering

Volatility clustering is concentrated periods of high volatility. There are some periods of time when information arrival is slow (weekends and holidays, for example), and other times when information arrival is rapid (elections, earnings releases, and mergers and acquisitions announcements). The graph in Figure II.A-11 shows a time series of weekly returns for the S&P 500 (black), sampled from the beginning of 2000 to the middle of 2005. The graph also includes 95% confidence interval bounds (grey) for the predicted return from a generalized autoregressive conditional heteroskedasticity (GARCH[1,1]) model calibrated to the time-series. From the gray lines it is evident that the GARCH[1,1] model predicts short periods of high volatility that eventually revert to normal levels.

■ **Figure II.A-11**

S & P Returns and GARCH Bounds

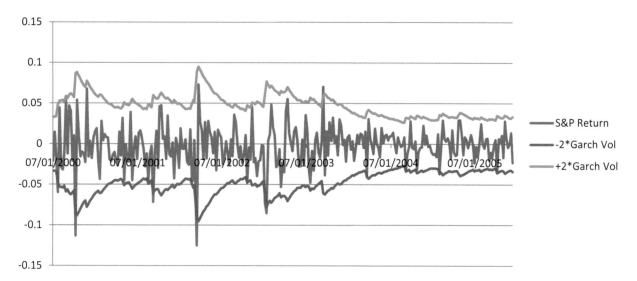

Note: Modeling Volatility Clustering

Volatility clustering can be modeled with two distinct components. The first component is a long-run volatility process that moves with the general economic cycle – low in economic expansions and high in recessions. The second component is a short-lived component, intended to model day-to-day information arrival. This component jumps up for short periods of time before quickly reverting back to a low level (about zero). This type of model is an involved extension of the Black-Scholes framework and is beyond the scope of this text.

Extensions of the Black-Scholes framework

The shortcomings of an assumption in the Black-Scholes framework – that the equity price follows a GBM – prevent extensions to the dynamics of the equity price at this time. The most common extensions involve modifying the σ_t in the SDE for GBM.

Local volatility models

Local volatility models attempt to explain the shape of the volatility surface by generalizing the function σ_t, which is a function of time only, to $\sigma(S_t, t)$. The SDE for the dynamics of the equity price becomes

$$dS_t = \mu_t S_t dt + \sigma(S_t, t) dW_t \qquad \text{(II.A-19)}$$

A simple function that satisfies the equation and can be easily calibrated is the constant elasticity of variance (CEV) model, which has the following form

$$dS_t = \mu_t S_t dt + \sigma(t) S_t^\alpha dW_t \qquad \text{(II.A-20)}$$

If α is equal to one, then GBM is recovered. Values of α less than one allow for natural skew in the model.

Stochastic volatility models

Stochastic volatility models attempt to explain the dynamics of the equity returns by generalizing the function σ_t to be a separate (possibly correlated) stochastic process with separate dynamics. Allowing σ_t to be stochastic allows for dynamics that are closer to what is observed in the historical market data. The most common stochastic volatility model is given by the Heston model for which the SDE can be described as follows:

$$
\begin{aligned}
dS_t &= \mu_t S_t dt + \sqrt{V_t} S_t dW_t \\
dV_t &= \kappa(\theta - V_t) dt + \nu \sqrt{V_t} dZ_t \\
d[S, V] &= \rho dt
\end{aligned}
\qquad \text{(II.A-21)}
$$

The last line means that the two processes are correlated with parameter Rho.

Realistic equity scenarios

Motivation for simulating realistic equity scenarios stems from their usefulness in determining the amount of liabilities to hold against an issued instrument. If the market risk of the instrument is not hedged, reserves provide protection based on certain probabilities. Otherwise, risk-neutral scenarios are appropriate for valuation.

The risk-neutral drift typically is not shown as the actual market expectation empirically. Historical equity return data seems to indicate a risk premium over the risk-free rate. The American Academy of Actuaries estimates the return on equity processes to range from 7% to 10%, which in a 5% interest rate environment indicates a 2% to 5% equity risk premium. To model realistic equity returns, use Equation II.A-16 with the function

$$\mu_t = F_t(t + dt) + rp \qquad \text{(II.A-22)}$$

Where rp is the equity risk premium over the risk-free rate. The drift specified by μ_t is now more aligned with empirical evidence, though it is no longer risk-neutral. Another aspect of realistic scenarios is the fact that volatility is stochastic, as can be seen from returns data in the previous

---

Another aspect of realistic scenarios is the fact that volatility is stochastic.

section. To model stochastic volatility, simulation of a separate volatility process is necessary. The parameters of a volatility process can be calibrated using maximum likelihood analysis of historical equity returns data, which is beyond the scope of this text.

Risk-neutral equity model calibration

Deterministic volatility calibration

Calibration of equity models is generally straightforward given simple dynamics for the equity process. For example, when calibrating a term structure of volatilities for GBM, one can simply look to the liquid option markets and retrieve quotes for at-the-money options. Each quote for implied volatility represents a point on the term structure, and then the forward volatilities can be bootstrapped. The bootstrapping algorithm to find the function σ_t can be found using the equation

$$\sigma_i^F = sqrt[\frac{(\sigma_i^S)^2 * t_i - \sigma_{i-1}^S * t_{i-1}}{t_i - t_{i-1}}]$$
(II.A-23)

Each parameter σ_i^F is the input for σ_t of Equation II.A-16. Note that this equation is similar to the equation used to calculate forward interest rates under continuous compounding.

Stochastic volatility calibration

Given that the Heston stochastic volatility model is the most commonly used, we will illustrate calibration techniques and results for this model on market data for the S&P 500 index volatility surface.

Calibration function

There are many objective functions to choose from when calibrating the Heston model to observed market data. They all are least squares functions, but have subtle differences in the implicit weights they give to each observation. Investigation into the performance of several objective functions has shown there are four objective functions that produce very good fits: absolute price, relative price, absolute implied volatility, and relative implied volatility. For example, the relative implied volatility function is

$$\min \sum_{i=1}^{n} w_i \frac{\left(\sigma_i^{\text{model}} - \sigma_i^{\text{market}}\right)^2}{\sigma_i^{\text{model}}}$$
(II.A-24)

Objective functions ... used to calibrate the Heston model to observed market data ... are least squares functions.

Optimization

To solve the above equation, we applied a sequential quadratic programming (SQP) method. This method is a gradient-based search, which will iterate until it converges on a solution with some tolerance on the result of the objective function. It is a local search, so the starting parameters influence the resulting calibrated parameters.

Data

The necessary inputs into the calibration are: the maturities, strike prices, and market prices of options, a risk-free rate curve bootstrapped from the observed LIBOR rates and swap rates, or Treasury rates, at the same date the option prices were observed, and an assumption for dividends that may be extracted from equity futures prices. Such data can be observed from market data providers such as Bloomberg Analytics.

Example

Using the process and data described above, we estimated Heston parameters on August 29, September 26, and October 31 of 2005. On each date, we observed a range of implied volatility quotes for European equity options. The options ranged in maturity from one month to two years, with strikes ranging from 100% to 120% of the spot equity level.

We bootstrapped the risk-free rates from the USD swap curve (available on Bloomberg Analytics) observed on each date. Our estimated dividend yield was 1.99% for all maturities. The observations were equally weighted. The objective function minimized the differences between observed and model call option prices.

The parameter estimates (corresponding to those in Equation II.A-19) are shown in Figure II.A-12.

▌ Figure II.A-12

	8-29-2005	9-26-2005	10-31-2005
V_0	13%	13%	14%
Kappa	2.11	2.67	2.10
Theta	17%	17%	18%
Nu	35%	39%	37%
Rho	-79%	-78%	-80%

This shows that, as of August 29, 2005, the Heston model dynamics resulted in a mean reverting process that started at 13% volatility and reverted to 17% volatility at a rate of 2.11 per annum. The volatility was 35% and the correlation among movements in volatility and movements in the equity price was -79%. Using these parameters, we can project an implied volatility surface and compare it to the market-implied volatility surface, shown in Figure II.A-13.

Figure II.A-13

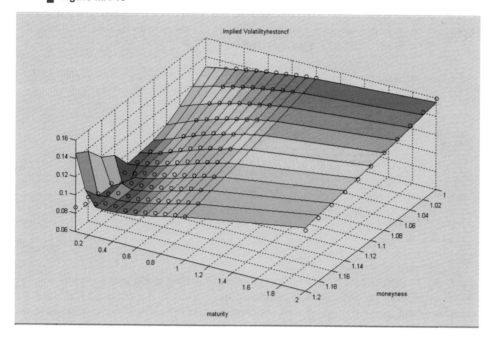

The black circles represent the actual market prices, and the coloured surface represents the Heston implied volatility surface. It becomes clear the Heston model fit the data extremely well in this example.

II.A.4 Credit Risks

This book describes credit risk scenario generation techniques commonly employed to model risks associated with investment portfolios, including plain vanilla and structured credit fixed-income assets.

Modeling default risks

Pricing and modeling default or credit risk has become an important component of risk management at banks and insurers because every financial instrument carries an element of credit risk. Increasing scrutiny from regulators and the dramatic growth followed by a sharp downturn in credit markets has put an increased focus on understanding and modeling credit risk. While there are many quantitative techniques used to model credit risk, most of them can be categorized into two main approaches: "structural" and "reduced form" models.

Structural models

Structural models use information from the equity markets and corporate balance sheets to estimate the likelihood of default, thus reflecting the risk in a company's assets and liabilities. Such a model was first proposed by Merton (1974) with an approach focusing on the value of the firm. Moody's KMV and CreditGrades are two companies that commonly employ structural models to infer default probabilities and fair market spreads in current markets.

While there are many quantitative techniques used to model credit risk, most of them can be categorized into two main approaches: "structural" and "reduced form" models.

Under the Black-Scholes-Merton (BSM) approach, equity is valued as a call option on the firm's assets using the standard Black-Scholes formula. The implied asset volatility and the implied spread can be calculated using the volatility of equity. The model can then be used to estimate the risk-neutral probability of default and the expected recovery rate.

$$E \, (Value \, of \, Equity) = A \, (Value \, of \, Assets) * N(d_1) - F \, (Face \, Value \, of \, Debt) * e^{-rT} * N(d_2)$$

$$d_1 = \frac{\log(A/F) + (r + \sigma_A^2/2) * T}{\sigma_A * \sqrt{T}}$$

$$d_2 = d_1 - \sigma_A * \sqrt{T}$$

$$\sigma_E = \sigma_A * N(d_1) * \frac{A}{E}$$

$$Risk \, Neutral \, \Pr obability \, of \, Default = N(-d_2)$$

$$\mathrm{Re} \cos eryRate = \frac{A * N(-d_1)}{N(-d_2)}$$

(II.A-25)

Simulating the risk of default for a company under the Merton model involves monitoring the change in its asset value in relation to the default threshold. Default is expected to occur if the asset value falls below the default threshold. Asset values for an individual company can be assumed to follow a normal distribution, and its default threshold can be estimated based on rating and historical default data.

At a given time t, if a company's asset value is A, the threshold is T, and the probability that the company will default is $P_{A<T}$. If at time t the cumulative default rate for this company is D, the default threshold is the inverse value of standard normal cumulative distribution at D.

$$Threshold = \Phi^{-1}(D)$$

(II.A-26)

Simulating default risk for portfolios of companies requires the model to incorporate correlation relationships across a group of companies. Li (2000) provided a solution for this problem using the copula function, which links together each asset's univariate cumulative density function (CDenF).

Structural models can be complex and difficult to calibrate in practice, depending on the level of detail captured about the issuers, and large variations in subordination level, tenor, quality, sector, and other idiosyncratic characteristics of individual debt instruments.

It must be noted that a simplistic BSM model does not generate realistic short-term spreads; therefore, Moody's KMV and CreditGrades have refined the model in their own proprietary ways for commercial implementations.

Unlike structural models, reduced form models rely on information in the fixed-income markets to infer risks of default.

Reduced form models

The second group of models comes under the rubric of reduced form or "default intensity" approaches. Unlike structural models, reduced form models rely on information in the fixed-income markets to infer risks of default. This approach uses stochastic processes similar to those used in the modeling of the riskless term structure of interest rates to model default.

Reduced form models have proven to be much more tractable for practical applications. Rather than modeling the value of the firm's assets as is done in structural models, this approach directly models the probability of default using information from the credit default swaps (CDS) and asset swaps markets. The recovery rate is derived endogenously, as in the case of structural models, or estimated exogenously. Reduced-form approaches range from pure default rate models, such as Jarrow and Turnbull (1995), to transition matrix models, such as Jarrow, Lando, and Turnbull (1997).

The variable modeled in reduced form models is the hazard rate, which is the forward probability of default, akin to the forward rate calculated for an interest rate yield curve. In reduced form models, default is linked to a stochastic jump process. Hazard rates can have a term structure and can be assumed to evolve randomly over time using a lognormal model, such as the Cox-Ingersoll-Rand model, which can incorporate jumps at random times.

The risk-neutral hazard rate, $h(t)$, is defined such that $[h(t)*\Delta t]$ is the probability of default between times t and $(t + \Delta t)$, assuming no prior defaults. The default probability density $q(t)$ is defined such that $[q(t)*\Delta t]$ is the unconditional probability of default between times t and $(t + \Delta t)$ as seen at time zero.

$$q(t) = h(t) * e^{-\int_0^t h(\tau)d\tau} \qquad \text{(II.A-27)}$$

Hull and White (2000) used a two-stage procedure to value a CDS. The first step is to calculate the risk-neutral default probability at future times from the yields on default-risky bonds and default-free bonds. The second step is to calculate the present value of both the expected future payoff and expected future payments on the CDS, where the CDS value is the difference between these two present values. The CDS spread is the value of the total annual premium payment that makes the CDS value in the second step equal to zero.

The probability that a company will survive to time t is:

$$\pi(t) = 1 - \int_{\tau=0}^t q(\tau)d\tau \qquad \text{(II.A-28)}$$

Hull and White (2000) showed that the CDS spread for maturity T is:

$$Spread = \frac{\int_{\tau=0}^T [1 - R - A(t)*r]q(t)v(t)dt}{\int_{\tau=0}^T q(t)*\{u(t) + e(t)\}dt + \pi(T)*u(T)} \qquad \text{(II.A-29)}$$

Credit risk and spread scenario generation techniques can be based on modeling the hazard rate as a stochastic process.

where R is the expected risk-neutral recovery rate, $A(t)$ is the accrual interest on the reference bond, $v(t)$ is the present value of one received at time t, $u(t)$ is the PV of payments at the rate of one on CDS payment dates, and $q(t)$ and $\pi(t)$ are as defined above.

Credit risk and spread scenario generation techniques can be based on modeling the hazard rate as a stochastic process, as noted by Lin (2006), with the default intensity evolving as per the following process with a lognormal distribution:

$$d \ln(h_t) = \alpha(\beta - \ln(h_t))dt + \gamma dz_t \tag{II.A-30}$$

where α is the mean reversion velocity, β is the long-term mean value, and γ is the volatility of the default intensity; dz is a Weiner process, and α, β, and γ are all constants.

Models can be calibrated to CDS and asset swap spreads in fixed-income markets. Furthermore, the same methodology can be used in a portfolio context to generate correlated hazard rates and correlated default densities. Credit rating migration can also be handled based on generating a risk-neutral transition matrix.

Alternatively, a simpler approach would be to assume that credit risk premiums follow a stochastic process similar to the Cox-Ingersoll-Ross interest rate model with mean reversion, positive spreads, and analytic bond prices, along with fixed recoveries.

Conclusions

Simulation scenarios can be generated under both structural approaches as well as reduced form or default intensity models. The decision to select one approach over another often depends on the information set available. The market practice at present appears to be to use variations of structural models, such as those offered by Moody's KMV or CreditGrades, or reduced form approaches that model the hazard rate as a stochastic process.

II.A.5 Inflation

This section describes two principal approaches used to model inflation: models based on past inflation, and Phillips curve models based on past inflation combined with other explanatory economic variables, such as unemployment. Both approaches are commonly used; however, models based on past inflation are used more often for insurance modeling.

Models based on past inflation

This approach includes univariate time series models, such as autoregressive integrated moving average (ARIMA) models, as well as non-linear or time-varying univariate models. Three variations exist within this approach. The first is a direct restricted autoregressive (AR) model

$$\pi_{t+h}^{h} - \pi_t = \mu^h + \alpha^h(L)\Delta\pi_t + v_t^h \tag{II.A-31}$$

where h period ahead inflation is defined as $\pi_t^h = h^{-1}\sum_{t=0}^{h-1}\pi_{t-i}$, π_t is the quarterly rate of inflation at an annual rate that is $\pi_t = 400 \ln\left(P_t \middle/ P_{t-1}\right)$ (using the log approximation), P_t is the price index at month t, μ^h is a constant, $\alpha^h(L)$ is a lag polynomial written in terms of the lag operator L, v_t^h is the h-step ahead error term, and the superscript h denotes the quantity for h-step ahead direct regression.

The second model variation of models using past inflation is the Atkenson-Ohanian (2001) random walk model

$$\pi_{t+4}^4 = \pi_t^4 + v_t^4 \qquad\qquad \text{(II.A-32)}$$

where π_{t+4}^4 is the forecast of the four-quarter ahead rate of inflation, and π_t^4 is the average of inflation over the previous four quarters, that is $\pi_t^4 = 100 \ln\left(P_t \middle/ P_{t-4}\right)$.

Stock and Watson (2008), who used the U.S. data to estimate both models in Equations II.A-31 and II.A-32, converted monthly data to quarterly data by computing the average value for the three months in the quarter prior to any other transformations. As measures of price inflation, the following five variables are used: the GDP deflator, the Consumer Price Index (CPI) for all items, CPI excluding food and energy, the personal consumption expenditure deflator, and the personal consumption expenditure multiplier, excluding food and energy.

Another variation in this approach is the model by Ahlgrim, D'arcy, and Gorvett (2005), which assumes inflation (q) to follow an Ornstein-Uhlenbeck process of the following form in continuous time:

$$dq_t = k_q(\mu_q - q_t)dt + \sigma dB_q \qquad\qquad \text{(II.A-33)}$$

For simulation model, we can use the discrete form of Equation II.A-31,

$$q_{t+1} = q_t + k_q(\mu_q - q_t)\Delta t + \varepsilon_q \sigma_q \sqrt{\Delta t} \qquad\qquad \text{(II.A-34)}$$

In Equation II.A-34, k_q is speed of reversion to mean, μ_q is mean reversion level of inflation, σ_q is volatility of inflation, and ε_q is a standardized normal random variable. To derive parameters k_q, μ_q, and σ_q, we rewrite Equation II.A-34 as

$$q_{t+1} - \mu_q = \varphi_1(q_t - \mu_q) + \varepsilon_q \sigma_q \sqrt{\Delta t} \qquad\qquad \text{(II.A-35)}$$

Based on Equation II.A-35, the following regression is run to estimate parameters:

$$q_{t+1} = \alpha + \beta q_t + \varepsilon'_{qt} \qquad\qquad \text{(II.A-36)}$$

Regression coefficients found in Equation II.A-36 could be transformed in the following way to find parameters of the inflation process:

$$k_q = \frac{1-\beta}{\Delta t} \qquad\qquad \text{(II.A-37)}$$

$$\alpha = k_q \mu_q \Delta t \qquad\qquad \text{(II.A-38)}$$

$$\mu_q = \frac{\alpha}{1-\beta} \qquad\qquad \text{(II.A-39)}$$

For the United States, inflation data from the CPI collected by the U.S. Bureau of Labor Statistics are usually used to estimate Equation II.A-36. Annual rate of inflation is measured as

$$q_t = \ln \frac{CPI_t}{CPI_{t-1}} \qquad \text{(II.A-40)}$$

Parameters k_q and μ_q are derived using the estimated parameters from the regression in Equation II.A-36. For other countries, appropriate inflation data from government or other sources can be used to derive the parameters based on estimated regression.

Using the regressions in Equation II.A-36, Ahlgrim, D'arcy, and Gorvett (2005) calculated the parameters for two time periods, 1913-2001 and 1946-2001, shown in Figure II.A-14.

■ Figure II.A-14

Time Period	k_q	μ_q	σ_q
1913-2001	0.37	3.3%	4.0%
1946-2001	0.47	4.8%	3.0%

Phillips curve modeling is based on the assumption that significant excess capacity in the economy should exert downward pressure on inflation.

Models based on Phillips curve

Phillips curve modeling is based on the assumption that significant excess capacity in the economy should exert downward pressure on inflation. This assumption stems from the empirical regularity that with widespread current and excess capacity, firms find raising prices increasingly difficult. Worker's expectations about inflation, in turn, decline, resulting in demand for smaller wage increases.

When modeling empirically, a common practice is to use the "triangle model" based on Gordon (1982). The following model is a modified version of the original "triangle model":

$$\pi_{t+1} = \mu + \alpha^G(L)\Delta\pi_t + \beta(L)u_{t+1} + \gamma(L)z_t + v_{t+1} \qquad \text{(II.A-41)}$$

where π_{t+1} is the inflation rate at period $t + 1$, μ is a constant, $\alpha^G(L)$, $\beta(L)$, and $\gamma(L)$ are lag polynomials written in terms of the lag operator L, μ_{t+1} is the unemployment rate, and z_t is a vector of supply shock variables. Gordon (1990) determines the lags in the context of the U.S. economy to be four for both unemployment and supply shock variables. The supply shocks used in his study are: rate of inflation of food and energy prices, relative price of imports, and two dummy variables for the Nixon wage-price control period.

The second variation in this modeling approach is a direct version of Equation II.A-41. Change in inflation in this model depends on lagged inflation and unemployment rate

$$\pi_{t+h} - \pi_t = \mu^h + \alpha^h(L)\Delta\pi_t + \beta^h(L)u_t + v_t^h \qquad \text{(II.A-42)}$$

Where π_{t+h} and π_t are inflation rates at period $(t + h)$ and t, and u_t is the unemployment rate at period t. The degrees of $\alpha^h(L)$, and $\beta^h(L)$ are chosen by the Akaike information criterion (AIC) and the specification imposes a unit root in the autoregressive dynamics for π_t.

A more detailed discussion on model implementation can be found in Atkenson and Ohanian (2001), Stock and Watson (2007), Stock and Watson (2008), Gordon (1982), Gordon (1990), and Ahlgrim, D'Arcy, and Gorvett (2005).

When modeling empirically, a common practice is to use the "triangle model" based on Gordon (1982).

References for Section II.A

Ahlgrim, Kevin C., D'Arcy, Stephen P., & Gorvett, Richard W. (2005). Modeling financial scenarios: A framework for the actuarial profession. Proceedings of the Casualty Actuarial Society, Vol. XCII: pp. 60-98.

American Academy of Actuaries (Jan. 13, 2006). Construction and use of pre-packaged scenarios to support the determination of regulatory and risk-based capital requirements for variable annuities and similar products.

Atkenson, A. & Ohanian, L.E. (2001). Are Phillips curves useful for forecasting inflation. *Federal Reserve Bank of Minneapolis Quarterly Review* 25(1):2-11.

Brigo, D. & Mercurio, F. (2006). *Interest rate models – theory and practice*. Springer.

Frye, J. (1997). Principals of risk: Finding VAR through factor-based Interest rate scenarios. *VAR: Understanding and Applying Value at Risk*, p. 275. Risk Publications.

Gill, P.E., Murray, W., & Wright, M.H. (1981). *Practical optimization*. London: Academic Press.

Gordon, Robert J. (1982). Inflation, flexible exchange rates, and the natural rate of unemployment. *Workers, Jobs and Inflation*, Martin N. Bailey (ed.). Washington D.C.: The Brookings Institution: 89-158.

Gordon, Robert J. (1990). U.S. inflation, labor's share, and the natural rate of unemployment. *Economics of Wage Determination*, Heinz Konig (ed.). Berlin: Springer-Verlag.

Heston, S. (1993). A closed-form solution for options with stochastic volatility with application to bond and currency options. *The Review of Financial Studies*.

Hull, J. C. (2006). *Options, futures and other derivatives*. Prentice Hall.

Hull, J. & White, A. (2000). Forward rate volatilities, swap rate volatilities, and the implementation of the Libor market model. *Journal of Fixed Income* 10, 2: 46.

Hull, John C. & White, Alan (Fall 2000). Valuing credit default swaps I: No counterparty default risk. *Journal of Derivatives* Vol. 8, No. 1.

Jarrow, Robert A. & Turnbull, Stuart M. (1995). Pricing derivatives on financial securities subject to credit risk." *Journal of Finance* 50: 53-86.

Jarrow, Robert A., Lando, David, & Turnbull, Stuart M. (Summer 1997). A Markov Model for the term structure of credit risk spreads. *Review of Financial Studies* Vol. 10, No. 2.

Klugman, S. et al. (1998). *Loss models*. John Wiley and Sons Inc.

Li, David X. (2000). On default correlation: A copula function approach. *Journal of Fixed Income* Vol. 9.

Lin, Fangxia (December 2006). Pricing credit default swaps when interest rate process and hazard rate process are stochastic. CUNY Seminar Paper.

Merton, Robert C. (1974). On the pricing of corporate debt. *Journal of Finance* Vol. 29.

Overhaus, M. et al. (2007). *Equity hybrid derivatives*. John Wiley and Sons Inc.

Solnik, B. & McLeavey, D. (2004). *International investments* 5th edition: p. 100.

Stock, J.H. & Watson, M.W. (2007). Why has U.S. inflation become harder to forecast? *Journal of Money, Credit, and Banking* 39: 3-34.

Stock, J.H. & Watson, M.W. (2008). Phillips curve inflation forecasts. Prepared for the Federal Reserve Bank of Boston Conference, *Understanding Inflation and the Implications for the Monetary Policy*.

Tuckman, B. (2002). *Fixed income securities*. John Wiley and Sons Inc.

U.S. Federal Reserve. Selected Interest Rates: Historical data (updated every business day, excluding holidays). Retrieved September 12, 2009, from–http://www.federalreserve.gov/releases/H15/data.htm.

II.B Life and Health Models

II.B.1 Catastrophic Mortality Modeling

In this section, we'll examine a methodology that can be used to model events producing catastrophic increases in mortality. This will be done by considering a hypothetical cohort of lives in the United States, described below, and projecting mortality rates for this cohort of lives through the models. While the example focuses on the United States, the modeling methodology can be extended to other developed countries where data exists for calibrating the model. For the purposes of this discussion, a catastrophic increase in mortality is one that causes additional deaths in the range of hundreds of thousands.

Overview of the model

The model can be visualized as three separate mortality models that feed into a "Combined Model" as shown in the diagram in Figure II.B-1.

Figure II.B-1

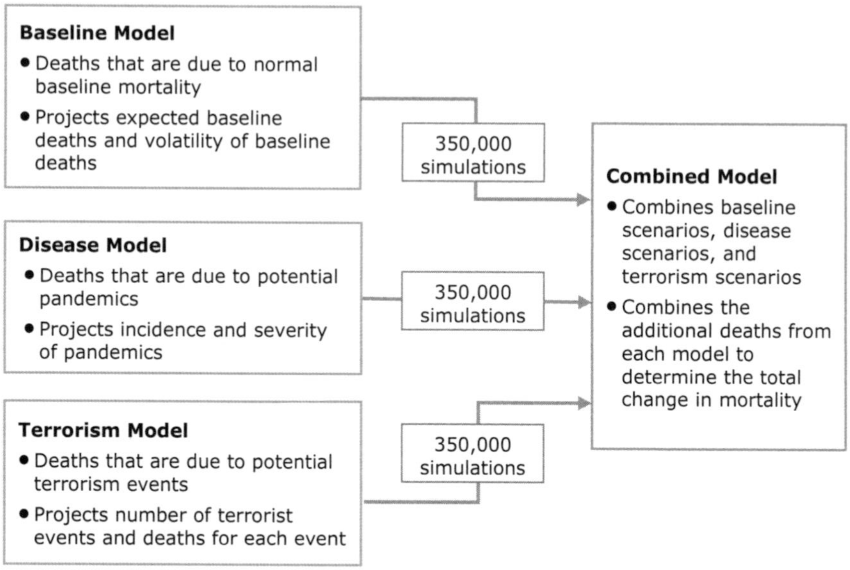

Mortality scenarios are generated by the three models shown in the left column of Figure II.B-1.

Each of these models generates 350,000 scenarios. All models are calibrated to historic data. The baseline, disease, and terrorism models are discussed in greater detail below.

Non-modeled items

The models used focus on those risks most likely to cause catastrophic increases in mortality based on historical experience. The following items are not modeled, except to the extent that their impact is included in the historical data used to calibrate the models:

- **Natural disasters**

In the past 100 years, and especially in the past 50 years, devastating natural disasters in developed countries have primarily resulted in significant property damage, but not a sufficient number of deaths to be considered a catastrophic event from a mortality perspective . This is largely because developed countries have better building codes, modern medical facilities, and good emergency response/early warning systems.

It is also important to note that some past natural disasters may already be reflected in the baseline model. For example, the data for 1995 Kobe earthquake, which caused 5,297 deaths in Japan, may be included in the country's actual mortality data used for calibrating a model; therefore, this event would not need to be separately considered when developing a baseline model. Otherwise, no explicit modeling is done for any extraordinary impact related to natural disasters, other than that contained in the historical period used to fit the baseline model.

The table in Figure II.B-2 provides the deaths that are due to natural disasters over the last 100 years for several developed countries, according to the World Health Organization (WHO).

Figure II.B-2: Natural Disasters – Recent History

Event	Country	Year	Deaths
Earthquake	Japan	1923	143,000
Earthquake	Italy	1908	75,000
Earthquake	Italy	1915	30,000
Hurricane	United States	1900	6,000
Earthquake	Japan	1948	5,131
Wind Storm	Japan	1959	5,098
Wind Storm	United Kingdom	1952	4,000
Wind Storm	Japan	1917	4,000
Wind Storm	Japan	1945	3,746
Earthquake	Japan	1933	3,008
Wind Storm	Japan	1934	3,006
Wind Storm	Japan	1923	3,000
Wave / Surge	Japan	1933	3,000
More Recent (1980-2005)			
Heat Wave	Europe	2003	19,000
Earthquake	Japan	1995	5,297
Earthquake	Italy	1980	4,689
Hurricane (Katrina)	United States	2005	1,836
Heat Wave	United States	1995	670
Tornado	United States	1984	600
Winter Storm	United States	1983	500
Flood	Japan	1982	345
Winter Storm	United States	1982	270

While the numbers of deaths in Figure II.B-2 are high, they are not high enough to be considered a catastrophic mortality increase. One exception is the 1923 Great Kanto Earthquake in Japan, which caused 143,000 deaths when that country's population was 58.1 million compared with 126.2 million in 2004, according to the Japan Ministry of Health. A similar event today would be expected to cause 310,000 deaths, if improvements in building codes, medical facilities, and emergency response and early warning systems had not changed.

More recently, the tsunami disaster of December 26, 2004, caused by underwater earthquakes in Southeast Asia, had a devastating impact on human life, resulting in over 186,000 deaths across a number of countries, none of which were developed countries.

- **Industrial accidents**

Industrial accidents – such as explosions, toxic spills, and nuclear power plant incidents – tend to raise mortality over an extended period of time; therefore, the impact on the analysis over a four-year period may be limited. Chernobyl, the worst nuclear accident in history, is estimated to have caused less than 1,000 deaths immediately following the release, with a 2% increase in long-term cancer rates in the region. We have not reflected any impact of industrial accidents in the analysis beyond those in the historical data.

- **Traditional war**

Historically, only World War I and World War II caused deaths in a magnitude sufficient to be considered catastrophic. The recent wars, such as those in Afghanistan and Iraq, have not resulted in a large enough number of deaths for the developed countries engaged in them. As such, limited military activity is only reflected in the model to the extent that it is included in the historical data.

- **Nuclear war**

While a nuclear war could certainly cause a large number of deaths, its impact is not projected.

- **Other risks**

Other potential risks, such as a meteor hitting the earth or various other remote natural calamities, are also not considered.

- **United States case study cohort**

The table in Figure II.B-3 shows the age and gender distribution of the U.S. cohort that will be analyzed throughout the catastrophic mortality modeling section.

Figure II.B-3

Age and Gender Distribution		
Age Range	**Males**	**Females**
<1	0.00%	0.00%
1 to 4	0.00	0.00
5 to 14	0.00	0.00
15 to 24	0.00	0.00
25 to 34	7.50	7.50
35 to 44	12.50	12.50
45 to 54	17.50	17.50
55 to 64	10.00	10.00
65 to 74	2.50	2.50
75 to 84	0.00	0.00
85+	0.00	0.00

In modeling the baseline model, historical mortality rates are used to calibrate the time series model.

II.B.1.a Baseline Model

The baseline model uses a time series model to project base mortality rates into the future. The general approach is to test different modeling methods and to consider the goodness of fit for various algebraic models using different parameters. To the extent that the baseline mortality for more than one country is projected, the underlying time series model and the parameters for the models can be different for each country.

In modeling the baseline model, historical mortality rates are used to calibrate the time series model. These historic mortality rates can generally be obtained from governmental organizations, such as the Centers for Disease Control (CDC) in the United States. A time series of baseline mortality rates are calculated using the following formula:

$$q_t = \sum_x a_{m,x} \times q_{m,x,t} + a_{f,x} \times q_{f,x,t} \qquad \text{(II.B-1)}$$

where:

q_t = the combined mortality rate for year t

$a_{m,x}$ = the weight applied to male mortality rates for age group x

$a_{f,x}$ = the weight applied to female mortality rates for age group x

$q_{m,x,t}$ = the mortality rate for males of age group x for year t

$q_{f,x,t}$ = the mortality rate for females of age group x for year t

The baseline model for the United States will be fitted by calibrating to the combined mortality rates for the period 1969 to 2003. The combined mortality rates for the years 1995 to 2003 are shown in the table in Figure II.B-4. The combined mortality rates are based on population mortality rates obtained from the CDC.

■ Figure II.B-4

U.S. Combined Mortality Rates per 100,000	
Year	Mortality Rate
1995	601.2
1996	583.3
1997	563.7
1998	552.0
1999	550.3
2000	537.4
2001	532.3
2002	527.7
2003	522.9

Modeling process

The historic mortality data are tested against the following models:

The parameters of the baseline model are selected to minimize the sum of squared errors between actual and modeled mortality rates.

- **Linear autoregressive model applied to mortality rates directly and rates of change in mortality rates**

- **Log autoregressive model applied to mortality rates directly and rates of change in mortality rates**

In each case, two to seven parameters are tested for each model. The parameters of the baseline model are selected to minimize the sum of squared errors between actual and modeled mortality rates.

The following primary criteria are used in selecting a model:

- The model should minimize the squared error term, and the primary statistical measure used is the adjusted R^2. The R^2 is a common statistical method of measuring how well a model fits the actual data. It determines the proportion of the change in the dependent variable that is explained by changes in the independent variables. Since adding additional variables cannot reduce the R^2 (i.e., adding variables cannot take away from the explanatory power of the model), an adjusted R^2 is calculated. The adjusted R^2 adjusts the R^2 for the number of variables used in the model.

- The projected results produced by the fitted model should be consistent with the historical trend.

For the United States cohort described above, the linear autoregressive model applied to the annual rate of change in mortality rates provided an optimal fit to the historical data. Algebraically, this linear autoregressive formulation can be represented as follows:

$$x_t = a_0 + a_1 x_{t-1} + a_2 x_{t-2} + \ldots + a_n x_{t-n} + error \qquad \text{(II.B-2)}$$

where:

x_t = the rate of change in the mortality rate from time $t - 1$ to time t

$error$ = the error term

The rate of change in the mortality rate is defined as one less the mortality rate for time t divided by the mortality rate for time $t - 1$.

The parameters selected for the United States model are shown in the table in Figure II.B-5.

Figure II.B-5

U.S. Baseline Model Parameters						
a_0	a_1	A_2	a_3	a_4	a_5	a_6
0.0137	0.0455	-	-	-	-	-

The graph in Figure II.B-6 illustrates how the historical mortality rates compare with those projected using actual data by applying the linear autoregressive model.

Figure II.B-6

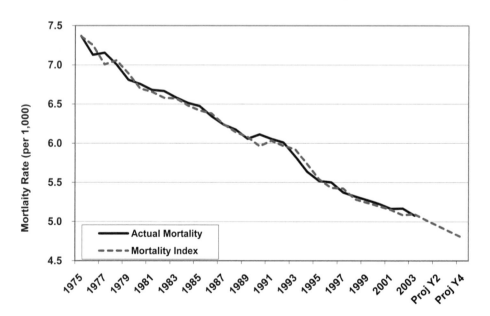

Actual versus Modeled Mortality

In developing this projection, the above model parameters were used to project an expected value for mortality rates in each future year. The expected value is then modified for the random variation around this mean. The random variation is modeled assuming the error component in the model has a normal distribution. The mean and standard deviation for the error term is determined using the mean and standard deviation of the historical difference between the modeled and actual mortality rates. The parameters used for each country are shown in the table in Figure II.B-7.

▌Figure II.B-7

Error Component Parameters	
Mean	**Standard Deviation**
0.00015%	0.00681%

The mean and standard deviation is calculated over the same period for which the data was used to fit the baseline mortality, i.e., 1969 to 2003.

Model results

The table in Figure II.B-8 shows the distribution of annual changes in mortality rates as projected by the baseline model.

▌Figure II.B-8

Distribution of Mortality Increase			
Mortality Increase Range		**With Mortality Improvements**	**Without Mortality Improvements**
Lower Percentage	**Upper Percentage**		
0.0	0.5	0.000%	36.186%
0.5	1.0	0.000	38.367
1.0	1.5	0.000	25.447
1.5+	-	0.000	0.000

Because of the low volatility of the baseline mortality, the baseline model does not project large increases in mortality rates. Even when the effect of the projected mortality improvements is removed, the increases in mortality projected are not large enough to be considered of a catastrophic nature.

II.B.1.b Disease Model

The disease model projects the additional deaths that are due to potential disease pandemics.

Overview of recent pandemics

Pandemics have occurred throughout human history. Some causes have been essentially eradicated (such as smallpox), others such as influenza remain with us, and still others, including

AIDS, SARS, H1N1, have recently emerged. Modeling considerations for these potentially high-impact pandemics is discussed below.

Influenza

Influenza has been well recognized as an unpredictable life hazard to humanity over recorded history. In the 1930s, the viral agents causing influenza were identified for the first time, a discovery that allowed medical professionals to begin understanding the different strains of influenza affecting humans over the past 100 years, if not longer.

Historically, influenza and pneumonia death rates have been higher among children and young adults. One potential explanation relates these deaths to a stronger immune response in younger persons, which, in turn, results in multiple organ failure.

A widespread pandemic is one of the major causes of sudden and unexpected adverse mortality.

The genetic strain of influenza is constantly cross-mixing with other genetic strains found in birds or other mammals. For this reason, the disease is ever-evolving, such that variant forms of influenza continue to emerge. While there is no reliable mechanism for predicting the particular frequency at which this occurs, the probabilities related to the interactions of billions of people and animals and many millions of influenza cases worldwide each year indicate that pandemics will strike periodically. At the same time, however, advancements in medicine have allowed for less severe and less widespread pandemics, especially in recent years.

Generally regarded as the most severe pandemic, the 1918-1920 "Spanish Flu" pandemic is estimated to have killed 40 to 50 million people worldwide, and possibly as many as 100 million, according to the Congressional Budget Office (2005).

For modeling purposes, it is these severe pandemics that serve as the important guideposts for estimating the possibility of highly adverse mortality. A widespread pandemic is one of the major causes of sudden and unexpected adverse mortality.

AIDS

Deaths from the AIDS virus (HIV) in developed countries have been declining over the last 10 years and the virus is not readily transmitted by casual contact. Therefore, a projection of future possible AIDS pandemics would not be likely to cause enough additional deaths in developed countries to be considered catastrophic.

SARS

First identified in Hong Kong in the spring of 2003, SARS has infected people in 29 countries or political entities, and resulted in case fatality rates of approximately 10% in the 11 countries where deaths occurred, according to WHO (*Summary of probably SARS cases*). Of these 11 countries, two had fatality rates that exceeded 15%.

The virus apparently resides in certain animal populations, but is not often transmitted to humans, which may be the reason that, to date, the total number of SARS deaths has been less than 1,000 worldwide. It appears that a SARS-like pandemic spread more effectively could have had a much more devastating effect.

Other diseases

Other diseases include:

- **Vector-borne diseases, such as Dengue fever, the plague, Rift Valley fever, yellow fever, and malaria, which is spread by insects such as mosquitoes**

- **Diseases such as Crimean-Congo fever, Ebola, hepatitis, Lassa fever, meningococcal disease, smallpox, cholera, and tuberculosis**

While some of these diseases have caused significant deaths in underdeveloped and/or tropical countries over the past 50 years, there has been no record of severe mortality resulting from these diseases in developed countries. Drastic changes in weather patterns and/or major breakdowns in public health systems would have to occur for any of these diseases to become significant risks in developed countries.

General modeling approach

Given the potentially catastrophic impact of a deathly disease, the approach taken in modeling a severe pandemic is to assume a somewhat regularly occurring spike in deaths that is due to an infectious disease outbreak. Historically, the greatest threat has been the influenza virus, so this virus has guided the development of the methods and assumptions for the disease model.

The modeling process starts with a random variable that determines if a pandemic has occurred in any given year. If a pandemic C has occurred, another random variable is sampled to determine the degree of severity of the pandemic in terms of percentages of excess mortality. The percentage of excess mortality is then applied to the baseline level of mortality. The assumptions and methodology used in the disease model are discussed in further detail below.

Modeling the frequency of disease pandemics

Some epidemiologists, such as Lazzari and Stohr (2004), believe that 31 influenza pandemics have occurred over the past 420 years, an average of one every 13.5 years. But others think the figure is as low as 10 influenza pandemics over the past 300 years, indicating a 3% to 4% probability of a pandemic occurring in a given year.

For the purposes of the present example, our disease model assumes a probability of a pandemic in any given year to be 7.38% based on the higher estimated frequency of 31 pandemics. But as the above estimates indicate, actual pandemic frequency may vary widely, a possibility that underscores the need to carefully consider this potentially highly variable, but basic, assumption when evaluating the contribution of the disease model to the various modeled scenarios.

> If a pandemic C has occurred, another random variable is sampled to determine the degree of severity of the pandemic in terms of percentages of excess mortality.

Potential of repeating a 1918-1920 pandemic

One distinct feature of the 1918-1920 pandemic was the high influenza and pneumonia death rates reported for children and adults, especially those between the ages of 25 and 34, as compared to the rates for older individuals. One theory, known as the "cytokine storm," holds that this disparity in death rates occurred because of an immune response in young adult cohorts whose typically strong systems overreacted, causing multiple organ failure. Like some other influenza pandemics, the 1918-1920 pandemic came in waves of varying severity, which may have resulted from changes in weather and behaviour that interrupted the spread of disease. The most severe episode occurred in October 1918. When a broadly similar strain (in the same H1N1 class) emerged in 1977, as noted by Hampson (1997), it was not extraordinarily deadly.

And while increased mobility and population concentration in urban areas could hasten the spread of an influenza pandemic, other factors such as increased public awareness and knowledge, a better scientific understanding of disease mechanisms, the use of early international warnings systems, and more effective vaccines and treatment options could also offset its spread.

Based on these factors, it is assumed that a severe influenza pandemic today would have a smaller impact on overall mortality rates (in terms of absolute mortality rates) than it did in 1918-1920.

Data points

A detailed record of severity of mortality from influenza pandemics is available for the 1918, 1957, 1968, and 1977 pandemics. In addition to these points, the 2003 SARS pandemic in Hong Kong was included as another data point.

For the 1918-1920 influenza pandemic, an excess mortality rate of 413.50 extra deaths per 100,000 lives was calculated and represents the 1918-1920 influenza pandemic in today's terms ("1918-1920 pandemic"). This 413.50 excess mortality rate is an increase of 25.50% over 1,621.71 per 100,000, which is 1917's combined mortality rate. In addition, an "adjusted 1918-1920 pandemic" component was calculated with 245.00 extra deaths per 100,000 to represent the 1918-1920 influenza pandemic if only 60% of the broad improvements in mortality over the past 85 years can be used to estimate today's impact of such an pandemic. Both rates were calculated as shown in the table in Figure II.B-9 using publicly available data sources (U.S. Census Bureau and CDC).

Based on these factors, it is assumed that a severe influenza pandemic today would have a smaller impact on overall mortality rates (in terms of absolute mortality rates) than it did in 1918-1920.

▌ **Figure II.B-9**

Derivation of 1918-1920 Influenza Pandemic Severity		
Total Death Rate per 100,000 for 1917	A	1,621.71
Total Death Rate per 100,000 for 1918	B	1,912.67
Total Death Rate per 100,000 for 1919	C	1,465.96
Total Death Rate per 100,000 for 1920	D	1,463.35
Influenza Death Rate per 100,000 for 1917	E	170.83
Influenza Death Rate per 100,000 for 1918	F	515.55
Influenza Death Rate per 100,000 for 1919	G	206.82
Influenza Death Rate per 100,000 for 1920	H	203.64
Excess Influenza Death Rate per 100,000 for 1918-1920	$I = (F + G + H) - 3 \times E$	413.50
1918-1920 Pandemic	**$J = I / A$**	**25.50%**
Total Death Rate per 100,000 for 2003	K	520.32
2003 Death Rate / 1917 Death Rate ratio	$L = K / A$	32.08%
Adjusted Influenza Death Rate per 100,000 for 1918	$M = L \times I$	132.67
Modern Health and Medicine Adjustment	N	60.00%
Adjusted Influenza Death Rate per 100,000 for 1918	$O = N \times M + (1 - N) \times I$	245.00
Adjusted 1918-1920 Pandemic	**$P = O / K$**	**47.09%**

When using the 47.09% excess mortality factor, it is assumed that the excess mortality rate from a potential influenza pandemic has improved along with base mortality. From a modeling perspective, this is equivalent to taking the view that, in the event of a pandemic , mortality is more likely to increase in proportionate rather than in absolute terms. Between 1917 and 2003, baseline combined mortality rates decreased by 68% in total (equivalent to an overall rate of mortality improvement of 1.3% per annum over this period).

The "Adjusted 1918-1920 Pandemic " is an additional data point used in the analysis of the degree of severity of a pandemic . This is calculated using a weighted average death rate by applying a 40% weight to the actual excess death rate in 1918-1920 (of 413.50 per 100,000). This calculation assumes there is no benefit of modern medicine, public health, or science.

Several reports can be used to give context to the rate of 245.00 per 100,000. Meltzer, Cox, and Fukuda (1999) in a CDC report projected the most pessimistic estimate of deaths from a severe influenza outbreak in the United States across all ages at 285,000, or slightly over 100.00 extra deaths per 100,000. Similar results were also indicated in Piercy and Miles (2003) in a report on the impact of an influenza epidemic in Switzerland. But a more recent document from the U.S. Department of Health and Human Services (HHS, 2005), which focused on morbidity and the potential burden on the healthcare system, gives a much higher mortality estimate, comparing the potential to a "severe (1918-like)" pandemic, which could cause 1.9 million deaths or 630.00 extra deaths per 100,000.[23]

Additional data points were calculated using excess influenza mortality rates for the 1918, 1957, and 1968 pandemics from data in the CDC's historical mortality database. These excess mortality rates were compared to the total mortality rates (from all causes) in the year prior to the pandemic to arrive at the increase in the total mortality rate that is due to influenza. The table in Figure II.B-10 shows the calculated increase in the mortality rates.

▌ Figure II.B-10

20th Century Pandemic – Increase in Mortality			
Pandemic Year	Excess Mortality Rate (per 100,000) from Influenza and Pneumonia	Total Mortality Rate (per 100,000) for Prior Year	Increase in Mortality Rates over Prior Year (%)
Adjusted 1918*	245.00	520.32	47.09
1918	413.50	1,621.71	25.50
1957[24]	11.78	898.24	1.30
1968	6.36	870.59	0.73

*Subsequently adjusted when fitting the extreme component at the 0.5 percentile level

---

[23] The report notes, in part, "Because the virulence of the Influenza virus that causes the next pandemic cannot be predicted, two scenarios are presented" of which the more severe involved 1,903,000 deaths; it goes on, "these estimates do not include the potential impact of interventions not available during the 20th century pandemics."

[24] A general analysis of mortality rates that are due to influenza and pneumonia indicate that mortality levels during 1957 and 1958 were elevated in comparison to non-pandemic years at that time. As such, the total excess mortality rate that is due to influenza and pneumonia in both 1957 and 1958 has been used, expressed as a percentage of the average of 1956 and 1959 mortality rates from all causes.

In addition, the 2003 SARS and the 1977 influenza pandemics were used as additional data points to fit the disease severity curve. According to WHO (*Summary of probable SARS cases*), in 2003 the SARS pandemic produced 299 deaths in Hong Kong. Those deaths came out of a total population, according to the U.S. CIA, of 6.9 million. If an epidemic of the same severity (in terms of mortality rate) occurred in the United States, base mortality rates would increase by 0.83%.

According to Viboud et al. (2004), the influenza pandemic of 1977 resulted in 10,000 deaths in the United States. The estimated population for the United States in 1977 was 221,412,000. The extra death rate is 4.52 per 100,000, compared to a combined mortality rate of 748.69 per 100,000 in 1977. Hence, the influenza pandemic of 1977-1978 was assumed to increase mortality rates by 0.60%.

In 2003 the SARS pandemic produced 299 deaths in Hong Kong ... out of a total population, according to the U.S. CIA, of 6.9 million.

Modeling the severity of disease pandemics

In developing a model for the severity of an infectious disease pandemic, a disease severity curve is plotted by fitting excess disease mortality points against the probability of achieving the excess mortality, given that a disease event has occurred.

As a first step in fitting the severity curve, the adjusted 1918-1920 pandemic is initially assumed to be the worst possible pandemic that can occur. This data point is placed at the zero percentile level, and is initially the uppermost endpoint of the severity curve.

As a second step, a separate curve is attached at the 0.5 percentile level to allow the model to simulate events that are worse than the mortality implied by the adjusted 1918-1920 pandemic data point. Given that it is assumed the probability of a disease pandemic occurring in any given year is 7.38%, the corresponding probability of an extreme disease pandemic occurring in a given year (where extreme is defined as a pandemic event in which the severity is a function of the extreme component) is 7.38% x 0.5% = 0.037% (or a one-in-2,700 year event). This curve has been chosen so that there is no maximum limit of excess mortality that can be generated by the disease model.

The resulting disease severity curve is, therefore, a construction of two curves that correspond to two components:

- **A main component representing the more probable outcomes of excess mortality associated with more probable pandemic events.**

- **An extreme component representing extremely severe levels of excess mortality significantly beyond historically experienced worst cases, such as the 1918-1920 pandemic event.**

The main component models severity for percentile levels higher than the 0.5 percentile level, while the extreme component models severity for percentile levels less than the 0.5 percentile level.

Severity curve: Fitting the main component

The table in Figure II.B-11 shows the percentiles with respect to the six data points at which the various pandemics were plotted for the main component of the disease severity curve.

Figure II.B-11

Percentile Plots for Main Component				
Pandemic	Percentile	Actual Excess Mortality Percentage	Fitted Excess Mortality Percentage	Fitted Excess Mortality Rate (per 100,000)[25]
Adjusted 1918*	0.0%	47.09%	47.83%	248.86
1918	3.2	25.50	23.27	121.07
1957	27.4	1.30	5.85	30.45
2003 SARS	51.6	0.83	2.68	13.94
1968	75.8	0.73	1.45	7.57
1977	100.0	0.60	0.87	4.50

Subsequently adjusted when fitting the extreme component at the 0.5 percentile level

The 1918 event resulted in an excess mortality of 25.50% over the previous year. Assumed to be the worst of the 31 influenza pandemics thought to have occurred over the last 420 years, the 1918-1920 pandemic is plotted at the 3.2 percentile (= 1/31) level. This is based on the assumption that, given that a pandemic has occurred, there is a one-in-31 probability of a pandemic with a similar impact on mortality rates occurring again.

The 1977 pandemic has the smallest increase in mortality for pandemics for which reliable data is available. The 1977 pandemic resulted in an excess mortality of 0.62%. This event is assumed to occur at the 100th percentile level. The remaining data points, representing the 1957, 1968, and 2003 SARS pandemics, were equally spaced between these two points.

For the main component, an exponential formula was fitted to the data. The parameters for the formula were determined by minimizing the least squares between the actual and modeled increases in the mortality rates. The squared differences between the actual and modeled mortality rates for the 1918 data points were multiplied by a factor of two to give more weight to the more severe pandemics. The formula for the exponential curve fitted to the data is as follows:

$$\text{Excess mortality percentage} = \frac{a \times \exp^{b\sqrt{percentile}}}{c} \qquad \text{(II.B-3)}$$

where:

a = 0.002489

b = -4.011781

c = 0.0052032 (the 2003 combined mortality rate)

$percentile$ = the percentile level

---

[25] Developed as the 2003 combined mortality rate of 520.32 per 1,000 times the fitted excess mortality percentages.

Severity curve: Fitting the extreme component

The extreme component (at percentile levels below 0.5%) utilizes a tangent function that approaches the severity axis asymptotically. The formula for the tangent curve is as follows:

$$\text{Excess mortality percentage} = \text{TAN}\left(\left(90 - percentile \times d\right) \times \frac{\pi}{180}\right) \qquad \text{(II.B-4)}$$

where:

d = 14,038.71

$percentile$ = the percentile level

The d factor ensures that the tangent function and the exponential function produce the same percentage increase in mortality at the 0.5 percentile level.

Given that a disease pandemic has occurred, the range of excess mortality as a percent of current mortality predicted by the disease model is shown in Figure II.B-12.

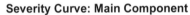

Figure II.B-12

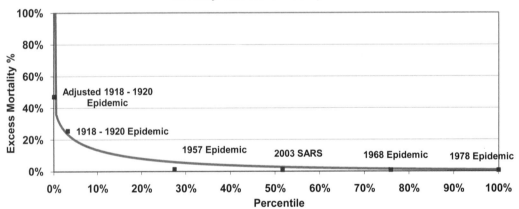

The extreme component of the disease severity curve has no upper limit on the excess mortality. The graph in Figure II.B-13 shows the disease severity curve for percentiles of 1.0% and lower.

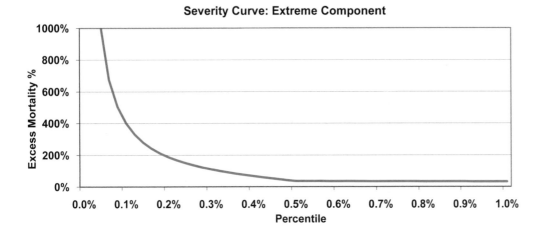

Figure II.B-13

Other supporting assumptions

- The disease model assumes that, in the event of a pandemic occurring, the incidence in any given year is not correlated to subsequent calendar years. This assumption may be appropriate given that historical evidence suggests that the occurrence of pandemics tends to either be uncorrelated or negatively correlated.

- The disease model also assumes that the increase in mortality rates applies proportionately to all ages; it does not assume there is a greater or smaller impact across age bands.

Model results

The table in Figure II.B-14 shows the distribution of the annual increase in mortality projected by the disease model. These mortality increases are based on the cohort described above.

Figure II.B-14

Distribution of Mortality Increase		
Mortality Increase Range		Proportion of Scenarios
Lower Percentage	Upper Percentage	
No Pandemic		92.64%
0	5	5.04
5	10	1.21
10	15	0.50
15	20	0.26
20	25	0.15
25	30	0.09
30+	-	0.10

II.B.1.c Terrorism Model

In this section, we examine the structure of a terrorism model, which is used to project the additional deaths that are due to potential events caused by hostile actions.

Model design

One objective of such a model is to determine whether a potential terrorist attack would cause catastrophic increases in mortality rates; however, a lack of historical data for the probability of such an event poses a serious challenge to constructing the model. For this reason, a multi-level trinomial lattice model was used.

A lack of historical data for the probability of a terrorist attack poses a serious challenge to constructing the model.

The terrorism model is split into 20 levels, each of which represents an increasing severity of loss and difficulty in carrying out a potential terrorist act. At each level, there is also the probability of success or failure. The lattice structure can be visualized as shown in Figure II.B-15.

Figure II.B-15

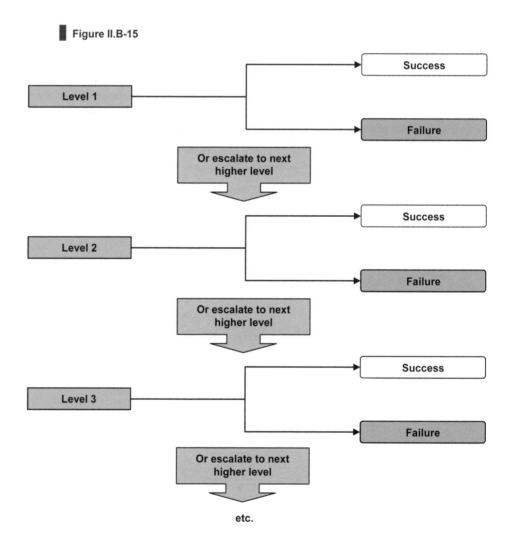

etc.

The approach for building the terrorism model is to fit the data that exists at the lower levels of the model structure above. The model structure then naturally extrapolates to larger and larger terrorist events that may ultimately cause catastrophic increases in mortality.

Data

To model the cohort described above, data on world terrorism events from 1980 through 2004 were taken from annual reports on world terrorism published by the U.S. Department of State. Similar data for 2004 were taken from "Patterns of Global Terrorism," a report on world terrorism published by the National Counterterrorism Center (NCTC), the "knowledge bank" of the U.S. government on international terrorism created in 2004.

The U.S. State Department data for the United States excludes events that occurred in Afghanistan or Iraq.

Modeling the frequency of terrorist events

The number of terrorist events per year is modeled as a normal distribution based on the data published by the U.S. State Department. Using this data, the parameters used in the terrorism model are shown in the table in Figure II.B-16.

Figure II.B-16

Annual Number of Terrorist Events	
Mean	Standard Deviation
27.20	8.6

The number of terrorist events per year is modeled as a normal distribution based on the data published by the U.S. State Department.

The parameters above include events affecting U.S. "interests" abroad, in addition to events happening in the United States. When referring to U.S. interests abroad, events in Afghanistan or Iraq linked to military action are not included in calibrating the terrorism model.

Defining levels

Levels are defined by the number of deaths with endpoints whose upper range is assumed to be double that of the previous level as shown in Figure II.B-17. The model's highest level reflects terrorist events causing between 393,216 and 786,432 deaths.

Using this structure and the data from the U.S. State Department, model parameters were selected by minimizing the sum of the squares of the difference between model and actual number of deaths.

Figure II.B-17

Once an event is found to be within a particular level, the number of deaths within that level is determined using a uniform distribution.

Number of Deaths by Level		
Level	Lower	Upper
1	-	-
2	1	3
3	4	6
4	7	12
5	13	24
6	25	48
7	49	96
8	97	192
9	193	384
10	385	768
11	769	1,536
12	1,537	3,072
13	3,073	6,144
14	6,145	12,288
15	12,289	24,576
16	24,577	49,152
17	49,153	98,304
18	98,305	196,608
19	196,609	393,216
20	393,217	786,432

Once an event is found to be within a particular level, the number of deaths within that level is determined using a uniform distribution.

The table in Figure II.B-18 presents examples of possible events that might reach the levels represented in the terrorism model.

Figure II.B-18

Example Events – Range of Number of Deaths		
Lower	Upper	Example Event
1	24	Shooting
25	192	Car or truck bombing
193	1,536	Hijacked airliner crash
1,537	12,288	Stadium bombing
12,289	98,304	Dirty bomb
98,305	786,432	Nuclear attack in a large city

Defining probabilities

Using the same data set and the levels defined in the prior section, the probabilities are established for success and failure and movement to the next level. For our purposes, failure is defined as an attempted terrorist event that resulted in no deaths. The parameters were selected based on minimizing the sum of the squared differences between actual and modeled number of deaths calculated using an exponential function. The table in Figure II.B-19 shows the results for each country.

▌ Figure II.B-19

Terrorism Model Parameters		
Success	**Failure**	**Movement to Next Level**
70.3%	29.7%	49.6%

For example, the probability of the event being successful at a given level is 70.3%, the probability of it being unsuccessful is 29.7%.

Other assumptions

It is assumed that the terrorism model is independent of other potential mortality events. For example, a rise in general mortality or an influenza epidemic does not indicate whether a terrorist event is more likely or less likely. Terrorism events are also assumed to be independent from each other whether in the same country or otherwise. A simultaneous attack, such as the terrorist attacks of September 11, 2001, is viewed as a single event rather than four events.

For our purposes, failure is defined as an attempted terrorist event that resulted in no deaths.

Model results

The table in Figure II.B-20 shows the distribution of the annual increase in mortality projected by the terrorism model. These mortality increases are based on the cohort described above.

▌ Figure II.B-20

Terrorism Model – Distribution of Maximum Additional Mortality		
Range		**Proportion of Scenarios**
Lower (%)	**Upper (%)**	
0.0	0.5	79.375%
0.5	1.0	17.495
1.0	1.5	2.239
1.5	2.0	0.574
2.0	2.5	0.150
2.5	3.0	0.100
3.0	3.5	0.029
3.5	4.0	0.032
4.0+	-	0.000

The terrorism model does not project large enough increases in mortality to be considered catastrophic.

II.B.1.d Combined Model Results

The table in Figure II.B-21 shows the distribution of the annual mortality increases projected by the combination of the baseline, disease, and terrorism models. The baseline model includes the effect of mortality improvements.

Figure II.B-21

Distribution of Mortality Increase		
Mortality Increase Range		**Proportion of Scenarios**
Lower Percentage	**Upper Percentage**	
0	5	6.103%
5	10	1.059
10	15	0.459
15	20	0.242
20	25	0.152
25	30	0.090
30	35	0.053
35+	-	0.043

The projected increases in mortality are slightly lower than for the disease model, because of the beneficial effect of the mortality improvements projected in the base model.

II.B.2 Dynamic Policyholder Behaviour

One important aspect of modeling insurance products is policyholder behaviour, typically estimated using lapses. For traditional insurance products, policyholder behaviour is usually modeled deterministically using historical data analysis to determine policy persistency in the model. The best estimate assumption might produce reasonable results in the context of deterministic modeling, but it would not provide the same level of risk assessment as provided by stochastic modeling.

Stochastic modeling typically involves capturing the dynamics of one or more economic or demographic factors, which may affect policyholder behaviour in a given scenario.

Stochastic modeling typically involves capturing the dynamics of one or more economic or demographic factors, which may affect policyholder behaviour in a given scenario. Of most interest are those scenarios that would prompt policyholders to behave in such a way as to financially imperil an insurance company. Dynamically modeling this type of policyholder behaviour will be our focus in the following section. We will also discuss in some detail the modeling of dynamic lapse in the context of variable annuity.

II.B.2.a Traditional Non-par Life Products

Traditional non-par life products usually offer a minimum cash surrender value, which essentially guarantees the policyholder a minimum return, regardless of the actual interest environment. This guarantee can be exercised at the policyholder's discretion. Assuming policyholders behave rationally and are more likely to exercise their surrender option when interest rates are low, it makes sense when modeling to assume that lapses are driven by different levels of interest rates.

Offering fixed-rate policy loans as part of its insurance product, as some insurers do, would expose a company to risks. Understanding how policy loan take-ups and defaults are driven by market economy also becomes an important aspect in modeling.

II.B.2.b Traditional Par Life Products

While much of the discussions related to non-par products also apply to par products, par products offer non-guaranteed bonuses that could mitigate the risk of lapse to a certain extent. A policyholder may be dissuaded from exercising the interest guarantee, even when market interest is low, in anticipation of future bonuses. These par products, however, could create a new problem for insurance companies in that they must now manage policyholder expectations regarding bonus declarations. This could be difficult to model, because poorly managed expectations could spark lawsuits whose financial impact is difficult to quantify. Nonetheless, consideration should be given to how policyholders would react to different market economies.

II.B.2.c Universal Life and Fixed Annuity

Though universal life and fixed annuity differ in many ways, they typically offer a credited interest to policyholders. This feature might alter lapse behaviour, because policyholders are more likely to terminate a policy when the credit rate is lower than the market interest or a competitor's credit rate; conversely, policyholders would be less likely to terminate when the reverse is true. Because these products are considered interest-sensitive, they are modeled dynamically for lapses as interest rates change.

II.B.2.d Variable Annuity

Variable annuity (VA) is perhaps the most complicated product to model for dynamic policyholder behaviour, because behaviour is likely to differ based on which embedded guaranteed minimum benefit (GMB) rider is offered, if any.

The base VA product is similar to a mutual fund. Policyholders invest premiums in various types of equity funds, and the policy benefit is determined by the performance of these funds. Arguably, policyholders are likely to either take more withdrawals from the funds, or they might lapse the entire contract when funds perform exceptionally well, in order to lock in their gains.

By introducing a GMB rider, the product offers a protection against poor fund performance, but also offers another wrinkle in modeling. Buyers of VA products with GMB can be said to value this protection and act according to the perceived value of the GMB. This means that a dynamic model needs to not only include assumptions about full lapses, the topic of the next section, but also partial withdrawal assumptions, GMB take-up assumptions, and GMB exercise assumptions.

Variable annuity (VA) is perhaps the most complicated product to model for dynamic policyholder behaviour.

Dynamic lapse in VA

VA lapse rates are influenced by various factors. Some policyholders may lapse simply because of the need for money. Some may lapse because of the inducement from the distributors who want to earn commissions by promoting conversions to other products. Others may lapse if the fund performance falls below expectations. GMB can encourage better consistency; however, GMB usually incurs additional charges and may increase lapse rates when the perceived value of the benefit is no longer attractive to policyholders.

In order to reflect such dynamic policyholder behaviour, it is common in VA to assume lapse rates behave according to the following formula:

$$\text{Base Lapse * Dynamic Factor} \tag{II.B-5}$$

Base lapse rates are those that occur because of the need for money not resulting from any measurable external influence. The dynamic factor is typically driven by the ratio of the account value to the perceived value of the GMB, or the "in-the-money" ratio. The dynamic factor is constrained between zero and one. It effectively decreases the lapse rate when the guarantee is in-the-money, or when the account value is lower than the value of the GMB. Base lapse rate applies when the guarantee is out-of-the-money, or when the account value is higher than the value of the GMB. The exact function could differ greatly from company to company, depending on how the company calculates the value of the GMB, and how the company performs the lapse experience study, relevant to the different degrees of in-the-money ratio. When the product offers more than one GMB, the analysis should also take into consideration how the multiple GMBs interact.

However, not all policyholders behave rationally, and companies may model the irrationality explicitly. For example, even when the guarantee is in-the-money and attractive, the policyholder may still lapse the policy. This could be because of an immediate need of cash, or because the policyholder values the GMB differently from the way it is valued by the company. This "irrational" behaviour can be reflected by:

- **Setting a non-zero minimum floor to the dynamic factor**
- **Setting a non-zero minimum lapse rate in the form of "minimum lapse rate + (dynamic factor * base lapse rate)"**

Summary

Modeling a dynamic policyholder is imperative in stochastic modeling, but there is, perhaps, no consensus in how to model this, because practically every company has its own unique experience with policyholder behaviour. To formulate the exact modeling function, companies would need to identify the external factors that drive policyholders and perform an experience study that distinctly illustrates this behaviour.

II.B.3 Morbidity and Claims Experience

Many of the approaches for generating a stochastic rates book are applicable to health risks as well. The key risks generated stochastically for health insurance valuation are:

- **Incidence rates**

- **Severity of claim**

- **Inflation – medical cost of benefits**

- **Utilization trends and other trends**

- **Termination rates – both voluntary lapse and mortality**

- **Claim continuance rates – once a claim occurs, the probability that the claim will continue for a period of time**

Depending on the product, other factors in addition to the interest rates and credit risk discussed earlier will be important to the projection risks for products modeled on a stand-alone basis. This section focuses on a discussion of these key risks specifically applicable to accident and health products.

Another modeling consideration is the availability of public healthcare systems in many developed countries, which greatly reduces the materiality of modeling the impact of private accident and health insurance products in these countries.

Incidence rates

A key component of insurance projections is incidence rate, or the probability that a claim will occur in a specified period. Incidence rates vary for each type of insurance coverage. For some coverage like critical illness, incidence rates are quite low until a specified age is attained. Others have consistently high incidence rates across all ages.

Similar to mortality projections, the Monte Carlo method has been the predominant method utilized to stochastically generate this component. For each policy, a random number is chosen and a claim or no-claim is determined. A sum of the claims in each period divided by the exposures in that period can be compared to the incidence rate or probability.

Other approaches have also been utilized including normal distributions, lognormal distributions, Poisson distributions, and various claim probability methods. Each of these approaches has various merits in specific situations or for certain types of coverage. It is important to first determine the distribution based on historical experience, before assuming future projected occurrences.

One disadvantage of any model is that, if a model office cell represents multiple policies, all with the same characteristics, then running a stochastic analysis only on the cells does not produce the desired answer. In this case, every policy in the model cell will be assumed to have the same hit or miss, which distorts the analysis. It is imperative that the stochastic generator apply to each projection unit. For example, if a benefit has a 20% chance of occurring and the model cell has five policies, a simple Monte Carlo simulation produces a "hit" for this cell. If the hit is applied to the cell in aggregate, all five policies in the cell experience a claim. If each policy is run through the model separately (seriatim), on average only one policy will have a claim, which more accurately reflects the average incidence rate.

Severity of claim

Severity of a claim – another key component of health insurance projections – is typically measured in cost of the benefit when a benefit is payable for service. This can be a monetary amount, such as dollars for costs incurred during a hospital visit, number of days of service when a benefit amount is paid daily, or weeks of disability as in the case of unemployment or disability benefits. Often an underlying claim distribution already exists. For example, determining severity for hospital benefits often relies on a continuance table (a sample of which is shown in Figure II.B-22), which provides the probability of incurring an amount, as well as a claim amount that can be multiplied together to arrive at a claim cost or average cost of the benefit.

▌ **Figure II.B-22**

Probability	Amount of Claim
60%	0
20	700
10	1,600
6	5,000
4	10,000
Total	1,000

Often a claim cost for this purpose would be utilized in deterministic analyses equal to 1,000 times the probability of incurring a claim.

It is also possible to randomly select the amount of claim. In the example above, a uniform distribution might be used to select a probability between 0 and 1. Once the probability is chosen, the appropriate claim level could be looked up in the table. There are many other possibilities of utilizing stochastic modeling in this way, but they are beyond the scope of this book.

Inflation

If benefits are subject to trend or inflation, as is the case in the United States where medical inflation has historically outpaced the general inflation rates by a wide margin, it may be essential to analyze results using a stochastic inflation or medical trend component. This can be particularly true for Market-Consistent Embedded Value (MCEV) calculations, which call for payment of benefits incurred and guaranteed during the policy effective period when premiums may not be adjusted. In some countries, premiums may be adjusted periodically, but the adjustment may not be tied to the increase in claims. For this reason, each situation should be carefully reviewed relative to the purpose of the analysis.

It is critical to note that the "inflation" component of a model may not be linked to monetary inflation, a situation that would necessitate a stochastic generator for medical trends as well as general inflation. The authors have utilized approaches such as 1) an additive factor to general inflation, 2) a compound equation utilizing short-term risk-free interest rates, and 3) a combination of the two. Based on historical data, a mean excess as well as a standard deviation can be determined. For example, suppose average medical trends are equal to average six-month risk-free rates times 150% plus 300%. If the 150% multiplicative factor has a standard deviation of 20%, and the additive factor has a standard deviation of 100%, a Monte Carlo approach generating normal distribution percentages could then be devised to randomly generate medical trends relative to these risk-free rates. These could be applied to a deterministic set of rates or stochastically generated rates.

Utilization

Utilization, typically viewed as the change in incidence rates over time, may also be a key component of claims. Utilization can vary separately from the medical trend assumption, as is the case for certain types of coverage that pay indemnity benefits and whose use can change over time. But certain types of coverage subject to medical trends may also be subject to utilization trends. While utilization trends should be separately considered, the methods utilized to randomly generate this component of claim costs would be similar to the methodology discussed for medical inflation. If it is stochastically generated, it would be multiplied by the other stochastically generated components of claims to develop the overall morbidity level for the period.

Voluntary terminations

For products sold to individual policyholders subject to individual underwriting, lapse, discussed in some detail above, is another key component of any analysis. And, as mentioned in the dynamic policyholder behaviour section, it is not uncommon to utilize a dynamic lapse component in an analysis that pertains to policies whose premiums may be changed.

One example occurs in long-term care (LTC) insurance or Medicare supplement insurance, whose premiums are typically guaranteed renewable and subject to periodic change for all members of a class. If adverse claims experience emerges, insurers may request a rate increase. But this action is assumed to produce a "shock" lapse, because some insureds, who can qualify for coverage under a more competitive plan or who can no longer afford coverage, may voluntarily lapse their policies. Part of shock stems from lapses. For example, an actuary may estimate that a 5% medical trend and 10% rate increase will result in an additional lapse of 200% of the difference between the rate increase and the medical trend. But another part of the shock also may come from an increase in claims that could occur if "healthier" lives lapse before unhealthy lives. The actuary may then believe that claims will increase by 50% of the shock lapse. In this example, the model would generate a shock lapse of 10%, and a subsequent claim adjustment in all future years of 105%.

As discussed in the dynamic policyholder behaviour section, a deterministic or stochastic approach can be used. This analysis could be performed in conjunction with stochastically generated lapse, trend, and/or other factors. Moreover, assumptions used in the analysis must be geared to the type of coverage under review, the availability of competitive products, and the historical or industry experience, among other factors.

For group products, voluntary lapse and mortality are typically not critical components of the analysis, particularly if pricing is the purpose of the analysis. Depending on the type of coverage, group terminations could occur and affect the future projection of the business. In this case, a similar approach to previously discussed methods would be appropriate.

Claim continuance

Claim continuance is a critical component of the pricing for some types of coverage, such as disability insurance or long-term care. Similar to immediate annuities, a benefit may be paid for a period of time, such as that covering the life of the insured, or a shorter period up to a specific age or date. More recently, insurers have been generating claim continuance or claim termination stochastically. These generations allow an insurer to measure the risk of longevity once an insured is on claim.

Typically, probabilities in a claim continuance table are based on large amounts of data, and while a binomial approach could be used, other distributions may be more appropriate. Any of the methods discussed in the first section of the book could be utilized to generate stochastic results once the user has selected a table.

References for II.B

Hampson, Alan W. (1997). Surveillance for pandemic influenza. *The Journal of Infectious Diseases* 176, Suppl 1: S8-13.

Japan Ministry of Health, Welfare and Labour Vital Statistics database.

Lazzari, Stefano & Stohr, Klaus (April 2004). Avian influenza and influenza pandemics [editorial]. *Bulletin of the World Health Organization* 82 (4): 242. Retrieved Sept. 15, 2009, from http://www.who.int/bulletin/volumes/82/4/242.pdf.

Meltzer, Martin I., Cox, Nancy J., & Fukuda, Keiji (1999). The economic impact of pandemic influenza in the United States: Priorities for intervention. *Emerging Infectious Diseases* Vol. 5, No. 5.

Piercy, James & Miles, Adrian (March 2003). The economics of pandemic influenza in Switzerland. Swiss Federal Office of Public Health.

U.S. CDC. Death rates from selected causes, by 10-year groups, race, and sex: Death-registration states, 1900-1932, and United States, 1933-1939. Retrieved Sept. 15, 2009, from http://www.cdc.gov/nchs/datawh/statab/unpubd/mortabs/hist290.htm.

U.S. CDC. Leading causes of death, 1900-1998. Retrieved Sept. 15, 2009, from http://www.cdc.gov/nchs/data/statab/lead1900_98.pdf.

U.S. Census Bureau (2009). Historic national population estimates 1900 to 1999. Retrieved Sept. 15, 2009, from http://www.census.gov/popest/archives/pre-1980/.

U.S. CIA. The World Factbook. Retrieved Sept. 15, 2009, from https://www.cia.gov/library/publications/the-world-factbook/index.html.

U.S. Congressional Budget Office (December 8, 2005; revised July 27, 2006). A potential influenza pandemic: Possible macroeconomic effects and policy issues. Retrieved Sept. 15, 2009, from http://www.cbo.gov/ftpdocs/69xx/doc6946/12-08-BirdFlu.pdf.

U.S. Dept. of Health and Human Services (November 2005). HHS pandemic influenza plan: 18.

U.S. National Counterterrorism Center (NCTC) (2004). Patterns of global terrorism 2003. Retrieved Sept. 15, 2009, from http://terrorisminfo.mipt.org/pdf/2003PoGT.pdf.

Viboud, Cécile, et al. (2004). *Influenza Epidemics in the United States, France and Australia 1972-1997*.

World Health Organization (2003). Summary of probable SARS cases with onset of illness from 1 November 2002 to 31 July 2003. Retrieved Sept. 15, 2009, from http://www.who.int/csr/sars/country/table2004_04_21/en/index.html.

World Health Organization, Emergency Events database.

II.C   Non-life Claim Models

Traditional non-life unpaid claim projection methods – many of which are based on averages of an insurer's data that produce a "best estimate" unpaid claim indication – provide an estimate for an insurer's financial statement or a rate amount, but they are generally not intended to consider the variability of the actual future claim payment emergence or the uncertainty of the parameter selections. These traditional methods provide a "central estimate" that is quite useful for accounting purposes, but without further risk information which is needed for a stochastic model. Indeed as it is very likely that the actual future claim payment emergence will prove to be different than the central estimate of the unpaid claims, it is the possible extent of these differences that we need to estimate.

Stochastic and distributional models of both claims as they occur during the projection period and the changes in estimate on unpaid claims should be the major risk components of a companywide stochastic model for a non-life insurer. The unpaid claim models address the fundamental variability associated with the currently held unpaid claim and unearned premium liability amounts and the losses for policies to be issued, which effectively define the basic risk transfer nature of insurance. Hayne (*Measurement of Reserve Variability*) discusses the uncertainty in unpaid claim estimation from three sources:

- **Process uncertainty, the fundamental uncertainty that is due to the presence of randomness, even when all other aspects of the distribution are known**

- **Parameter uncertainty, the uncertainty that arises due to unknown parameters of statistical models for the distribution, even if the selection of those models is perfectly correct**

- **Model or specification uncertainty, the uncertainty that arises if the specified distributions or underlying models are unknown**

The non-life models in this section attempt, for the most part, to incorporate process and parameter uncertainty into their respective standard error or distributional indications.

> It is very likely that the actual future claim payment emergence will prove to be different than the central estimate of the unpaid claims, it is the possible extent of these differences that we need to estimate.

The third source of uncertainty – model risk – has two parts. First, there is the risk that the model is not a good representation of the current claim process. This risk can be estimated or reduced by testing the assumptions of the model(s) being used and studying the results from different models. Second, there is the risk that, even if the model is a good representation of the current claim process, this process will experience unforeseeable changes in the future. Examples include the emergence of asbestos claims and the financial crisis of 2008/2009. This kind of risk is the most difficult to quantify.

This section provides a brief review of non-life models that will produce a distribution for unpaid claims (which typically can include allocated loss adjustment expenses associated with individual claim loss amounts). Some models presented are based on commonly applied actuarial methodology, such as loss development projections and associated methods. For estimating unpaid claim variability, the process derived by Thomas Mack (1993) might be the most well known, perhaps because the Mack methodology provides variance estimates by formulas that extend from a basic loss development analysis. Other models use curve fit models of loss development factors.

The discussions that follow serve to introduce some of the more common models, but they are not intended to be exhaustive. All of the models discussed can be used for estimating liabilities for accounting purposes, for parameterizing a stochastic model and for pricing new business. While we will discuss each of these, our primary focus is on the first two applications. As a way of organizing the discussion, we have grouped the models into three broad categories: 1) aggregate triangle-based models, 2) individual claim frequency/severity models, and 3) catastrophe models.[26] The references guide the reader to the published works that document the statistical derivation and application of these methodologies.

If the original data (e.g., triangle) is not of a sufficient size and with enough experience, then estimates of unpaid claims at high percentiles lose accuracy.

While we have described the main assumptions, advantages, and disadvantages of each model, it is also worth noting that these characteristics are similarly not intended to be exhaustive. For example, most, if not all, of the models described suffer from the disadvantage that the distribution of unpaid claims they produce is based solely on experience to date. If the original data (e.g., triangle) is not of a sufficient size and with enough experience, then estimates of unpaid claims at high percentiles lose accuracy. This issue can often be mitigated by including more historical data or looking at similar industry data or modifying the model's framework to fit additional distributions or introduce additional uncertainty, but such modification, in turn, introduces parameter error.

Finally, it should be noted that the process of updating an analysis of unpaid claims on a regular basis (e.g., annually or quarterly) will have an impact on stochastic modeling and solvency estimation. For example, typically older data is excluded from an analysis as new data is added, but it could be saved and used to increase the credibility of the parameters, or older parameters could be saved to compare with new parameters, or the model could be back tested to see how well it predicted the new data. More importantly, as actual data "emerges" this will cause the unpaid claim estimates to change (i.e., the total estimate can be split into the first estimate of unpaid for the new data and the new estimate of the unpaid for the old data). As the interim estimates change, this can in turn cause short term solvency issues (e.g., a large spike in payments in the current period) even if long term solvency is not an issue.

---

[26] Indeed, even the categories reveal that the models described in this section are not exhaustive, because aggregate claim count / average severity models could be considered another category.

II.C.1 Aggregate Triangle-based Models

Advantages

- These models typically only require triangle data input, which is usually readily available.

Disadvantages

- Triangle-based models provide results in aggregate, for groups of claims. They do not model each individual claim, as is done in the frequency / severity models. Therefore, they are not suitable to be used in cases where individual claim projections are needed, for example, in evaluating excess of loss reinsurance contracts.

Stochastic loss development model

In the stochastic loss development model, the loss development factors are assumed to follow a probability distribution (Hayne ["Estimate of Statistical Variation"] uses a lognormal distribution, although other distributions may be used[27]). The parameters of the distribution can be estimated from the triangle of incremental loss development factors.

Assumptions

The stochastic loss development model is built around the chain ladder algorithm, so it should only be applied to claims processes that follow the chain ladder assumptions.[28]

> The stochastic loss development model is built around the chain ladder algorithm, so it should only be applied to claims processes that follow the chain ladder assumptions.

Advantages

- The model is based on the chain ladder method, which is easily understood.

- For the lognormal model, a closed form distribution for the cumulative development factors (product of loss development factors, or LDFs) can be obtained; for other distributions, simulation is required.

- Negative incremental values are allowed.

Disadvantages

- According to Murphy (2007), the model does not explicitly incorporate parameter risk, although it can be incorporated with judgment.

- The model does not incorporate a tail factor, although this can be estimated separately.

- A large number of parameters are estimated (relative to the data points used), which reduces the ability to gauge the applicability of the model to the underlying process.

- Unable to recognize change in calendar period trends, which is a general chain-ladder limitation.

---

[27] Kelly ("Practical Loss Reserving Method") describes a variety of other distributions that can be applied to the stochastic loss development model.

[28] Venter (1998) describes six testable implications of assuming that claim emergence follow a chain ladder algorithm.

Hoerl curve

A Hoerl curve, as described by England and Verrall (2002), is not a stochastic model in itself, but rather is a parametric curve fit to incremental losses through the use of weighted linear regression. The shape of the Hoerl curve follows the typical claim development in that it increases to a peak then decreases exponentially. It can be used as a substitute for loss development factors in stochastic models that follow the chain-ladder structure.

Assumptions

- **The expected incremental loss follows the form:**

$$E[Incremental\ Loss(i,j)] = A(i) \times j^{\beta(i)} \times e^{\gamma(i) \times j}$$ (II.C-1)

where i and j refer to the exposure periods and development periods, respectively, of the loss triangle.

Advantages

- **Reduces the number of parameters in a chain-ladder based model. A typical model requires one loss development factor for each development period. The Hoerl Curve uses just one parametric curve to describe the whole run-off pattern.**

- **Allows for extrapolation to obtain an estimate of the tail factor.**

- **Parameter error is incorporated explicitly.**

Disadvantages

- **The curve does not usually fit well for the whole length of loss development. This can be remedied by removing the first one or two development periods from the fit.**

Mack's distribution-free model

Mack's model (1993) calculates the mean and standard errors of the chain ladder unpaid claim estimate. The error term incorporates both the process and parameter variance of the model.

Mack's model (1993) calculates the mean and standard errors of the chain ladder unpaid claim estimate. The error term incorporates both the process and parameter variance of the model.

The model is distribution-free. In order to calculate percentiles, a probability distribution must be selected for the outstanding claim liabilities. As noted by Houltram (2003), Mack proposes a lognormal model; Li (2006) observes that other distributions can be used depending on the required thickness of the tail.

Assumptions

Mack's model is built around the chain ladder algorithm, and Venter (1998) notes that it should only be applied to claim processes that also follow the chain ladder assumptions. Consistent with the chain ladder framework, Mack makes the following three assumptions:

- **Cumulative claims in each exposure period are independent.**

- **The expected value of cumulative claims for the next evaluation date (C_{j+1}) is equal to the cumulative claims at the current evaluation date (C_j) multiplied by the corresponding LDF.**

- **The variance of an LDF is inversely proportional to the cumulative claims (at the evaluation to which the LDF will be applied).**

Advantages

As described by England and Verrall (2004):

- **Able to handle negative incremental values.**
- **Calculations can be performed easily, with no simulation required.**
- **Assumptions can be made to estimate tail factor variability.**
- **Incorporates parameter risk explicitly.**

Disadvantages

- **Unable to recognize change in calendar year trends, which is a general chain ladder limitation.**
- **It is based on the chain-ladder method and uses LDFs. Therefore, the model could be seen as being over-parameterized, as one LDF is required for each development period pairing.**

Bootstrap model

Bootstrapping is a versatile framework that can be used in combination with many other models. The bootstrap premise is that there is an assumed model framework that provides a perfect "fitted" version of the data, and the difference between this fitted version and the actual historical data gives an indication of how different the actual data can be from the model framework. This is captured by calculating residuals from this difference. The residuals are placed in a "pool" that is sampled from and added to the fitted model to generate new versions of simulated "actual" data. For each simulated dataset, the model framework is applied to develop the claims to ultimate. If this process is simulated 10,000 times it will yield 10,000 values for the unpaid claims, forming an empirical estimate of the unpaid claim distribution.

> Bootstrapping is a versatile framework that can be used in combination with many other models.

The most common version of the bootstrap model is from England and Verrall (1999, with an update in 2002), using the chain ladder method.

Assumptions

- **The bootstrap framework inherits the assumptions of whatever underlying best estimate model is used.**
- **The bootstrap framework assumes that the best estimate model fits the data well and completely explains all past trends. If, for instance, the chain ladder model is used, and there are calendar year trends that have not been accounted for in the model, then the resulting residuals will not be independent and identically distributed.**

Advantages

- The bootstrap model is easy to explain and understand, and it is one of the best known and most used stochastic liability frameworks.

- The framework is very versatile and can be applied to a number of best estimate models.

- In its simplest form, distributions do not need to be assumed or parameterized, reducing parameter error.

- A tail factor can be easily incorporated

- Parameter risk is incorporated explicitly. Process risk can be incorporated as an enhancement to the basic bootstrap model (as illustrated in Section IV.D)

- The basic model can be modified to handle negative incremental losses.

Disadvantages

- In its basic form, the residuals calculated in a chain ladder bootstrap model cannot be considered to be identically distributed; to fix this problem, Pinheiro et al. (2001) outlined the use of a "hat matrix" that can be applied to the residuals.

- The model requires stochastic simulation to obtain a distribution result. Therefore, a simulation model must be built

- In its basic form, the model is unable to recognize changes in calendar year trends, although the model can be modified to allow this

- The basic bootstrap model uses the chain ladder method, which could be seen as being over-parameterized, as one LDF is required for each development period pairing. This can also be modified, for example, by fitting a curve to replace the LDFs.

Because the bootstrap model is so versatile, it is used in Section IV.D to illustrate the use of a model to estimate one of the primary inputs into a company-wide stochastic model: unpaid claim variability. Additional information is included in Appendix D.

Schnieper

The Schnieper (1991) model separates the incurred losses that arise from new claims from the incurred losses that arise from existing claims.

The Schnieper (1991) model separates the incurred losses that arise from new claims from the incurred losses that arise from existing claims. Subsequent development by Liu and Verrall (2006) show how this framework can be bootstrapped. In the common bootstrap method, there is only one set of residuals for all claims. In the Schnieper model, there are two sets of residuals: one for the new claims emergence, and one for the development of existing claims.

Assumptions

The Schnieper model assumes:

- There is independence among accident years.

- The development of existing claims follows chain ladder assumptions.

- The development of the new claims follows Bornhuetter-Ferguson assumptions in that the expected value is the exposure multiplied by an a priori factor for that accident year; the variance is the exposure multiplied by a variance factor for that accident year.

Advantages

- Able to separately model pure incurred but not reported (IBNR) claims and incurred but not enough reported (IBNER) claims.
- Parameter risk is modeled explicitly.
- Can handle negative incremental values.

Disadvantages

- The model requires data that allows the separation of IBNR and IBNER movements, as well as exposure data.
- Although it is possible to model IBNR and IBNER claims separately, Liu and Verrall (2006) do not provide guidance on obtaining a separate distribution for IBNR and IBNER.
- The basic Schnieper model does not accommodate a tail factor.

All disadvantages outlined for the bootstrap model also apply here.

Generalized linear modeling framework

The generalized linear modeling (GLM) framework is a powerful statistical tool that models the outcome of an event depending on other variables. It provides a structured process for the important drivers of an outcome to be identified and their effect to the estimated. The term "linear" is used because there is a linear function of the explanatory variables. This linear function is passed through a link function, which relates it to the dependent variable. In this way, the relationship between the dependent and explanatory variable do not need to be linear because of the link function, which can provide for different relationships. For instance, if a multiplicative relationship is desired, then the log-link function is used. The basic steps in GLM are:

> The generalized linear modeling (GLM) framework is a powerful statistical tool that models the outcome of an event depending on other variables.

1. Obtain data.
2. Select initial set of explanatory variables, using judgment as well as simple diagnostic tests.
3. Select a model (multiplicative, linear, etc.).
4. Fit the model in an iterative process. With each fit, decisions will be made such as the weights assigned to each variable, the inclusion/exclusion of a variable, or the variable change from, say, the "age" variable as continuous integers to "age" in groups.
5. Test the fitted model. A good test is to keep a portion of original data to one side and do not use it to fit the model. The predictions of the fitted model can then be compared to this original data to help prevent over-fitting.

Advantages

- **GLM is extremely flexible.**

  a) It can incorporate desired variables in many different ways, and it uses a rigorous process to identify these variables and structure the model. For example, calendar year trends can be incorporated into a GLM. Additionally, the number of parameters used is a modeling decision, so over-parameterization can be avoided.

  b) In addition to providing unpaid claim distributions, GLMs can also be used to rate insurance, to model demand, to identify good customers, to identify large claims early, to provide statistical case estimation and to stream claims.

Disadvantages

- **The GLM is very sensitive to the data input. If the data has errors, then the resulting model could also have errors.**

- **Some statistical knowledge is needed to fit and interpret results.**

- **GLM is still a process of judgment and, as a result, the process can be difficult to review. A large number of iterations are usually required to fit a model, where, at each iteration, decisions of judgment are made that lead the model down different paths; therefore, it is possible to end up with many different, equally valid models.**

- **High-powered computer hardware is needed and processing time is long because of the need for many trial and error iterations.**

II.C.2 Individual Claims Frequency/Severity Models

Individual models allow for the modeling of individual claims, which is necessary for the analysis of reinsurance products operating under an individual claims basis, for example, excess of loss reinsurance.

Advantages

- **Allows for the modeling of individual claims, which is necessary for the analysis of reinsurance products operating under an individual claims basis, for example, excess of loss reinsurance.**

- **Frequency/severity models provide a more granular level of modeling, which can be used for many different types of actuarial analysis, including pricing, reserving and reinsurance modeling. This would allow more synchronization of models across an organization.**

Disadvantages

- **These models typically require individual claim data, which may not be readily available.**

- **Because of the level of detail the need for computing power and data storage is usually greatly increased compared to triangle based models.**

Collective risk model

The collective risk model calculates the total loss from an insurance portfolio as the sum of N claims with ultimate claim size S, where N and S are specified by frequency and severity distributions, respectively.

As noted by Hayne (1994), it is assumed that the ultimate claim sizes are independent and identically distributed random variables. Common severity distributions are the lognormal and gamma distributions.

N is a random variable, usually following a Poisson distribution or negative binomial, unless no IBNR claims are expected, in which case N would be fixed.

In its simplest form, the Poisson distribution for claim frequency is parameterized by equating the Poisson parameter with the expected number of claims. The severity distribution can be parameterized by fitting to the historical distribution of individual ultimate claims, all adjusted for inflation so that they are on a comparable basis. For each iteration, a value for N is simulated, n, and n values of the severity distribution are simulated.

In this form, the collective risk model only accounts for process variance, not parameter variance. Heckman and Meyers (1983) address the problem of parameter uncertainty. They add a "contagion" parameter to the model to address the potential that an external event could affect the frequency across all years or lines, and another "mixing" parameter that reflects the possibility that external events could affect the future claim severity.

Hayne (*Measurement of Reserve Variability*) illustrates the parameterization of this model, using the variance of the projection methods (e.g., chain ladder, Berquist-Sherman, or Bornhuetter-Ferguson methods) around the weighted mean to parameterize the variability of the unpaid claims (the model combines the distribution of N and S to create an algorithm for the aggregate unpaid claims).

The collective risk model falls into the more widely recognized family of models known as the Markov chain Monte Carlo method. A Markov Chain is a stochastic process with the following property: given the current outcome, future outcomes are independent of past outcomes. A random walk is an example of a Markov Chain. Monte Carlo simulation defines the domain of all possible inputs into a model (i.e., the variables and their parameters). Then, for each iteration, randomly selects inputs for that model from the domain, performs a deterministic calculation using the inputs, aggregates the results of the individual computations into the output and repeats. The end result is a distribution of outputs.

> The collective risk model falls into the more widely recognized family of models known as the Markov chain Monte Carlo method.

Assumptions

- **In its basic form, the collective risk model assumes that the number of claims in a year is independent from one year to the next, and the severities of each claim are all independent from each other.**

- **Correlations could be explicitly included in the model.**

Advantages

- Allows for the modeling of individual claim severities, which is necessary for analysis of all reinsurance operating on an individual claim basis (e.g., excess of loss).

- Provides a more granular level of modeling, which can be used for many different types of actuarial analysis, including pricing, liability, and reinsurance modeling. This would allow more synchronization of models across an organization.

- Simulated results can be made arbitrarily close to the model results simply by increasing the number of simulations, subject to the constraints of time and computing power.

- Advances in computing power have made the time constraints associated with simulation reasonable.

- Specification of the underlying model is often far easier in a simulation environment as closed-form solutions quickly become exceedingly difficult to construct for all but the most simple models.

- Simulation allows the stochastic elements of the model to be separated from the deterministic elements. This separation can simplify the development, testing, and communication of a complex model.

Disadvantages

- In its basic form, the parameterization of the severity distribution involves estimating the historical ultimate loss on a claim-by-claim basis. This information is not usually readily available, because traditional loss development factors develop pure IBNR, as well as IBNER. One method to obtain the ultimate loss for each claim is to use a transition matrix. (See below.)

It is also possible to model losses by layer. Historical losses are trended, and the loss amounts and loss counts in a layer are calculated.

Collective risk model by layer

It is also possible to model losses by layer. Historical losses are trended, and the loss amounts and loss counts in a layer are calculated. The mean of the frequency distribution can be obtained by developing an aggregate count triangle to ultimate. A Poisson distribution can be used. Alternatively, in those instances where claim counts show substantial variability, a negative binomial can be used, with the mean to variance ratio selected by judgment. For the severity distribution, we have several options: (1) create a triangle of aggregate losses in the layer and develop to obtain the mean ultimate aggregate loss. Because we have the mean of the frequency distribution, the mean of the severity distribution can be obtained. The distribution and further parameterization of the severity distribution can be obtained by judgment or through the analysis of the distribution of historical losses closed in the layer. Alternatively, per Papush (1997), (2) develop claims to ultimate that are open in the nth development period, compile a triangle on those claims open in the nth development period, and use these development factors. A severity distribution can then be fit to these ultimate claims using the maximum likelihood method.

Assumptions

- It is assumed that the number of claims in a year is independent from one year to the next, and the severities of each claim are all independent from each other.

Advantages

- **By narrowing development down to specific layers, more accurate results in the layer may be possible than if we analyzed losses from the ground up.**

Disadvantages

- **Can be difficult if attempting to model high layers, because of lack of historical data.**

Transition matrix

The transition matrix is not a stochastic model in itself, but a method used to obtain a distribution of ultimate claim costs, which can be used as part of a collective risk model.

When dealing with excess loss pricing, correct estimates of individual large losses are needed. A common method is to trend and develop individual claims to ultimate, using one set of development factors, and fitting a severity distribution to these claims. This, however, produces only one ultimate for each claim, which in reality has many different possible outcomes. Using transition matrices, as noted by Mahon (2005), allows for these different outcomes.

In the transition matrix method, each claim is bucketed into a state denoting the current information on the claim. Mahon (2005) uses the size of the incurred claim and considers whether the claim is open or closed. The transition matrix contains the probabilities that a claim will move from a given state to each of the other states during a particular development period. By successive multiplication of the matrices, one gets an ultimate matrix for each maturity level. Transition matrices are estimated by analyzing the historical movement of claims. The results will be a series of possible outcomes and their probabilities for each and all existing claims. A distribution can then be fit to this from which ultimate claim costs can be simulated.

Assumptions

The transition matrix assumes that the movement of the claim from one development period to the next, or from transition to transition, is independent of the previous movement. That is, the development has no memory. For this reason, there is a tendency for the ultimate distribution result to be overly dispersed.

Advantages

- **Provides a more realistic estimation of the distribution of individual ultimate claim costs than the straight application of the selected loss development factors.**

- **Negative incremental losses can be incorporated into the model.**

- **Can accommodate the explicit modeling of re-opened claims.**

Disadvantages

- **Generates a large number of parameters and does not incorporate an allowance for parameter risk.**

- **Requires individual claim data to be maintained at each evaluation period to estimate the transition matrices.**

- **Requires data with sufficiently long history such that a tail factor is not required.**

Generalized linear modeling applied to unpaid claim estimation

Taylor and McGuire (2004) provide a well documented application of generalized linear modeling (GLM) methodology to a specific unpaid claim estimation example. The structure of the model is presented in contrast to models using loss development factors. The GLM model systematically and subjectively incorporates the most representative and significant trends in the historical loss data that are poorly addressed by chain ladder methodology, such as when the loss development factors appear to be increasing by accident year. The case study relied on individual claim data but the authors note that the basic GLM methodology could be applied to triangle loss data.

Assumptions

- **The observation or dependent variable being modeled is assumed to follow a distribution from the exponential family (normal, gamma, Poisson, binomial or inverse Gaussian).**

- **Further assumptions are made about the relationship of the independent and dependent variables to each other once the link function has been selected. For example, a log-link function assumes the relationship is multiplicative.**

Advantages

- **GLM provides a structured and rigorous form of data analysis. It enables the investigation and modeling of a number of complex features that invalidate the chain ladder process. For example, it allows the modeling of:**

  a) Superimposed inflation

  b) Changes in rates of claim payment. In Taylor and McGuire's example (2004), the loss development factors were increasing by accident year. This can be explicitly modeled using GLMs.

- **It allows trends to be detected in more than one dimension simultaneously, which is very difficult for the human eye to do.**

Disadvantages

- **Structuring and estimating parameters for a GLM is often a lengthy and challenging exercise; if this methodology is used, the analyst should be prepared to perform detailed data "scrubbing" on top of the statistical modeling work.**

Wright's model

Wright's model (1990) is a frequency/severity model. Claim counts are assumed to follow a Poisson distribution, where the Poisson parameter is set as a function of the development period and the exposure in that period of origin. Severities are assumed to be Gamma-like[29] random variables with the mean set as a function of the development period, a possible adjustment for claims inflation, and the variance proportional to the mean squared. The models for claim

---

[29] The severity distribution is "Gamma-like," since, like the Gamma distribution, the standard deviation is proportional to the mean. When claim amounts are all positive, Wright's severity random variables are Gamma-distributed.

frequency and severity are then combined to form a model for aggregate losses, which in turn can be transformed into a generalized linear model.

Assumptions

- All claim severities are independent from each other, as are the number of claim payments from year to year.

- Claim severities follow a Gamma, or Gamma-like distribution.

- Claim counts follow a Poisson distribution.

Advantages

- Allows for an inflation effect (i.e., a calendar year effect) to be included in the severity modeling.

- Negative incremental losses are allowed.

- Over-parameterization is avoided by using a Kalman filter to produce smoothed parameter estimates.

- The model explicitly accounts for parameter risk.

- The model is able to produce estimates of liabilities and the standard error past the last observed development period, and so can account for tail variability.

Disadvantages

Implementing this model requires a sophisticated understanding of stochastic claims models.

> Wright's model (1990) is a frequency/severity model. Claim counts are assumed to follow a Poisson distribution, where the Poisson parameter is set as a function of the development period and the exposure in that period of origin.

II.C.3 Catastrophe Modeling

Catastrophe modeling helps insurers assess the potential losses caused by natural and man-made catastrophes.

Catastrophe models can be seen as a unique type of frequency / severity model, with three segments:

- **Hazard:** This models the hazard itself, where it will spread, at what speed, and with what force.

- **Inventory:** This models the properties at risk, capturing location as well as information on the property itself (e.g., construction and use of the property).

- **Loss:** This combines the hazard and inventory models with policy information (e.g., sum insured, attachment points and limits), so that the total loss to the insurer can be estimated. Loss models include the physical loss of property as well as losses from business interruption and expenses and reflect the percent damaged. Recently, the models have also included loss assessment for workers compensation policies, and for life and health insurance products.

Catastrophe models are parameterized using a large database of historical catastrophes, meteorological information, engineering data, and insurer-specific exposure information.

Insurers, risk managers, rating agencies, and insurance brokers tend to license models from the major catastrophe modeling firms: AIR Worldwide, Risk Management Solutions (RMS), and EQECAT (EQE). Many use multiple catastrophe models to better understand the model risk. The models are used for risk management, underwriting, and pricing.

The Catastrophe Insurance Working Group of the National Association of Insurance Commissioners (NAIC) published the *Catastrophe Computer Modeling Handbook* (2001), which investigates catastrophe models and the issues surrounding them.

Advantages

Catastrophe models allow estimates of the catastrophe risks faced by insurers, using expertise from a range of fields including meteorologists, seismologists, geologists, engineers, mathematicians, actuaries, and other scientists and statisticians.

Disadvantages

- **Catastrophe models are proprietary, so they have a "black box" feel to the practitioner who uses the output.**

- **Catastrophe models can be over-parameterized, which can create correlation among the parameters, compounding the effect of parameter uncertainty.**

References for II.C

Actuarial Standards Board (2000). Actuarial standard of practice no. 38: Using models outside the actuary's area of expertise (property and casualty). Retrieved Sept. 15, 2009, from http://actuarialstandardsboard.net/pdf/asops/asop038_071.pdf.

Andrade, Pinheiro P., Silva, J., & Centeno, M. (2001). Bootstrap methodology in claim reserving.

Bouska, A. *From disability income to mega-risk: Policy-event based loss.*

Clark, D. *LDF Curve-fitting and stochastic reserving: A maximum likelihood.*

de Jong, P. (2004). *Forecasting general insurance liabilities.*

England P, and Verrall, R. (1999). Analytic and bootstrap estimates of prediction errors in claims reserving.

England, P. and Verrall, R. (2002). Stochastic claims reserving in general insurance. Institute of Actuaries and Faculty of Actuaries. Retrieved Sept. 15, 2009, from http://www.emb.com/EMBDOTCOM/Netherlands/Nieuws%20-%20News/SCRinGI-EnglandVerrall.pdf.

England, P. and Verrall, R. (2004). More on stochastic reserving in general insurance. GIRO Convention.

Hayne, R. (1985). An estimate of statistical variation in development factor methods. Proceedings of the CAS. Retrieved Sept. 16, 2009, from http://www.casact.org/pubs/proceed/proceed85/85025.pdf.

Hayne, R. (1994). A method to estimate probability level for loss reserves.

Hayne, R. Measurement of reserve variability. Retrieved Sept. 15, 2009, from http://www.casact.org/pubs/forum/03fforum/03ff141.pdf.

Heckman, P.E. & Meyers, G.G. (1983). The calculation of aggregate loss distributions from claim severity and claim count distributions. *Proceedings of the Casualty Actuarial Society* LXX (1983): 22-61. (Addendum in LXXI (1984): 49-66.)

Hesseslager, O. (1994). A Markov Model for loss reserving. *ASTIN Bulletin* Vol. 24-2: 183-193. Retrieved Sept. 15, 2009, from http://www.casact.org/library/astin/vol24no2/183.pdf.

Houltram, A. (2003). Reserving judgement. The Institute of Actuaries of Australia XIVth General Insurance Seminar.

Kelly, Mary V. *Practical loss reserving method with stochastic development factors.*

Klugman, S., Panjer, H., & Willmot, G. (2004). *Loss models: From data to decisions* 2nd edition. Wiley.

Li, J. (2006). Comparison of stochastic reserving methods. *Australian Actuarial Journal* Vol. 12 issue 4: 489-569. Retrieved Sept. 15, 2009, from http://www.actuaries.asn.au/IAA/upload/public/ Vol12_Issue4(web).pdf.

Liu, H. & Verrall, R. (2006). Predictive distributions for reserves which separate true IBNR and IBNER claims. Presented at the International Congress on Insurance: Mathematics and Economics, July 18-20, 2006. Retrieved Sept. 15, 2009, from http://www.kuleuven.be/ime2006/full/27.pdf.

Mack, T. (1993). Distribution-free calculation of the standard error of chain ladder reserve estimates. *ASTIN Bulletin* 23, no. 2: 213-25.

Mahon, J. (Spring 2005). Transition matrix theory and individual claim loss development. *CAS Forum*. Retrieved Sept. 15, 2009, from http://www.casact.org/pubs/forum/05spforum/05spf115.pdf.

McGuire, G. & Taylor, G. (2004). Loss reserving with GLMs: A case study. CAS Discussion Paper Program. Retrieved Sept. 15, 2009, from http://www.casact.org/pubs/dpp/dpp04/04dpp327.pdf.

Murphy, D. (2007). The language of uncertainty: Terminology surrounding loss reserve variability/ranges. Casualty Loss Reserve Seminar.

National Association of Insurance Commissioners (NAIC), Catastrophe Insurance Working Group (January 2001). *Catastrophe computer modeling handbook*. (Available for purchase online at http://www.naic.org/store_pub_special.htm#catastrophe.)

Papush, D. (1997). A simulation approach in excess reinsurance pricing.

Scollnik, D. (2001). Actuarial modeling with MCMC and BUGS. *North American Actuarial Journal* Vol. 5 No. 2. Retrieved Sept. 15, 2009, from http://math.ucalgary.ca/~scollnik/abcd/naaj0104_7.pdf.

Scollnik, D. (2004). *Bayesian reserving models inspired by chain ladder methods and implemented using Win BUGS.* Retrieved Sept. 15, 2009, from http://www.soa.org/library/proceedings/arch/2004/ arch04v38n2_3.pdf.

Venter, G. (1998). Testing the assumptions of age-to-Age factors. *PCAS* LXXXV: 807-47.

Verrall, R. (2004). A Bayesian generalized linear model for the Bornhuetter-Ferguson method of claims reserving.

Wacek, M. *Parameter uncertainty in loss ratio distributions and its implications.*

Walsh, B. (2004). Markov chain Monte Carlo and Gibbs sampling. Lecture Notes for EEB 581, version 26. Retrieved Sept. 16, 2009, from http://www.stat.columbia.edu/~liam/teaching/neurostat-spr07/papers/mcmc/mcmc-gibbs-intro.pdf.

Wright, T.S. (1990). A stochastic method for claims reserving in general insurance.

II.D Non-life Financial Models

II.D.1 Types of Models

The goal of dynamic risk modeling is not to forecast the future. Instead, dynamic risk modeling helps company managers understand how best to manage the financial affairs of their company.

The Finnish and British working groups on solvency[30] were the first to publish research on dynamic risk models for the insurance industry. These groups were largely responsible for evolving the notion of solvency, moving it from a static accounting basis to a dynamic, cash flow focused approach that views the entity as an ongoing concern. Their works, however, were just the beginning of an evolution in insurance modeling that has drawn on techniques used by strategic planners, financial analysts, and investment professionals.

Dynamic risk modeling aims to provide information that allows management to make better informed, more rewarding decisions. This rich trove of information includes:

- **Solid information about the *interaction* of decisions within all areas of company operations and their *impact* on results**
- **A quantitative review of the *risk and return trade-offs* inherent in emerging strategic opportunities**
- **A *structured process* for evaluating alternative operating plans**

The goal of dynamic risk modeling is *not* to forecast the future. Instead, dynamic risk modeling helps company managers understand how best to manage the financial affairs of their company.

---

[30] See Pentikainen (1988); Coutts and Devitt (1989); Daykin et al. (1989); and Daykin, Pentikainen, and Pesonen (1994).

As noted in the CAS Dynamic Risk Modeling Handbook (2006), these tools allow managers to better position their companies to absorb the transfer of risk, to earn an appropriate return, and to minimize the company's exposure to insolvency.

II.D.1.a The Evolution of Models

While dynamic risk models evolved from more traditional models, each stage in the evolutionary process has involved a quantum leap in modeling capabilities. The Dynamic Risk Modeling Handbook (2006) defined four stages or types of financial models:

- **Financial budgeting.** Essentially a deterministic or static model that uses only one set of assumptions about future operating results from a company's various divisions or business units.

- **Sensitivity or stress testing.** Perhaps most accurately described as incorporating "best case" and "worst case" scenarios along with the expected outcome.

- **Stochastic modeling.**[31] Makes it possible to describe critical assumptions, and their combined financial implications, in terms of ranges of possible outcomes rather than fixed values and results.

- **Dynamic modeling.** As the most recent evolutionary step, dynamic modeling, described in the Dynamic Risk Modeling Handbook, incorporates feedback loops and "management intervention decisions" into the models.

II.D.1.b Uses of Dynamic Risk Models

> **Dynamic risk models are concerned with the relationship among assets and liabilities; dynamic risk models also concern the resultant risks to income and cash flows.**

Dynamic risk models (DRMs) are concerned with the relationship among assets and liabilities; DRMs also concern the resultant risks to income and cash flows. By explicitly recognizing all of the company's operations, dynamic risk models can: a) reveal the links between different strategies and possible outcomes, b) illustrate the uncertainty related to contingent events occurring during the potentially long delay between creating or assuming risk and the liabilities arising from that risk, and c) evaluate the impact of time, the interrelationships among different aspects of an operation, and alternative outcomes of contingent events. In this way, dynamic risk models make a unique contribution to the analytical tools available for performing financial analyses.

There are virtually unlimited possibilities for modeling this financial information. If it can be put in a spreadsheet, it can be dynamically modeled. Common examples include:

- **Realistic business planning**

- **Product and market development**

- **Claims management**

- **Capital adequacy and regulatory support**

- **Capital allocation**

---

[31] Footnote 26 on page 419 of Feller (1968) states, "The term 'stochastic process' and 'random process' are synonyms and cover practically all theory of probability from coin tossing to harmonic analysis. In practice, the term 'stochastic process' is used mostly when a time parameter is introduced."

- **Liquidity**

- **Reinsurance or securitization structure**

- **Asset/investment strategy analysis**

- **Rating agency support**

- **Merger and acquisition opportunities**

This is not necessarily a complete list and it could be different based on what is customary in each country. (For a description of some of the country-specific uses, see Section II.E.) For the interested reader, the "Dynamic Risk Modeling Handbook" is a very useful source for a description of many aspects of building a model. For the remainder of Section II.D we will describe a specific model (which is one option among many) that the reader should be able to tailor or adapt to specific situations rather than trying to discuss all of the possible options.

An insurance company dynamic risk model can easily become complicated because of the interrelationships among economic conditions, underwriting results, investment results, asset management, and decision making.

II.D.2 Description of a Non-life Dynamic Risk Model

An insurance company dynamic risk model can easily become complicated because of the interrelationships among economic conditions, underwriting results, investment results, asset management, and decision making. It is, therefore, useful to break the model into a number of smaller modules, examples of which are shown in the diagram in Figure II.D-1 that will be used in this discussion. While Figure II.D-1 illustrates the major components of the model and their interactions, it is important to remember that each of those components is critically dependent on the assumptions, stochastic parameters and business logic which drive all of the simulations.

Figure II.D-1

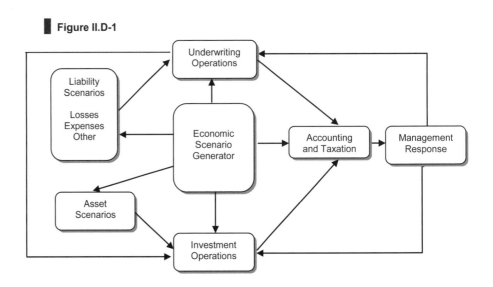

The centerpiece of the model, the economic scenario generator, creates the economic variables used as inputs to:

- **Determine loss and expense frequencies and severities (the liability scenarios module)**

- Update market values of bonds and equities and calculate market values and cash flows of financial derivatives (the asset scenarios module)

- Calculate the cash flows resulting from insurance operations (the underwriting operations module premium)

- Invest the net cash flows generated by the underwriting operations and funds from bond coupons and maturities or equity dividends (the investment operations module, whose operations also include implementation of investment strategies and asset allocations)

- Calculate income taxes and financial statement values using the desired accounting rules (the accounting and taxation module)

- Evaluate and modify assumptions of the operations modules for future periods (the management response module)

II.D.2.a General Model Description

The non-life dynamic risk model discussed in this section is a stochastic Monte Carlo model, which is used to simulate insurance company financial results for a specified number of projection periods over a specified period of time. Model inputs are parameterized based on historical company, insurance industry, and economic data. The model simulates premiums, losses, expenses, and investment outcomes. Losses are modeled using a combination of premiums, loss ratios, claim frequencies, and claim severities.

II.D.2.b Economic Scenarios

Central to the model is the economic scenario generator (ESG). The economic variables affect all of the other modules either directly or indirectly. Interest rates and default rates are used by the asset scenarios module to determine the market price of bonds. Equity returns and dividend yields determine equity prices and income. Inflation rates, economic growth, and unemployment may be used to determine liability frequencies and severities or changes in company expenses. In the investment operations module, economic variables are often used to make asset allocation decisions. Underwriting operations, such as pricing levels, depend on future expectations for the interest rates that can be used for underwriting cash flows. Accounting may depend on risk-free or risk-adjusted interest rates for discounting of liabilities.

The non-life dynamic risk model needs the following variables from the ESG (a description of the calculation of most these variables is in Section II.A of this book):

- Interest rates

- Bond default rates

- Equity returns

- Equity dividends

- Inflation rates

- Changes to gross domestic product (GDP)

> Central to the model is the economic scenario generator. The economic variables affect all of the other modules either directly or indirectly.

- **Unemployment rates**
- **Exchange rates**

II.D.2.c Asset Scenarios

The asset scenarios module uses the economic variables produced by the ESG to calculate cash flows and other variables needed to model assets. The variables needed depend on the accounting basis used, but usually include: coupons and maturities; market value, par value, amortized value, and acquisition cost for bonds; dividends, market value, and acquisition cost for equities; and real estate rental income, market value, and acquisition costs.

Returns for additional asset types, beyond those provided by the ESG, may be calculated in the asset scenarios module. For example, using government bond yields produced by the ESG as the base, a credit risk spread can be superimposed to produce corporate bonds of the desired credit quality. Other derivative assets, such as mortgage-backed securities or inflation-protected securities, may be modeled in the asset scenarios module.

Assets may be modeled at varying degrees of detail depending on the purpose of the dynamic risk model. A model used to evaluate asset strategies would require assets to be modeled at a detailed level, perhaps even at the individual asset level. By contrast, a model used to evaluate underwriting strategies could group assets into broad categories, perhaps as simple as modeling in three groups: bonds, equities, and cash. A trade-off exists between ease of use and time to parameterize and run the model versus the accuracy of model results.

Details of asset modeling can be found in many finance textbooks, for example Hull (2006).

II.D.2.d Underwriting Operations

While the calculations are done separately by line of business, the assumptions used in the calculation may be correlated among lines of business.

The underwriting operations module calculates the cash flows from premiums, claims, and company expenses. The calculations in this module are generally done separately for each line of business. One exception is the reinsurance calculation, which may have contracts that aggregate multiple lines of business. While the calculations are done separately by line of business, the assumptions used in the calculation may be correlated among lines of business. Correlation and model parameterization are discussed in Section IV.D of this book.

Premium

The base for both the premium and loss projections is exposure. The amounts of premium and loss are both proportional to the amounts of exposure. Exposure can be measured using whatever units are appropriate for a particular line of business, for example number of cars for an automobile liability or payroll for workers' compensation.

The projected exposure for each period starts with the exposure for the prior period. The prior year exposure is then adjusted. These adjustments can be made based on economic variables, such as growth in GDP; on company strategy, such as planned growth in a line of business; or on random variation between budgeted amounts and actual results.

■ **Prior period exposure**

   ×   Planned changes

   ×   Changes based on economic variables (GDP, inflation)

   ×   Random changes

   =   Projected exposure

Once projected exposure is calculated, written premium is calculated by multiplying the exposure by an average rate. Similar to exposure, the average rate can be adjusted based on strategy, economic conditions, and random variation.

■ **Prior average rate**

   ×   Planned changes

   ×   Changes based on economic variables (inflation, anticipated investment yields)

   ×   Random changes

   =   Projected average rate

Random changes for both the exposure and the average rate may also include a change that is due to insurance market conditions (the underwriting cycle). The underwriting cycle may be modeled using a state matrix approach. A transition matrix gives the probability of moving from one market condition to another. Once the market condition is stochastically generated, the random change is generated from a distribution appropriate for that market condition.

> **Random changes for both the exposure and the average rate may also include a change that is due to insurance market conditions (the underwriting cycle).**

A hypothetical example of a transition matrix is shown in the table in Figure II.D-2.

■ **Figure II.D-2**

Current Market Condition	Market Condition Next Period		
	Hard	Normal	Soft
Hard	8%	90%	2%
Normal	15%	70%	15%
Soft	6%	84%	10%

When calculating income, premiums should be earned in the periods in which a policy can incur losses, a practice that gave rise to the term "earned premium." For example, if a policy runs from July 1 through June 30, half of the premium is usually earned in the year the policy is written, and the remaining half in the following year. This approach allows the income from the premium to be matched with costs of the losses. This calculation is also done using exposure in addition to premium. The resulting earned exposure is used in the loss calculation.

A similar calculation is used for premium collection. Not all of the premium is collected when the policy is written. Some policies bill at inception, some bill monthly during the policy period, and some may be audited and have additional premiums collected after the policy has expired.

Historical patterns of collected premium may be used to calculate a collection pattern that will apply to premiums projected by the model.

Loss payments and liabilities

Losses are modeled by line of business in four groups:

- **Individual large losses**
- **Aggregate small losses**
- **Catastrophe losses**
- **Runoff of starting liability**

With unlimited computing power the model could simply generate each claim individually; however, to save computing time, the model generates the large claims and catastrophic events individually with only the total for all small claims. The size of each individual large claim and catastrophic event is needed for the excess of loss reinsurance calculation.

Large claims are generated by first generating the number of claims using a unit of expected frequency of claims per exposure, adjusted for changes in economic variables and a random error term. This frequency is multiplied by earned exposure to get the number of large claims.

- **Expected large-loss frequency**
    - ×   Changes based on economic variables (GDP, inflation) up to occurrence date
    - ×   Earned exposure
    - ×   Random variation
    - ×   Number of large claims

For each large claim, a stochastic severity is generated.

- **Expected large-loss severity**
    - ×   Changes based on economic variables (inflation, unemployment) up to occurrence date
    - ×   Random variation
    - ×   Large-claim severity

Small losses are generated by adjusting the prior year loss ratio for rate changes, changes in economic variables, and random variation. The adjusted loss ratio is multiplied by earned premium to calculate small losses.

- **Prior year small-loss ratio**
    - ×   Rate changes
    - ×   Changes based on economic variables (inflation, interest rates, unemployment) up to occurrence date

    ×   Random variation

    ×   Earned premium

    ×   Small losses incurred

The runoff of the existing liability may be calculated using the same procedure as for large losses and small losses. It may also be calculated using a simplified procedure that adjusts the starting liability for differences in future actual inflation versus expected inflation and random variation. The modeling of liability variability is discussed in further detail in Section IV.D of this book.

■ **Existing liability estimate**

    ×   Change that is due to differences in inflation

    ×   Random variation

    ×   Projected runoff of existing liability

Catastrophe losses are often modeled by using the output of a catastrophe model. They may also be modeled using a procedure similar to large losses, where the number of catastrophe events is modeled using a frequency distribution, and the size of each event is modeled using a severity distribution.

Many claims are not paid during the period in which they occur. In some lines of business, such as workers' compensation, payments may be made over the lifetime of the claimant. The timing of payments may be modeled using a payment pattern (percentage of payments made during each period). The payment pattern may be adjusted based on changes in economic variables, planned changes in company operations, and random variation.

> **Many claims are not paid during the period in which they occur. In some lines of business, such as workers' compensation, payments may be made over the lifetime of the claimant..**

■ **Ultimate losses incurred**

    ×   Expected payment pattern

    ×   Changes based on economic variables (inflation – from occurrence date to payment date)

    ×   Changes that are due to company operations

    ×   Random variation

    ×   Losses paid

Expense payments and liabilities

In the dynamic risk model, acquisition expenses (commissions and premium taxes) are modeled as a percentage of written premium; other underwriting expenses (general company expenses) are modeled as a percentage of earned premium, and loss adjustment expenses (claim settlement expenses) are modeled as a percentage of paid losses plus a percentage of earned premium.

The percentages for each type of expense are modeled using an expected percentage and a stochastic random variation.

- **Acquisition expense incurred**

  × Written premium

  × Expected percentage

  × Random variation

- **Other underwriting expense incurred**

  × Earned premium

  × Expected percentage

  × Random variation

- **Loss adjustment expense incurred**

  × Paid losses

  × Expected percentage

  × Earned premiums

  × Expected percentage

  × Random variation

Each type of expense has an associated payment pattern. Expenses paid and expense liabilities are calculated in a fashion similar to loss payments and liabilities.

Reinsurance

Once the direct losses and premiums have been stochastically generated, the reinsurance accounting calculations are deterministic.

Once the direct losses and premiums have been stochastically generated, the reinsurance accounting calculations are deterministic. The reinsurance module calculates the amounts of losses and premium that are ceded to the reinsurers as well as the amounts retained by the company based on the provisions of the historical and proposed reinsurance programs.

Modeling of the following three types of reinsurance are described in this section:

- **Quota share (QS)**
- **Excess of loss (XOL)**
- **Aggregate (AGG)**

Except for XOL, the reinsurance calculation may be done with any of the four loss types described earlier (individual, aggregate, catastrophe, and runoff). The reinsurance calculations are described here in their simplest forms. In a realistic model, there may be many additional features that need to be calculated as part of the reinsurance accounting. These additional features include items such as ceding commissions (fixed or sliding scale), loss caps and corridors, reinstatement premiums, and interest accruals, among others.

QS reinsurance cedes a fixed percentage of losses and the same percentage of premiums. The only parameter needed for QS is the percentage to be ceded.

XOL reinsurance operates only on the large loss and catastrophe types. Its calculation requires three parameters: the rate (the percentage of premiums ceded to the reinsurer), the retention (the amount of each individual claim that must be paid by the company before the reinsurance begins to pay), and the limit (the maximum amount for each claim that the reinsurer will pay).

The calculation of AGG reinsurance is similar to the calculation of XOL; however, instead of being applied to each individual claim separately, the retention and limit apply to the aggregate total of all claims within a specified time period. For AGG reinsurance, the retention and limit may be specified as fixed amounts, but they are often specified as a percentage of premiums.

The reinsurance calculation may be applied to losses that have already occurred (the liability runoff loss type), termed "retrospective reinsurance," or to losses that will occur in the future (the small, large, and catastrophe loss types), termed "prospective reinsurance."

The reinsurance types may also be combined to form more complicated reinsurance programs. For example, an XOL contract may apply first, and then a QS contract may apply to the remaining amount of retained loss. All of these reinsurance schemes would need to be carefully incorporated into the model.

Once reinsurance amounts incurred have been determined, the amount that will actually be collected from the reinsurers may be stochastically modeled. A simple model would include the effects of reinsurer credit quality and economic conditions on the probability and amount of collection. Realistic models may also include other considerations, such as letters of credit, reinsurer deposits, and offsetting balances. Additional model considerations are the occurrence of large industry wide catastrophe events, changes in reinsurer credit quality and willingness to pay.

Investment operations

The investment operations module calculates investment-related variables and implements investment strategies. Returns from the ESG are used to determine cash produced by investments (bond coupons, stock dividends, matured bonds, and proceeds from investments sold). Cash from investments plus net cash from underwriting operations (premiums collected, less losses and expenses paid, less taxes paid) are invested according to a predetermined asset mix. Assets can be rebalanced at the end of each projection period to produce a desired mix or cash flow. Investment strategies may vary depending on whether cash flows are positive or negative during the period.

Accounting and taxation

The accounting and taxation module creates the financial statement variables from the underwriting and investment cash flows developed by the earlier modules. The calculations in this module are deterministic.

Management response

The management response module allows the simulation to model the type of changes to company operations that company management could make in response to observed financial results and economic conditions. Rules are created prior to the simulation model run that change assumptions for future periods. A hypothetical example of a rule is:

The management response module allows the simulation to model the type of changes to company operations that company management could make in response to observed financial results and economic conditions.

If capital at the end of the period is less than a target level, then increase rates by 5%.

Rules can be based on any of the observed financial or economic variables from prior periods, and they can modify any assumptions used to model future periods.

A management response module is necessary for a realistic simulation, especially over longer modeling horizons. It is unrealistic to model assuming that management would not make adjustments in case of adverse results. It is also unrealistic to assume that management consistently takes the proper corrective action immediately.

II.D.3 Parameterization and Correlation

Stochastic financial models typically involve the complex aggregation of multiple underlying processes and the application of various financial and accounting rules in order to present distributions of items of interest. For this reason, most stochastic financial models employ Monte Carlo simulation methods in order to extract the distributions of the items of interest.

But if the stochastic components are not independent, then individual values need to be sampled in a manner such that the underlying dependency structure is maintained.

Any stochastic financial model of even moderate complexity will involve the aggregation of results from various multiple stochastic components, but the process varies greatly depending on interdependence of stochastic components. For independent components, the process simply involves sampling each value randomly from its distribution and using that value in all subsequent deterministic calculations. As long as each stochastic component is selected independently, no particular care need be taken in combining the individual elements. But if the stochastic components are not independent, then individual values need to be sampled in a manner such that the underlying dependency structure is maintained.

References for II.D

CAS Dynamic Risk Modeling Handbook Working Party (2006). *Dynamic risk modeling handbook.*

CAS Enterprise Risk Management Committee (Summer 2003). Overview of enterprise risk management. *CAS Forum:* 99-163. Retrieved Sept. 16, 2009, from http://www.casact.org/pubs/forum/03sforum/03sf099.pdf.

Coutts & Devitt (1989). The assessment of the financial strength of insurance companies - generalized cash flow model. *Financial Models of Insurance Solvency*, eds. J.D. Cummins and R.A. Derrig. United Kingdom: Kluwer Academic Publishers: 1-37.

Daykin, et al. (1989). The solvency of a general insurance company in terms of emerging costs. *Financial Models of Insurance Solvency*, eds. J.D. Cummins and R.A. Derrig. United Kingdom: Kluwer Academic Publishers: 87-151.

Daykin, Pentikainen, & Pesonen (1994). *Practical risk theory for actuaries.* Chapman & Hall: 546.

Feller, William (1968). *An introduction to probability theory and its uses,* volume 1, third edition. New York: John Wiley & Sons.

Forrester, Jay W. (1961). *Industrial dynamics.* MIT Press.

Hull, John C. (2006). *Options, futures, and other derivatives.* Prentice Hall.

Pentikainen (1988). On the solvency of insurers. *Classical Insurance Solvency Theory*, eds. J.D. Cummins and RA. Derrig. Finland: Kluwer Academic Publishers: 1-49.

II.E Country- and Region-specific Issues

The concept of stochastic modeling has had a rich diversity of applications in the sciences and stock market, among other fields, but has only recently been used as a technique for evaluating the risks embedded in insurers' asset and liability structures. Regulators, rating agencies, and, most importantly, managers are all applying stochastic modeling to gain deeper insight into the risks an enterprise faces, thereby allowing for better allocation of resources.

In this section, we will explore how stochastic modeling is changing regulation, financial reporting, pricing, and enterprise risk management.

II.E.1 Regulatory Reporting

It is widely accepted that the financial strength of an insurer is determined by more than the value of its assets and liabilities. Traditionally, supervisory systems relied on a formulaic approach to defining the required minimum level of capital solvency based on a prudent assessment of assets and liabilities. But this approach largely ignored the risk-sensitive attributes of an individual insurer.

More recently, in recognition of the need for a more risk-based approach, the European Insurance Chief Financial Officer (CFO) Forum (CFO Forum principles are outlined in Appendix A), a body formed by major European insurers, launched the European Embedded Value (EEV) principles in May 2004. These principles extended traditional embedded values techniques to include explicit valuations of options and guarantees, in an effort to standardize the way in which embedded values are reported. But definitional ambiguity in these principles left room for considerable discretion in the approaches used to determine the required capital an individual insurer must carry.

The development of consistent market-based standards made considerable progress with the promulgation of a new set of regulations in Europe known as Solvency II. Structured around three pillars, Solvency II regulations strive to establish a principles-based approach to supervision by linking capital requirements to risk on a market-consistent basis. As such, these regulations represent a fundamental change in valuation and solvency requirements. Rather than take a one-size-fits-all approach, Solvency II instead seeks to lay out a framework for assessing the individual risk characteristics of an insurer. This is accomplished through a provision for the use of internal models.

As part of the articles, the draft framework directive defines two levels of capital:

- **Solvency Capital Requirement (SCR), which reflects an insurer's level of capital calibrated to a probability of ruin of 0.5%, i.e., a 1-in-200 year event, over a one-year time horizon.**

- **Minimum Capital Requirement (MCR), which represents an absolute minimum level of capital that would be required to stave off urgent regulatory action.**

Under the directive, SCR is calculated using VaR techniques. Insurers are given the option of using a standard formula or an internal model subject to supervisory approval. The directive also requires that the SCR calculation be performed at least once a year and be continuously monitored. A significant change in the insurer's risk profile would trigger the need for a recalculation.

Articles 110-125 describe the requirements that apply to the use of an internal model for calculating SCR. Under these guidelines, internal models must pass five tests related to data quality, calibration, validation, documentation, and usage. The models can be used on a partial basis, given the modular structure of the standard formula calculation, or on a full basis.

Solvency II is expected to greatly advance the use of stochastic models, partly because of the lower levels of regulatory capital internal models are expected to generate, but also because of a large shift toward an economic capital framework.

Solvency II is expected to greatly advance the use of stochastic models, partly because of the lower levels of regulatory capital internal models are expected to generate, but also because of a large shift toward an economic capital framework.

It is important to point out that solvency is only part of the goal of these new regulations. Determining SCR is also meant to provide insurers with an assessment of their economic capital based on company-specific risk appetite. Indeed, the Committee on European Insurance and Occupational Pensions Supervisors (CEIOPS), the driving body behind the development of Solvency II, has said that SCR "shares many features with economic capital." In a tangible sense, this link reflects a convergence of economic and regulatory forces that have come to realize that profitability and well executed risk management go hand-in-hand with solvency.

As part of Solvency II, the European Commission requested CEIOPS to conduct a series of large-scale field tests of the proposed directives. Known as quantitative impact studies (QIS), these surveys were intended to assess feasibility and the impact of Solvency II proposals on insurers' assets, liabilities, and capital requirements.

While each QIS has been informative and helped to advance the goals of Solvency II, it is the fourth and final QIS (QIS4) that sheds considerable light on the growing importance of stochastic modeling.

As part of QIS4, participants were asked to compare standard formula solvency calculations and associated capital levels with the methodology and results produced by internal models. Among the survey findings, the CEIOPS reported that 13% of respondents, or 90 insurance entities, do not expect to develop internal models, but instead expect to use the standard formula, which was characterized as a good fit. But 63%, or approximately 450 respondents, indicated that they are considering the use of either a partial or full internal model, and more than half of these respondents plan to adopt full internal models. Improved risk management and governance were cited as the two main incentives for developing internal models.

The potential impact of internal models on the industry is perhaps most dramatically reflected in the QIS benchmark testing that compared SCR levels produced by standard formulas with those of internal models. Half of respondents indicated that they expect to see SCR decrease 20% with the use of internal models. The survey indicated that confidence in this expectation grew with the size of the insurer.

Risk modules in internal models that generated lower SCR include basic SCR (BSCR), market risk (interest rate risk), life underwriting risk (longevity risk, lapse risk), health underwriting risk (health short-term underwriting risk), and non-life underwriting risk (premium/liability risk). Conversely, operational risk, equity risk, property risk, and mortality risk produced higher capital requirements in internal models.

While the QIS4 also concluded that many firms still need to refine their models in order to be fully compliant with the Solvency II framework, expected to be implemented in 2012, these results provide further evidence of the far-reaching impact that stochastic modeling will likely have on the market in years to come.

Much like European regulators, their U.S. counterparts have been moving towards a risk-based capital prudential framework. Initially, efforts focused on developing principles-based tools that were able to better reflect the equity and interest rate risk in variable annuity products with enhanced guarantees. Taking its name from a component of the risk-based capital (RBC) formula, C3 Phase II regulations require, among other provisions, that scenario testing be used to set capital and liability levels for annuity products with guaranteed living benefits (GLB). Companies have the option of using a factor-based method for annuities without guaranteed living benefits, but the National Association of Insurance Commissioners (NAIC) effectively mandated the use of stochastic modeling for valuing products with GLBs in light of the fact that formulaic approaches lack the proprieties needed to assess these products.

Regulators in the U.S. also have developed new statutory liability requirements, known as the variable annuity commissioners' annuity reserve valuation method (VACARVM), which, like C3 Phase II, call for a scenario approach for valuing individual and group, deferred, and immediate variable annuity liabilities.

With the adoption of C3 Phase III, expected to become effective in 2010, the use of stochastic modeling in valuing liabilities and capital could be expanded to include all new and in-force business for all products, many of which have not been previously valued using a principles-based approach. Such an undertaking will not only greatly expand the use of stochastic modeling, but, at least initially, also tax insurers' working knowledge of the regulations as well as their modeling expertise.

II.E.2 Liability Valuations

Valuation of liabilities poses an especially unique issue for insurers. Traditionally, life insurance liabilities have been valued under different methods depending on the purpose to which they were used in the financial accounts. For example, each country in the European Union regulates the approach used based on the third life directive.

Valuation of liabilities poses an especially unique issue for insurers. Traditionally, life insurance liabilities have been valued under different methods depending on the purpose to which they were used in the financial accounts.

For non-linked traditional life insurance business, liabilities are valued using prospective methods. These calculations involve subtracting the present value of future premiums, if any, from the present value of future benefits, and also require assumptions for demographic variables such as mortality and policyholder behaviour variables such as lapses, as well as economic variables such as interest rates. Although these calculations could in theory be done stochastically, they have traditionally been done deterministically, subject to regulatory or accounting constraints associated with mortality tables and interest rates.

For unit-linked business whose benefit value can fluctuate with market performance, the value of the liability is simply the number of units allocated to the policies being valued multiplied by the unit price.

This approach, however, is not used for products that have embedded options within the benefit structure, such as a policyholder's right to convert the assured sum into another guaranteed benefit – for example, an annuity, often called a guaranteed annuity option.

Other exceptions include a guarantee to convert an annuity benefit into a lump sum cash amount (e.g., guaranteed commutation options) or variable annuity-style guarantees such as:

- **Guaranteed minimum accumulation benefit (GMAB), which provides a guaranteed amount at a specific maturity date contingent upon the policyholder being alive and the policy in-force.**

- **Guaranteed minimum death benefit (GMDB), which provides a guaranteed amount payable upon the death of the policyholder.**

- **Guaranteed minimum income benefit (GMIB), which provides a guaranteed minimum income stream upon annuitization at a specific maturity date.**

- **Guaranteed minimum withdrawal benefit (GMWB), which provides a guaranteed minimum withdrawal stream from a unit-linked account for either a specified duration, or for the lifetime of the policyholder.**

In each case, these embedded options need to be valued stochastically.

In valuing these products, the industry trend has been to use market-consistent, risk-neutral valuations as a starting point. Margins for adverse deviations are built into the basis, depending on the purpose of the valuation. For example, margins are typically more prudent for statutory accounts whose purposes are to demonstrate solvency than for those assumed on financial accounts geared to a realistic recognition of profits under financial standards, such as International Financial Reporting Standards (IFRS).

When stochastic models were first considered for this purpose, the approach was to simulate a large sample of the liability option outcomes, and then select a liability of a sufficiently prudent percentile observation. This approach was adopted by the Maturity Guarantees Working Party in the UK.

The industry practice now, however, is to stochastically simulate the economic risk variables only, with path-dependent demographic risks generally limited to dynamic policyholder behaviour functions, such as lapses.

The industry practice now, however, is to stochastically simulate the economic risk variables only, with path-dependent demographic risks generally limited to dynamic policyholder behaviour functions, such as lapses.

For a variable annuity business, the size of the margins for adverse deviations is often determined with reference to a stochastic analysis of the likely outcomes, and with benchmarking against a CTE65[32] of the observed outcomes, or CTE90 of the observed losses that could be made.

II.E.3 Financial Reporting and Embedded Values

In addition to the IFRS and local statutory reporting, nearly all listed life insurance companies use embedded value techniques to communicate financial performance to the shareholders. The embedded value of the business is the present value of future profits of the business, which is calculated using a constant deterministic projection scenario for non-guaranteed business and risk-neutral stochastic techniques to determine the value or cost of guarantees for guaranteed business. Embedded value is also an important operational decision making tool in optimising capital allocation across the various business units and investment opportunities.

These calculations have traditionally been made using deterministic methodologies, although recently there have been moves towards introducing a stochastic component to the calculation. A forum of CFOs of the leading multinational insurance companies in Europe (CFO Forum) has published a set of principles to be followed. A detailed outline of these principles is found in Appendix A, but for the purposes of a discussion of stochastic models and their calculation, we draw attention to principles 7 and 15. These state:

Principle 7:	Allowance must be made in the Market Consistent Embedded Value (MCEV) for the potential impact on future shareholder cash flows of all financial options and guarantees within the in-force covered business. The allowance for the time value of financial options and guarantees must be based on stochastic techniques using methods and assumptions consistent with the underlying embedded value. All projected cash flows should be valued using economic assumptions such that they are valued in line with the price of similar cash flows traded in the capital markets.
Principle 15:	Stochastic models and the associated parameters should be appropriate for the covered business being valued, internally consistent and, where appropriate, based on the most recent market data. Volatility assumptions should, wherever possible, be based on those implied from derivative prices rather than the historical observed volatilities of the underlying instruments.

Volatility assumptions should, wherever possible, be based on those implied from derivative prices rather than the historical observed volatilities of the underlying instruments.

In theory, the embedded value could and should be calculated using nested stochastic techniques that stimulate future stochastic variables, such as liabilities and liability option values at each future time step, in addition to future hedge rebalancing transactions providing the assets backing these liabilities are supported by hedge instruments. At issue is the fact that few companies have the

---

[32] A CTE65 (conditional tail expectation at the 65th percentile) is calculated as the average of the worst 35% of observations from the distribution of outcomes.

necessary technology to perform these nested stochastic valuations, at least at the time this discussion is being written.

A simplified approach has, therefore, been adopted under the CFO Forum principles, which involves calculating the time value component of the option using either closed-form solutions or stochastic Monte Carlo techniques. At present, most applications of the CFO Forum principles involve calculating the time values of options and guarantees (TVOG), which offer a pragmatic solution to the problem because they are relatively easy to implement for liability guarantees and static risk management hedging strategies. However, this approach has its limitations. One of its key drawbacks is the difficulty it poses in valuing the financial impact of dynamic risk management hedging strategies whose future impacts on rebalancing transactions are ignored.

The use of nested stochastic technique clearly provides much greater information about the trade-off between the reduction of risk and value created with different risk management strategies.
For non-life insurers, the risk-based assessment trend is also being followed by accounting standard organizations, such as the International Accounting Standards Board (IASB), which is scheduled to release a new International Financial Reporting Standard for insurance contracts in 2011.

If financial reporting is to represent faithfully the difference between a liability with fixed cash flows and a liability with uncertain cash flows, the measurement of liabilities needs to include an input that reflects the extent of uncertainty.

The anticipated IFRS balance sheet will differ from many local statutory and GAAP accounting practices in a number of ways. For example, an IASB discussion paper issued in May 2007, "Preliminary Views on Insurance Contracts," outlines the need for an explicit risk margin in the valuation of liabilities, stating:

> If financial reporting is to represent faithfully the difference between a liability with fixed cash flows and a liability with uncertain cash flows, the measurement of liabilities needs to include an input that reflects the extent of uncertainty.

The IASB specifies that the risk margin, together with the best or central estimate of liabilities, should be equal to the market value of those liabilities, i.e., including the market price of risk associated with the liability. Yet, since there is no deep and observable market for insurance liabilities, the IASB anticipates that models of risk will need to be used. The discussion paper lists some suggested methodologies for estimating the risk margin, including using explicit confidence levels, methods using the capital asset pricing model, and cost of capital methods.

Another difference could stem from an anticipated change by the IFRS, which provides that the appropriate valuation basis of the technical provisions is the discounted best estimate gross of reinsurance plus a risk margin net of reinsurance, with an asset held to account for the ceded amounts.[33]

As of QIS4, the guidance states:

- **Best estimate outstanding claims provisions should include claim handling expenses. Best estimate premium provisions should be calculated separately.**

- **At least two reliable and suitably different standard actuarial methods based on runoff triangles are to be used where practicable.**

---

[33] As of 2008, the Solvency II specifications for technical provisions differ from the latest IFRS specifications (the latter of which includes a service margin in addition to a risk margin). We anticipate eventual convergence between the two.

The risk margin should be derived via the use of an annual cost of capital factor of 6% above the risk-free interest rate. The level of the cost of capital factor is still under discussion with the possibility that it will be reduced.

The goal of the risk margin is to set the overall technical provisions (best estimate plus risk margin) at market value, similar to the IFRS.

Additional information can be found in Appendix B regarding country specific practices.

II.E.4 Product Design and Pricing

Consistent with the liability side of the balance sheet, traditional business tends to be priced using deterministic profit-testing cash flow techniques with the nested deterministic projections of the statutory or local GAAP liability volatility measurement.

For life insurance products, the main exception to this practice occurs in products with embedded options, such as the ones described above.

Another exception is the transfer of bulk annuity, which involves the movement of large blocks of existing payout annuities from one provider to another. Given the magnitude of the risk involved with such large transactions, stochastic models of mortality and longevity risk might be internally considered when pricing such a deal.

In these cases, stochastic methods would be used.

Generally the aim of the stochastic model is to determine the economic cost of hedging the embedded option. This information has become increasingly important, since these classes of liabilities need to be better managed, either through direct hedging techniques that rely on the insurance company's own activities or through indirect reinsurance or counterparty investment bank strategies.

During the product design process for variable annuity and similar hybrid products, stochastic models are used to illustrate the range of policyholder benefit outcomes for a product. This information is important for designing products that meet specific customer needs and provide fair value to the customer, but the information can also be used to develop tools to support the sales process.

In the non-life sector, stochastic modeling is primarily used in pricing lines of business, such as personal auto and homeowners insurance supported by large amounts of data. Its use has given insurers the ability to look beyond the traditional one-dimensional approach used in pricing many lines of business to a setting where they think about the interaction of rating factors. Stochastic modeling allows insurers to see how multiple variables, such as a driver's age, sex, and location interact. With this understanding, insurers can derive more precise rating measures than those provided by traditional ratings techniques that considered only a single dimension of experience.

Pricing information developed from stochastic modeling more closely mirrors an insurer's accurate experience; therefore, insurers can more readily identify which classes are being overcharged or undercharged, as well as address strategic questions like elasticity of demand. In this sense, stochastic modeling raises the efficiency of pricing from merely matching rate to exposure, to providing a competitive edge and determining market strategies.

In the non-life sector, stochastic modeling is primarily used in pricing lines of business, such as personal auto and homeowners insurance supported by large amounts of data.

While stochastic modeling and its benefits are available to many insurers in developed countries, this is not necessarily the case for local, non-life insurers in many emerging market countries. Regulators in these countries are still building a prudential supervision framework based in deterministic actuarial methodologies, and many have not yet introduced reporting regimes that require support by stochastic modeling.

Nevertheless, some stochastic modeling is practiced in these countries. For instance, insurers that are subsidiaries of multinational groups may participate in a group-wide internal stochastic model.

A major constraint on the use of stochastic models in emerging markets is the lack of credible and relevant statistical data needed to calibrate stochastic models. Moreover, it is unclear whether many of the assumptions on which such models are based (e.g., the efficient markets hypothesis) would hold. Consequently, the information used to construct stochastic models for insurance will involve a number of judgment calls as to how data obtained from these emerging markets will be blended with data from more mature markets.

II.E.5 Economic Capital Management

Insurance companies are also increasingly using stochastic models as part of their toolkit in internal business decisions, particularly as they apply to risk and capital management.

This trend has been largely driven by insurers' need to hold capital that will allow them to deliver on their obligations to customers, even given wide fluctuations in experience, while at the same time delivering an adequate return to shareholders. Determining the cost associated with return on capital when pricing insurance products has created the need to establish "correct" levels of capital for a given ruin probability, so that:

- **The capital on which the providers of capital are expecting to earn a risk return is not too high, a situation that would lead to an excessive cost of insurance.**

- **The capital is not too low, a situation that would lead to an unacceptable risk of insolvency.**

For these reasons, economic capital is an extremely useful tool for determining the financial health of an insurance company.

Economic capital can be defined as the capital required to support a business with a certain probability of default. It can be thought of as a function of the following: the risks to which the company is exposed, the targeted probability of ruin, and the time period over which it is assessed.

Economic capital can be defined as the capital required to support a business with a certain probability of default.

The notion of economic capital has emerged as a measure of capital adequacy at a time when insurers are attempting to better understand the capital requirements of their businesses and identify ways to justify their capital requirements to rating agencies and other users of company financial statements. Many companies believe the formulaic approach used by the rating agencies does not appropriately reflect a company's process for effectively managing risk. A prime example is the lack of credit that the formulaic approach gives to diversification of risk or superior risk management practices. Such a shortcoming could be rectified with the use of economic capital, which can positively reflect insurers' risk management practices.

Insurance company management could also measure performance, taking into account the capital that is effectively being employed in different business areas, as part of the modeling process. For example, insurers' various products – each of which has its specific risk characteristics – typically call for different amounts of economic capital, which should be recognized in a measure of return on equity. Given this premise, it would then be reasonable to look for the same return on economic capital for all businesses. This assumption, however, could be counterproductive, if another measure that does not sufficiently differentiate capital levels for high-risk and low-risk businesses (such as statutory solvency capital) were used. Less risk discriminating measures that apply the same targeted return across all business could result in a tendency to overprice the less risky products and underprice the more risky products.

For the purpose of enterprise risk management, economic capital is calculated to be sufficient to cover a certain level of possible losses associated with certain risks. In this context, the definition of risk can be viewed as asymmetric downside risk. A more detailed definition of insurers' risk categories is described in IAA (2004) as well as in Finkelstein et al. (2006). These risks are:

- **Underwriting risks:** pricing, product design, claims, mortality, morbidity, policyholder behaviour
- **Credit risks:** default, downgrade, concentration, counterparty
- **Market risks:** interest rate, equity and property, currency, reinvestment, concentration, asset/liability management, off-balance sheet
- **Operational risks:** people and processes failures, strategic (environmental change, catastrophic disasters)
- **Liquidity risks:** insufficient liquidity to meet cash flow requirements

Total risk is calculated by measuring the effect of each of these specific risks on a company's earning or capital, generally as a function of the probability distribution of losses. Several modeling approaches can be used to measure these losses, including scenario based models, static factor based models, stochastic factor models, and covariance models. (For further discussion on these alternative models, see Finkelstein et al., 2006.) Our focus is on stochastic analysis, which is commonly used to assess the impact of extreme events for economic capital modeling purposes. Economic capital calculations based upon stochastic models are typically performed on a real-world basis. This analysis involves calibrating the economic scenario generator according to real-world parameters, incorporating expected risk premiums and discounting the resulting cash flows at the risk discount rate, rather than the risk-free rate.

In general, insurers that have implemented internal capital models have tended to follow one of two methods in measuring risks and required capital. The first method has a one-year time horizon, and the second uses a multi-year time horizon of, for example, 30 years, or a liability runoff timeframe over which the economic balance sheet of the company is projected.

Under the first method, the insurer would test its solvency for a short-term shock, such as a sudden movement in equity market or interest rates. The shock is calibrated to represent a certain probability, such as a one-in-200-year event. Under this scenario, the capital adequacy is the amount of funds needed to ensure continued solvency, given the stated level of probability of the shock.

It should be noted that a one-year change in certain risk factors can have an impact on cash flows that extends beyond that time. For example, lapse rates can change over the year because of new

> In general, insurers that have implemented internal capital models have tended to follow one of two methods in measuring risks and required capital.

incoming information, such as market forecasts, which, in turn, affects the anticipated future lapse rates that underlie the liability value at the end of that year.

Although this method does not give information about the magnitude of the loss in the tail of the distribution, such that it cannot be used to calculate VaR or CTE measures, the short-term shock is an attractive approach for those companies wishing to avoid complex and time-consuming stochastic modeling, provided solvency can be adequately estimated using deterministic methods. Another version of the one-year method involves performing stochastic projections over one year and determining the capital required to remain solvent at the end of the current year, given a certain probability, for example, the worst 0.5% of the scenarios.

The second method, using a multi-year time horizon, can either be structured such that there is adequate capital throughout a certain percentage of these scenarios or only at the end of a certain percentage of these scenarios. Unlike the one-year horizon projection method, a multi-year time horizon can give a deeper understanding of the long-term risk exposures of the company. The multi-year approach does have limitations, however. First, it may require computationally intensive nested stochastic projections for exotic guarantees and hedge assets. And although most stochastic models allow for some dynamic management actions – such as the investment policy, risk management/dynamic hedging strategies, and dividend policy – it may be hard to realistically account for the full range of possible regulatory and management actions related to capital raising and hedging of risks. These limitations may be the reason that 10 of 13 respondents to the CFO Forum's 2004 "Benchmarking Study of Internal Models" indicated that they used a one-year time horizon to assess risks, while the remaining three participants indicated a multi-year time horizon (of 5 to 30 years).

Risk management is another prominent application of stochastic models, particularly for life companies that have guaranteed products, such as traditional annuities, variable annuities, with-profits, guaranteed investment bonds, and other structured products whose risk exposures need to be understood, appropriately priced, and hedged.

Stochastic asset liability models are now being used to manage the investment policy supporting traditional annuity and with-profits blocks of business.

Stochastic asset liability models are now being used to manage the investment policy supporting traditional annuity and with-profits blocks of business. For traditional annuity books, these models are generally used to assess reinvestment risk and, to some extent, credit risk. In the case of with-profits, these models can also incorporate dynamic management actions, such as the rebalancing of equity backing ratios in accordance with the principles and practices of financial management" of the company. For companies that manufacture guaranteed investment bonds through internal hedging, stochastic models are widely used to value the embedded options and generate some or all of the Greek risk measures for rebalancing a hedge portfolio.

Stochastic models are also commonly used for variable annuity products in hedge design and testing. In fact, nested stochastic financial projections are the only practical approach for assessing a given hedge strategy in accordance with current best practice, which suggests an investigation include the evaluation of a hedge strategy's expected effectiveness, residual risk, and impact on profitability. Such an analysis would involve projecting liabilities on frequent time steps (typically weekly) for the lifetime of the policy across a number of real-world scenarios. At each time step, multiple nested risk-neutral stochastic valuations would be performed in order to derive the Greek risk measures used to rebalance a dynamic hedge portfolio. This process enables insurers to generate the full balance sheet and profit and loss statement of the business at each time step on a consistent basis for each scenario. It also allows them to see the distribution of key items such as liabilities, assets, margin requirements, and net profit generated from the nested stochastic analysis. Armed with this information, managers can compare different hedge strategies and identify those scenarios for which a particular hedging strategy results in too much capital at risk, and how an alternative hedging strategy might be employed to address the issue.

While stochastic modeling is used to assess risk in a fairly wide range of functions across the life insurance enterprise, its use in the non-life sector is somewhat limited. Part of the reason rests with regulatory forces in the non-life sector that have not been as committed to adopting principles-based assessment measures. Another reason may be that policies for non-life products typically have much shorter time horizons.

The need for enormous amounts of underlying data has also confined the use of stochastic modeling to personal auto and homeowners insurance. But this is not to say that stochastic modeling won't eventually be used across the full range of non-life products. Its predictive capacity has particular value in estimating distribution outcome for exotic long-term lines, such as environmental or asbestos liabilities, which have a high level of uncertainty associated with their long-term potential payment obligations.

Indeed, the groundwork is now being laid for stochastic modeling in the non-life sector with the development of deterministic generalized linear models (GLM). GLMs allow insurers to look at the interactions of multiple rating variables, such as drivers' age, sex, and location, and their impact on experience. In fact, the large amount of detailed information and high level of technical expertise required to support deterministic GLMs have encouraged insurers to move to a truly stochastic environment where claims can be stimulated based on actual exposure, rather than historical underlying distribution. This next level of analysis will allow insurers to develop a true picture of their risk profile and distribution of risk for use in future pricing.

Even today, stochastic modeling is being used to assess liability variability and to determine reinsurance. Stochastic models allow insurers to go beyond a central estimate of their liability and to review the entire breadth of possible outcomes and probabilities as a way of allocating capital based on risks and expected profit.

Stochastic models allow insurers to go beyond a central estimate of their liability and to review the entire breadth of possible outcomes and probabilities as a way of allocating capital based on risks and expected profit.

References for II.E

CFO Forum (2004). Benchmarking study of internal models.

Commission of the European Communities (2008). Amended proposal for a directive of the European Parliament and of the Council on the taking up and pursuit of the business of insurance and reinsurance (Solvency II). Retrieved Sept. 16, 2009, from http://ec.europa.eu/internal_market/insurance/docs/solvency/proposal_en.pdf.

Finkelstein, G., Hoshino, T., Ino, R., & Morgan, E. (December 2006). Economic capital modeling: Practical considerations. Milliman Research.

IAA (2004). A global framework of insurer solvency assessment.

International Accounting Standards Board (May 2007). Discussion paper: Preliminary views on insurance contracts. Retrieved Sept. 16, 2009, from http://www.iasb.org/NR/rdonlyres/08C8BB09-61B7-4BE8-AA39-A1F71F665135/0/InsurancePart1.pdf

III. Evaluating and Discussing Results

After a stochastic analysis has been performed, the model's results will need to be scrutinized and evaluated by adjusting the model for specific situations and conducting peer review and other checking. The goal is to ensure that the scenarios reasonably reflect the range of potential outcomes over the projection period and to determine whether adequate information is available to arrive at a judgment independently. Special attention should be paid to extreme events, particularly if the model is intended to be used for capital adequacy or allocation, because these events generally have correlations across multiple lines of business or countries.

The first place to start an evaluation is to ask some basic questions.

The first place to start an evaluation is to ask some basic questions:

- **Do the scenarios reasonably reflect historical experience?**
- **Do they reflect the current environment?**
- **Which factors are expected to continue in the future?**
- **Should the scenarios reflect real-world or risk-neutral expectations?**
- **Do the model results use extreme scenarios consistent with real-world results for similar extreme events?**

Keeping in mind guidelines from Herget's *US GAAP for Life Insurers* (2007) can also help in the evaluation of the model and the presentation of its results. They state: "Reliable information meets an objective standard of accuracy, which includes verifiability. Although perfect exactness cannot be achieved, the accuracy must be such that incorrect decisions would not result from using the information provided. The information must be materially accurate."

The GAAP guidelines also advise that "Information is relevant if it provides an appropriate level of detail. Relevant information should contain adequate detail to have value to an informed user, but not so much detail that it becomes confusing or difficult to use." These principles can also be applied to the accounting treatment of other business segments, such as non-life businesses, as well as other accounting regimens such as IFRS 4.

While it is impossible to address every point when analyzing the results of a model, we recommend performing some simple tests, at a minimum, to ensure that the model is calibrated correctly and that it validates to the current environment. We also suggest reviewing and checking results after the analysis with consideration as to whether the model results can be clearly communicated and whether sufficient information is available for outside review. Lastly, we advise documenting those steps taken to calibrate a model and analyze results; this may prove especially useful in the event of an audit.

The goal of this discussion is not to dictate the level of testing and documentation required, but instead to emphasize the importance of calibration as part of the stochastic modeling process. We will explore a number of important considerations for evaluating a model's results, but this discussion should not be considered all-inclusive. It may be necessary to seek additional guidance on disclosures, audit requirements, and other items specific to jurisdictional accounting standards.

References for III

Herget, Thomas R. (2007). *US GAAP for life insurers*, Second Edition, p. 5.

III.A Calibrating the Model

When calibrating a model, it is important to keep in mind that the complexity of the process will vary according to the scope and purpose of the analysis, the data available for the generator assumptions, and the framework of the stochastic model generator itself.

When calibrating a model, it is important to keep in mind that the complexity of the process will vary according to the scope and purpose of the analysis, the data available for the generator assumptions, and the framework of the stochastic model generator itself. The implications of these factors can be overwhelming, but some basic checkpoints can provide perspective. Try asking the following questions:

- **Given the underlying assumptions, would the model generally track to the expected assumptions if you were to run a large number of scenarios going forward?**
- **Does it reasonably reflect expectations today?**
- **Does the model take into account historical experience, and does it reflect potential deviation from experience?**
- **What period of experience was reviewed to derive parameters? Why was this period chosen?**
- **Does the distribution of results look reasonable for today's environment?**
- **Does the model produce reasonable results for the future?**
- **Does the range of results reflect possible future outcomes?**
- **Did this period include any extreme events? How are these events incorporated into the parameters?**
- **If extreme occurrences are projected, have these been reviewed?**
- **How have extreme occurrences been calibrated to historical extreme occurrences?**

Additional considerations are likely to evolve in more complex models.

Perhaps the best way to start a discussion of calibration is with a simple example, in this case, a Canadian insurance company that has invested in multiple economies. For its annual embedded value (EV) analysis, the company needs to convert its foreign-denominated investments into Canadian dollars. The stochastic generator used in the calculation is the *current average* and *standard deviation* of each exchange rate for the conversion into Canadian dollars. This specification admittedly simplifies the process, given that exchange rate models tend to be based on the change in interest rate spreads among comparable rates in each economy, but it will serve for discussion purposes.

Information available on the Internet allows us to analyze the average historical monthly rates for the currencies shown in the table in Figure III.A-1. Changes in economic policy over time are captured by examining the exchange rate over 12-month, 30-month, and 9-year periods. The data in bold type represent the assumption base.

▌ Figure III.A-1

Exchange Rate Calculations as of July 1, 2008 Expressed in Canadian Dollars					
	US Dollars	Japanese Yen	British Pound	Euro	Hong Kong Dollars
Current	.98149	104.32700	.49380	.62255	7.65381
Average over last 12 months	**.99351**	108.22150	.49688	.66880	**7.74135**
Standard deviation over last 12 months	**.02331**	5.60752	.01099	.03400	**.17067**
Average over last 30 months	.92743	**105.85393**	.47955	.68170	7.22262
Standard deviation over last 30 months	.05912	**5.23942**	.02252	.03050	.46424
Average over last 9 years	.78812	90.38686	**.45458**	**.67532**	6.14400
Standard deviation over last 9 years	.12755	14.2813	**.02770**	**.04768**	.99507

Two approaches to model calibration

In general, calibration to historical experience and calibration to current market conditions are used to assess a model. The first approach is typically used for generating real-world scenarios, and the second approach is more commonly relied on when assessing risk-neutral scenarios, although exceptions to these also exist. (A discussion of the differences between real-world and risk-neutral scenarios can be found in Section I.B.)

Calibration to historical experience

Typically, calibration is based on experience analyzed over a period of time, which is then used to set the parameters for future scenarios. Models calibrated using historical experience will depend on certain required assumptions. For example, modeling that uses Monte Carlo simulation typically does not require calibration beyond a normal review of the assumptions. An assumption can be derived based on the experience of the business or another such variable. The assumption can then be used as the probability to test "hit or miss" at different points in time.

In general, calibration to historical experience and calibration to current market conditions are used to assess a model.

Assessing the implied incidence of extreme events over long periods is an important part of the process, particularly as it relates to outlying events. Examples of outlying events include a category 5 hurricane on the U.S. East Coast, a major winter storm in northern Europe, the current worldwide credit situation, or inflation in food costs that are due to the production of alternative grain-based fuels. If such an extreme event has occurred in the past, the modeler should question whether the simulated results of such outliers are consistent with past financial experience.

Probability distributions, such as normal or lognormal, and formulaic approaches also need to be calibrated, with special attention given to the mean and variance, or standard deviations. As a model becomes more complex, other assumptions or parameters, such as reversion targets and reversion strengths, may also become important.

A typical economic generator will produce a number of assumptions such as:

- **Current risk-free yield curve**
- **Expected risk-free curve (long-term target)**
- **Mean reversion strength**
- **Volatility**
- **Correlations to equity returns**
- **Correlations among various economies**
- **Exchange rate volatility**
- **Correlation of risk-free rates and inflation**
- **Expected equity risk returns and volatility**

Depending on the country, assumptions can frequently be derived from historical experience. For developed economies, relevant and readily available data can often be found on government or equity market Web sites.

The length of the historical period is one important parameterization consideration. In general, experience should cover more than one business cycle and should typically be longer than 10 years for credit assumptions in some countries.

Modelers should exercise caution when using data that spans decades, because that may include extreme conditions that skew the results.

Modelers should exercise caution when using data that spans decades, because that may include extreme conditions that skew the results. Examples include data from 1981 when U.S. government short-term bond rates exceeded 15%, and data from periods within the past 10 years when government bond returns in Japan were negative. A stochastic generator should be able to generate such rates, but other rates would also correlate to these extremes. Under the U.S. and Japanese extreme interest rates scenarios, it seems unlikely that short-term rates would exceed 20% and long-term rates would be less than 1% for any length of time.

In developing economies, the lack of data increases the difficulty of calibrating a model. Market conditions may not support a credible level of trading. In some cases, trading might also be closed to some degree. Parameters typically should be based on the trading market or a comparable measure. For example, if Australia's trading market is used as the basis for investment income and returns, the modeler should calibrate the parameters used by the generator based on a review of

Australian markets and generate the exchange rates accordingly. This process would reflect the company's approach within the market, a critical factor to validating the model. If multiple economies are involved, we recommend a review of each economy in order to appropriately calibrate the model to reflect current expectations.

Calibration to current market conditions

A model can also be calibrated in the context of current market conditions. This approach is particularly useful in the analysis of different scenarios for equity market return. For example, stock market volatility could be determined by examining current market prices on a "plain vanilla" call or put option. The implied volatility needed for the Black-Scholes pricing formula could then be calculated to arrive at the market price. Other information needed for this analysis includes:

- **The market price of a stock index**
- **The strike price of a call or put option on that stock index**
- **The time to expiration of the option**
- **The current assumption for risk-free interest rates**

With this information in hand, an assessment can be made regarding how close the market-implied volatilities (as calibrated to current market conditions) come to the volatilities developed from calibrating to historical experience. Differences, if they exist, may be explained by the degree to which assumptions developed from historical experience are out of sync with current market conditions.

Another way of solving for the unknown input or assumption can be illustrated by using the above example to generalize the calibration of other assumptions with the following:

- **An observed market price (or interest rate, exchange rate, etc.)**
- **A closed-form formula used to generate the market-observed price (or interest rate, exchange rate, etc.)**
- **All of the inputs/assumptions put into the closed-form formula except for one**

Calibrating to current market conditions offers a powerful technique for developing "difficult assumptions" such as market volatility when certain other assumptions are known. It also has the decided advantage of producing market-consistent assumptions, which, if ignored in pricing of financial instruments, could produce arbitrage opportunities that make (or lose) a great deal of money. Illustrative market-consistent assumptions are included in Appendix C.

III.B Validating the Model

Validating a model involves numerous aspects, many of which are beyond the scope of this book because of space or technical considerations. At a minimum, however, the process should involve cellular checking, a reasonableness review, an assumption review, and formula testing, which will be discussed below in some detail.

At a minimum, however, the process should involve cellular checking, a reasonableness review, an assumption review, and formula testing, which will be discussed below in some detail.

In nearly every review, determining whether each assumption can reasonably stand on its own is the first step in the validation process. One exception occurs when calculating a probability of ruin or capital, a process that requires analyzing multiple risks varying at the same time. In such cases, correlations observed in a "normal" setting may no longer apply.

To begin the discussion, it would be useful to consider the testing of a traditional life product, which, given its inherent fluctuations in mortality, the economic environment, and voluntary terminations, would call upon us to examine the scenario generator for each of these risks independently as a first step.

For this examination, all assumptions are held constant, except those for the generator under review. Once this step is completed, the collection of assumptions can then be tested.

For example, if the mortality generator is under review, the modeler would set and hold constant interest scenarios and use deterministic values for lapses.

For example, if the mortality generator is under review, the modeler would set and hold constant interest scenarios and use deterministic values for lapses. Under these conditions, mortality could be tested using changing variables.

To simplify the validation process, it is recommended that testing first be performed at the cellular level. For example, using Monte Carlo simulation for the mortality of 1,000 scenarios, it would be reasonable to expect the average in each future year to be closely tied to the mortality assumption, based on the principle of statistics. This principle implies that the larger the number of trials or scenarios, the smaller the difference between the sample mean and the actual mean. If assumed mortality is denoted by $q_{[x]+t-1}$, where n is the number of scenarios and d is the death rate in a given scenario, then

$$q_{[x]+t-1} \approx \Sigma_{s=1 \text{ to } n} d_s / n \qquad \text{(III.B-1)}$$

In a second example, let us suppose the base mortality is stochastically generated using a Monte Carlo approach, while the mortality improvement, also stochastically generated, follows a normal distribution in which the mean is an annual improvement of 0.6% and the standard deviation is 0.25%. In this case, the logic used to validate the model would be similar to the first example, but the process would now involve three tests: One with mortality only stochastically generated; a second with mortality improvement only stochastically generated; and a third in which both assumptions are allowed to vary.

Over a large number of scenarios, mortality might be expected to approximate the input assumption in the first test. Similarly, if a random number between 0 and 1 generated over a large number of scenarios is used as a probability to pick the "z-score" off the normal distribution table, and the implied improvement at that point in time is solved for, then the calculation should approximate the mean assumption of 0.6% per year in the second test.

A single scenario, such as a level interest rate, also should be tested, but it would produce quite different results. When testing both assumptions, moving stochastically over a large number of scenarios, the mean in this case should approximate

$$\mu \approx q_{[x]+t-1} \cdot \prod_{a=1,t} (1 - i_a) \qquad \text{(III.B-2)}$$

where i_a is the annual improvement.

Similarly, for products with non-life coverages, the modeler might first stochastically simulate the number of claims (or claim frequency in the case of exposure data) to assure that the mean and standard deviation criteria are satisfied. Claim size (severity distribution) could then be modeled to assure that the distribution by size criteria is also satisfied. At this point, both frequency and severity could be simulated to assess whether the aggregate distribution criteria are satisfied.

In our third example, interest rates are generated using a formula approach. Current government rates form the starting rate for projection, and future rates were generated stochastically, subject to a volatility constraint that is assumed to revert to a long-term historical mean. The resulting output is shown in Tables III.B-1 through III.B-5, and average interest rates for 1,000 and 100 scenarios are displayed in Tables III.B-1 and III.B-2, and Tables III.B-3 and III.B-4, respectively. Table III.B-5 shows a summary of the shape of the yield curves resulting from the stochastic analysis. From the results, it can be observed that the starting rate tends to move towards the mean rate over time.

Validating the model is more complex, and would involve capturing individual cells and checking the results to ensure that the mechanics are performing as expected.

> **From the results, it can be observed that the starting rate tends to move towards the mean rate over time.**

▌ Table III.B-1

Summary of Interest Rate Generator Output – Long Term Government Bonds										
Results of 1000 Scenarios										
	Yr 1	Yr 2	Yr 3	Yr 4	Yr 5	Yr 10	Yr 20	Yr 30	Across All Yrs	Average Across All Yrs
Mean	4.420%	4.385%	4.445%	4.491%	4.526%	4.859%	5.182%	5.282%	4.730%	4.730%
StdDev	0.693%	0.847%	0.906%	0.926%	0.939%	1.143%	1.446%	1.430%	1.065%	1.065%
Percentile Distribution										
0%	2.556%	2.135%	2.099%	2.291%	1.969%	2.140%	1.961%	2.155%	1.681%	2.096%
1%	2.926%	2.668%	2.450%	2.499%	2.449%	2.651%	2.746%	2.661%	2.358%	2.620%
5%	3.361%	3.055%	3.055%	2.980%	3.089%	3.109%	3.192%	3.270%	2.980%	3.134%
10%	3.568%	3.286%	3.286%	3.316%	3.357%	3.498%	3.646%	3.686%	3.286%	3.443%
25%	3.922%	3.772%	3.753%	3.870%	3.867%	4.020%	4.298%	4.393%	3.753%	3.996%
50%	4.367%	4.339%	4.426%	4.451%	4.483%	4.805%	5.044%	5.136%	4.339%	4.670%
75%	4.911%	4.956%	5.046%	5.070%	5.149%	5.544%	5.803%	5.979%	4.911%	5.365%
90%	5.366%	5.546%	5.704%	5.688%	5.737%	6.317%	6.728%	6.972%	5.366%	6.061%
95%	5.613%	5.848%	6.015%	6.017%	6.094%	6.833%	7.505%	7.718%	5.613%	6.490%
99%	6.054%	6.434%	6.470%	6.996%	6.845%	7.739%	10.433%	10.007%	6.054%	7.670%
100%	7.118%	7.041%	7.683%	7.751%	8.680%	11.304%	17.875%	13.422%	7.041%	10.463%

Table III.B-2

Summary of Interest Rate Generator Output – Short Term Government Bonds										
Results of 1000 Scenarios										
	Yr 1	Yr 2	Yr 3	Yr 4	Yr 5	Yr 10	Yr 20	Yr 30	Across All Yrs	Average Across All Yrs
Mean	2.498%	2.641%	2.774%	2.840%	2.953%	3.327%	3.634%	3.750%	3.126%	3.126%
StdDev	0.469%	0.665%	0.796%	0.887%	1.004%	1.340%	1.794%	1.779%	1.175%	1.175%
Percentile Distribution										
0%	1.442%	1.187%	1.139%	1.092%	1.094%	1.167%	1.056%	1.090%	1.000%	1.127%
1%	1.635%	1.440%	1.369%	1.378%	1.401%	1.393%	1.348%	1.485%	1.306%	1.403%
5%	1.797%	1.750%	1.706%	1.672%	1.687%	1.742%	1.764%	1.772%	1.645%	1.730%
10%	1.948%	1.899%	1.895%	1.843%	1.882%	1.910%	1.994%	2.062%	1.843%	1.926%
25%	2.160%	2.170%	2.215%	2.213%	2.239%	2.387%	2.482%	2.563%	2.160%	2.320%
50%	2.457%	2.537%	2.641%	2.700%	2.767%	3.026%	3.248%	3.325%	2.457%	2.880%
75%	2.769%	2.991%	3.208%	3.284%	3.451%	3.940%	4.230%	4.472%	2.769%	3.649%
90%	3.110%	3.506%	3.784%	3.979%	4.337%	5.132%	5.739%	5.771%	3.110%	4.630%
95%	3.333%	3.885%	4.244%	4.460%	4.920%	5.900%	7.099%	7.072%	3.333%	5.349%
99%	3.833%	4.472%	5.394%	5.728%	6.113%	7.561%	10.131%	10.599%	3.833%	7.033%
100%	5.082%	6.358%	6.250%	6.895%	8.748%	11.402%	20.921%	13.831%	5.082%	10.518%

Table III.B-3

Summary of Interest Rate Generator Output – Long Term Government Bonds										
Results of 100 Scenarios										
	Yr 1	Yr 2	Yr 3	Yr 4	Yr 5	Yr 10	Yr 20	Yr 30	Across All Yrs	Average Across All Yrs
Mean	4.347%	4.418%	4.400%	4.447%	4.436%	4.850%	5.116%	5.323%	4.696%	4.696%
StdDev	0.745%	0.889%	0.904%	0.930%	0.922%	0.896%	1.343%	1.549%	0.991%	0.991%
Percentile Distribution										
0%	2.645%	2.692%	2.315%	2.465%	2.372%	2.919%	2.238%	2.284%	2.157%	2.520%
1%	2.645%	2.692%	2.315%	2.465%	2.372%	2.919%	2.238%	2.284%	2.157%	2.520%
5%	3.242%	3.100%	2.924%	3.072%	2.923%	3.621%	3.119%	3.389%	2.923%	3.171%
10%	3.436%	3.246%	3.228%	3.236%	3.243%	3.779%	3.443%	3.768%	3.228%	3.457%
25%	3.814%	3.634%	3.757%	3.772%	3.731%	4.129%	4.254%	4.333%	3.634%	3.993%
50%	4.314%	4.353%	4.331%	4.387%	4.444%	4.818%	5.015%	5.099%	4.314%	4.644%
75%	4.741%	5.059%	4.851%	4.994%	5.031%	5.541%	5.769%	6.017%	4.741%	5.286%
90%	5.358%	5.648%	5.622%	5.596%	5.609%	5.988%	6.671%	6.980%	5.358%	5.905%
95%	5.668%	5.814%	5.987%	6.007%	5.786%	6.259%	7.199%	7.802%	5.668%	6.261%
99%	5.756%	6.493%	6.359%	6.953%	6.553%	6.900%	7.880%	11.280%	5.756%	7.109%
100%	7.118%	7.036%	6.868%	7.119%	6.902%	6.919%	11.614%	11.761%	6.868%	8.014%

▌Table III.B-4

										Average
Summary of Interest Rate Generator Output – Short Term Government Bonds										
Results of 100 Scenarios										
									Across	Across
	Yr 1	**Yr 2**	**Yr 3**	**Yr 4**	**Yr 5**	**Yr 10**	**Yr 20**	**Yr 30**	**All Yrs**	**All Yrs**
Mean	2.535%	2.612%	2.861%	2.913%	3.027%	3.270%	3.484%	3.615%	3.108%	3.108%
StdDev	0.488%	0.634%	0.864%	0.959%	0.992%	1.242%	1.574%	1.853%	1.128%	1.128%
Percentile Distribution										
0%	1.496%	1.255%	1.139%	1.092%	1.094%	1.167%	1.056%	1.306%	1.002%	1.203%
1%	1.496%	1.255%	1.139%	1.092%	1.094%	1.167%	1.056%	1.306%	1.002%	1.203%
5%	1.729%	1.613%	1.748%	1.554%	1.740%	1.719%	1.499%	1.876%	1.493%	1.670%
10%	1.867%	1.843%	1.876%	1.804%	1.933%	1.900%	1.890%	2.085%	1.769%	1.902%
25%	2.204%	2.113%	2.283%	2.223%	2.337%	2.295%	2.358%	2.558%	2.113%	2.316%
50%	2.537%	2.587%	2.723%	2.769%	2.773%	2.973%	3.143%	3.033%	2.537%	2.880%
75%	2.865%	2.937%	3.301%	3.394%	3.439%	4.040%	4.359%	4.141%	2.865%	3.634%
90%	3.154%	3.438%	3.838%	4.367%	4.724%	4.821%	5.450%	5.214%	3.154%	4.545%
95%	3.333%	3.717%	4.131%	4.844%	5.005%	5.791%	6.062%	6.147%	3.333%	5.089%
99%	3.590%	4.211%	5.651%	5.596%	5.698%	6.536%	8.123%	11.717%	3.590%	6.507%
100%	3.835%	4.391%	6.250%	5.718%	5.724%	6.885%	10.859%	13.831%	3.835%	7.314%

▌Table III.B-5

Summary of Interest Rate Generator Output – Shape of Yield Curve								
Results of 1000 Scenarios								
	Year 1	**Year 2**	**Year 3**	**Year 4**	**Year 5**	**Year 10**	**Year 20**	**Year 30**
Normal	81.0%	72.4%	69.4%	66.3%	62.6%	62.0%	62.6%	64.3%
Inverted	0.2%	1.0%	1.8%	1.8%	2.8%	2.6%	3.8%	4.2%
Flat	18.4%	25.5%	27.4%	29.8%	32.6%	32.8%	31.8%	29.5%
Other	0.4%	1.1%	1.4%	2.1%	2.0%	2.6%	1.8%	2.0%

Our fourth example, which focuses on non-life coverage, examines the impact of the aftermath of a major natural catastrophe on the cost of goods and services and overall economic growth. If widespread destruction has occurred, inflationary pressure could take its toll on construction and material costs and result in delays in rebuilding. The value of property surrounding the catastrophe zone may also be affected. As a result, standard model assumptions related to construction costs and reconstruction time might have to be updated to reflect the increase in building inflation and other costs related to the property damaged and destroyed.

Because validation can be a lengthy task, detailed documentation of the process is recommended. It should include:

- **The source of data**

- **Assumptions and reasoning supporting those assumptions (e.g., experience period)**

- **The tests performed, including those for individual cells**

- **Evidence of checks performed, both at the cell level and for overall reasonableness**

Because validation can be a lengthy task, detailed documentation of the process is recommended.

Simple tools like the one shown below for voluntary termination or lapse scaling factors can be developed for checking reasonableness. In this case, Microsoft Excel was used to produce a matrix showing statistical results by projection period. Scaling factors were applied to a traditional whole life insurance block with the base rates derived as 15% in the first policy duration; 9%, 7%, and 6% in the second, third, and fourth durations respectively; and 4% thereafter. The scenarios were assumed to form a normal distribution with a mean of 1.00 and a standard deviation of 0.16, and lapse rates were derived by product based on a review of experience over the last 10 years. The resulting table, seen in Table III.B-6, shows the mean and standard deviation, the minimum and the maximum, and a percentile distribution at various key risk levels at each point in time. This table can then be used to check the reasonableness of the scaling factors generated.

Table III.B-6

									Across	Average Across
Lapse Scaling Factors										
Projection Year Statistics										
	Yr 1	**Yr 2**	**Yr 3**	**Yr 4**	**Yr 5**	**Yr 10**	**Yr 20**	**Yr 30**	**All Yrs**	**All Yrs**
Mean	1.0045	1.0040	1.0032	0.9936	1.0018	0.9997	0.9992	1.0029	0.9984	0.9984
StdDev	0.1606	0.1615	0.1552	0.1561	0.1580	0.1597	0.1573	0.1546	0.1588	0.1587
Percentile Distribution										
0.0%	0.4725	0.3585	0.5557	0.5334	0.4869	0.4558	0.4964	0.4928	0.3585	0.4790
0.5%	0.5879	0.5837	0.5987	0.5925	0.5970	0.6029	0.5912	0.6350	0.5912	0.5942
1.0%	0.6094	0.6165	0.6372	0.6250	0.6433	0.6349	0.6301	0.6577	0.6254	0.6321
5.0%	0.7498	0.7318	0.7408	0.7348	0.7483	0.7387	0.7435	0.7402	0.7375	0.7379
10.0%	0.8036	0.7926	0.8001	0.7981	0.8030	0.8015	0.7970	0.8098	0.7954	0.7962
25.0%	0.8998	0.8974	0.8973	0.8837	0.8885	0.8861	0.9019	0.8982	0.8905	0.8906
50.0%	1.0077	1.0087	1.0044	0.9891	1.0027	1.0001	0.9971	1.0030	0.9979	0.9977
75.0%	1.1101	1.1087	1.1120	1.1025	1.1047	1.1069	1.1098	1.1002	1.1062	1.1060
90.0%	1.2113	1.2079	1.1945	1.2045	1.2053	1.2046	1.1958	1.2008	1.2023	1.2032
95.0%	1.2701	1.2750	1.2440	1.2549	1.2598	1.2616	1.2678	1.2589	1.2600	1.2592
99.0%	1.3677	1.3483	1.3580	1.3460	1.3505	1.3692	1.3825	1.3933	1.3624	1.3597
99.5%	1.3793	1.4248	1.3824	1.3707	1.4022	1.4085	1.3951	1.4314	1.3999	1.3957
100.0%	1.4740	1.5275	1.5484	1.5131	1.8583	1.5198	1.4579	1.6415	1.8583	1.5398

A review of historical experience shows that the variation in actual lapse rates ranges between 50% and 150% of the derived experience factors for various subsets of the business. Therefore, it provides evidence to support the reasonableness of factors developed in the above matrix with two exceptions. These two outliers, highlighted in the table, are caused by one scenario in each case. But given the realistic potential for variation, these alone should not negate the use of the resulting factors for our analysis. The resulting mean and standard deviations of the analysis are as expected in the 1,000-scenario example. Had the resulting mean for a given cell produced an unreasonable result in all years, it would call for an additional detailed review to determine the cause of the unexpected variation.

Remember to test and review for extremes. If, for example, the probability of a category 5 hurricane exceeds 5% in a given time and place, it is likely an extreme event has occurred and warrants a thorough review.

Remember to test and review for extremes.

III.C Conducting a Peer Review

An independent perspective can help test assumptions and parameters, validate results, check for errors, and provide an external perspective that can ensure that the modeling satisfies necessary levels of rigor and professionalism.

Peer review is typically a process in which someone other than the model developer or user reviews the model's development, arguments, assumptions, calibration, and generated results. Given the increasingly visible role that models play in reporting financial results and developing appropriate capital levels for companies, we strongly recommend conducting a peer review to further ensure the accuracy of a model's results.

Actuarial testing typically relies on two methods: Static validations that compare point-in-time outcomes to actual results, and dynamic validations that compare back-casting outcomes to historical actual results and review of forecasted trends. Of particular importance is the comparison of actual versus modeled extreme events in evaluating capital levels.

Peer review is typically a process in which someone other than the model developer or user reviews the model's development, arguments, assumptions, calibration, and generated results.

Depending on the complexity of the model, peer reviews can vary greatly, but they usually try to address many of the following questions:

- **Formulas:** Have the formulas been reviewed for accuracy?

- **Parameters:** How were the model parameters developed and how were they calibrated? Do they rely on credible data? Do they reflect common industry practice? Is the correlation among various economies appropriate? Are correlations among various assumptions appropriate? Are correlations among various lines of business or product types appropriate? Do the correlations appropriately change if one or more extreme events are incorporated?

- **Testing:** Does the model produce reasonable results? What checks have been performed? Have the extreme results been reviewed? If the parameters are changed, do the results change appropriately? If a new set of scenarios is used, does the generator produce different scenarios but similar statistical measurements?

- **Validation:** Does the model validate on both a static and dynamic basis?

This checklist is intended as a guide for developing a rigorous level of testing necessary in a peer review. As experienced modelers become more comfortable with generated results, the degree of testing and review may decrease. But while the level of testing for the formulas or mechanics can be scaled back on some existing models, the continual regeneration of parameters requires that a model be reviewed periodically.

III.D Communicating the Results

Often, the results of a stochastic analysis will need to be communicated to people with little or no background in statistics. In these cases, graphs or numerical tables can simplify the material and help illustrate the results and their implications.

One effective technique is the use of projection output, which provides a succinct picture of how the model performs on an isolated level, so that non-mathematically trained people can more easily assess the model results for reasonableness.

One effective technique is the use of projection output, which provides a succinct picture of how the model performs on an isolated level, so that non-mathematically trained people can more easily assess the model results for reasonableness.

Some useful projections might include:

- **An average projection based on a single cell or projection unit across all scenarios**
- **A worst-case projection based on either a worst-case scenario or the worst present value of a specific performance measure**
- **A best-case scenario based on either a best-case scenario or best present value**
- **A projection based on a specific random scenario.**

It is also helpful to provide a "total" projection that addresses the same four cases, as well as a projection at a specific evaluation point, e.g., the conditional tail expectation (CTE) of 99.5%. These projections demonstrate how the model works in aggregate and can be useful when walking an audience through the modeling process.

Much like hurricane predictions or economic movements, forecasting the outcome of events as they change over time is notoriously difficult. A simple graph like the one shown in Figure III.D-1 can be used to illustrate that as time moves forward, the potential variation widens. In this case, the audience can visualize not only the most likely track, but also consider the range of outcomes over time.

The graph in Figure III.D-2 also might have an extreme event scenario superimposed in one of the projection years to show the effect of an extreme event and the possible progression of results thereafter.

There are many useful methods available to illustrate the results of analyses, but ultimately, the way in which the information is communicated will depend on the target audience, the results, and, to some extent, on the presenter's comfort level as a public speaker.

Figure III.D-1

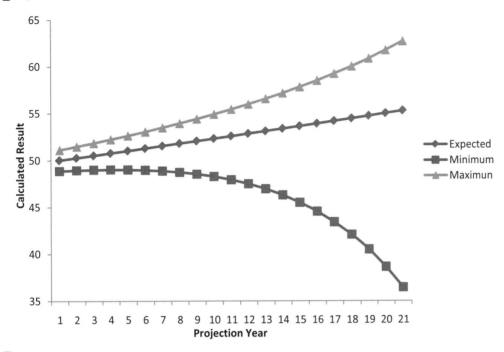

Figure III.D-2

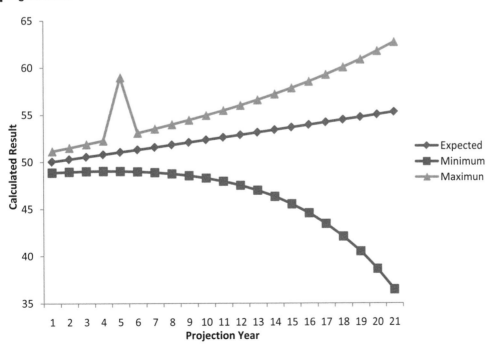

III.E Auditing the Process

Stochastic generators are sometimes viewed as "black boxes" in which information is fed into the model and an answer "pops out." For this reason, it is important to have thorough documentation readily available so that those reviewing the model can validate its results as well. Much like the steps described for peer review, a comprehensive audit will include testing, checking, and validation to provide a reasonable audit trail for outside reviewers.

The following checklist provides a basic framework that can be use to create documentation typically needed for audit purposes:

- **Parameter development**
  - □ Source of information
  - □ Development of assumptions
  - □ Development of correlation to other parameters
  - □ Expected assumptions
- **Stochastic generator analysis**
  - □ Cell checking performed
  - □ Review of range of outcomes
  - □ Correlation checking performed
  - □ Extreme cases investigated
  - □ Confirmation of similar results using different scenarios

Keep in mind that the level of detail required will vary according to the needs of the auditor and the purpose of the analysis.

Much like the steps described for peer review, a comprehensive audit will include testing, checking, and validation to provide a reasonable audit trail for outside reviewers.

IV. Case Studies

IV.A Development and Management of a Variable Annuity Product

This case study discusses the development and management of an individual variable annuity (VA) product. To lay a foundation for the discussion, we will start by describing a basic VA product, but our primary interest will focus on the technical aspects of modeling and pricing of the contract. In practice, marketing and sales considerations would also be part of the process. While there are many types of VA contracts, the product selected for this case study, a single-premium VA with guaranteed lifetime withdrawals benefits (GLWB), perhaps best demonstrates many important considerations of the modeling process.

All numerical results referenced herein were generated from a VA model built in a proprietary projection system, which does not accompany this text. A liability projection system that is capable of handling stochastic and nested stochastic projections would be expected to generate similar results.

General comments on issues related to risk management and product development on an international level are also discussed toward the end of this case study.

IV.A.1 Introduction

IV.A.1.a Variable Annuity

By combining an investment vehicle and an insurance product, VA products were initially viewed and marketed as an ideal retirement solution for the Baby Boomer generation in the United States. But they are also proving to be popular in Asia, Japan in particular, and are expected to grow in European markets as well.

Early VA products sold in the United States were basically mutual funds with an associated insurance wrapper. As such, the policyholder had the ability to participate in the market, and also to benefit from tax-deferred growth until funds were withdrawn. Market participation is indirect, however, because the policyholder does not invest directly in mutual funds, but rather mutual fund clones, commonly referred to as subaccounts in the United States. The premiums are invested across the subaccounts at the policyholder's discretion, and the policy value is governed by the performance of these subaccounts. In addition to the subaccounts, most VA products typically offer a fixed (or general) account option that credits interest at a guaranteed rate.

IV.A.1.b Embedded Guarantees

Early VA policies usually offered a principal guarantee in the form of a return of premium upon the death of the policyholder, the basic form of a guaranteed minimum death benefit (GMDB). More complicated GMDBs and other types of guarantee structures usually involve variations of so-called "roll-up" and "ratchet" features, which are commonly seen in VAs sold today. The roll-up provides an annual percentage increase in the guaranteed death benefit value at each contract anniversary, whereas the ratchet or step-up feature resets (usually annually) the guarantee value to the prevailing account value if the latter is higher. These features are sometimes sold in combination, which would entitle the policyholder to a guaranteed value equal to the larger of the two.

Guarantees provide a means for insurers to differentiate themselves from ordinary mutual funds by offering the benefit of upside market participation coupled with, at a minimum, principal protection in bearish markets.

Continued product innovation, competitive pressures, and consumer demand over the years have resulted in the introduction of considerably more flexible guarantee options. In particular, the living guarantees, such as the guaranteed minimum income benefit (GMIB), guaranteed minimum accumulation benefit (GMAB), and guaranteed minimum withdrawal benefit (GMWB), are proving popular with consumers as a means of ensuring adequate income in retirement. The focus of these benefits is on income distribution as well as wealth accumulation.

GMIBs, which can be a feature of many different types of annuities, allow for a minimum amount of income in retirement. The option is purchased based on certain assumptions made by the insurer regarding a minimum number of years that the policy is in force, usually referred to as a waiting period. GMIB is typically an elective benefit, because the conversion of the policyholder's account value to a payout annuity stream is at their discretion, and not required by the contract.

GMABs provide the policyholder with a minimum guaranteed accumulation balance at some future point in time. Some contracts may also allow certain options to be renewed. For example, the contract could guarantee a minimum fund balance of 110% of the initial premium (net of withdrawals) after 10 years, and the policyholder would have the option to renew the guarantee for a future term upon expiration.

GMWBs are a relatively more recent development. This guarantee ensures that the policyholder can make systematic annual withdrawals of a specified amount from their benefit base over a period of time, even though their account value might be depleted.

Perhaps the most exciting new guarantee in the VA market at present is the guaranteed lifetime withdrawal benefit (GLWB). A variation of GMWB, it allows for a guaranteed source of income for the life of the policyholder irrespective of market performance.

IV.A.1.c Revenues and Expenses

A VA policy generates most of its revenue from periodic asset-based fees, including mortality and expense (M&E) charges, investment management fees, and charges relating to the guarantees. In addition, such policies often have an annual or monthly per-policy fee, which may be waived for larger policies. The M&E fee usually composes the bulk of the revenue inflow for insurers, while the investment management fees are largely retained by the fund managers, though a portion is typically passed back to the insurer as revenue sharing.

Other sources of revenue include surrender charges, a fee usually based on a 5- to 10-year declining schedule, entitling the insurer to a portion of the policyholder's account value upon early surrender; and interest spread, the difference between the earned rate on a portion of the overall liability held to back the fixed account liability and the credited rate on the fixed account portion of the total account value.

An insurer's contract outflow includes an up-front commission, an acquisition expense that covers the business set-up costs, and often maintenance expenses that cover the administrative cost of managing the policy. Some contracts may also provide for a renewal commission, which can take the form of a percentage of the premium or of the account value in-force.

One of the larger outflows for a VA policy, however, stems from the payment of claims connected to the guarantee. For example, an insurer that issued a VA with a GMWB is still liable for the policyholder's withdrawals until the end of the term, even if the policyholder's account value has been depleted prior to the term end. Paid benefits are not necessarily a cash cost to the insurer, because they usually represent a one-to-one release of account value, but if the guaranteed benefit exceeds the account value at the time of payment, the shortfall represents a cost to the insurer.

IV.A.1.d Risks

The most obvious risk associated with VA is equity risk, particularly the risk related to a market downturn, which causes the guarantees associated with the contract to become in-the-money (ITM) as the underlying account value diminishes. VA contracts with GMIB also have longevity and interest rate risks, because the guaranteed payments are a function of both mortality and interest. Another risk associated with VA is policyholder behaviour risk, which relates to any action on the part of the policyholder that works against the insurer. For example, the fact that policyholders might be less likely to lapse when their guarantees are in-the-money becomes a risk for the insurer. Another potential risk would be that of policyholders allocating funds to subaccounts with higher volatility. Section IV.A.8 discusses the risks in more detail.

IV.A.2 Product Specifications and Pricing Assumptions

The subject of this case study is a single-premium VA product with a GMDB in the form of a simple return of initial premium and also with a GLWB option, whose benefit base is the higher of either an annual ratchet amount or a 5% roll-up. The roll-up is credited annually if there is no withdrawal in the year, and it stops upon the first withdrawal or at the end of the 10th policy year, whichever comes first. Any withdrawals reduce the GMDB by the same proportion as the withdrawals to total account values, but they do not reduce the GLWB. The detailed product specifications and the pricing assumptions are summarized in Figures IV.A-1 through IV.A-5.

▌ **Figure IV.A-1**

Base Variable Annuity Product Specifications	
M&E fee	110 basis points
Surrender charge	8, 7, 6, 5, 4, 3, 2, 0% of account value in policy years 1-7, and 8 and beyond, respectively
Free withdrawal amount	10% of account value
Return of premium death benefit	Death benefit equals the greater of premiums paid and the account value. Partial withdrawal reduces the death benefit on a pro-rata basis
Commission	7% of premium with a 100% chargeback for lapses in the first six months and a 50% chargeback for lapses in months 7-12.

Figure IV.A-2

Guaranteed Lifetime Withdrawals Benefits Product Specifications	
Benefit base	Maximum of 5% compound roll-up and annual ratchet for up to 10 years or until first withdrawal, whichever comes first, and annual ratchet thereafter
Charge as a percent of benefit base	0.6%
Maximum benefit percent	5% "for life" at ages 60-69 6% "for life" at ages 70-79 7% "for life" at ages 80-85 Attained age at first withdrawal sets maximum benefit percent
Ratchet once withdrawals have started	If the account value is above the benefit base on any anniversary after withdrawals have started, the benefit base will be reset to the account value and a new maximum benefit amount will be calculated The maximum benefit percent will not be changed

Assumed Fund Allocation	S&P 500	Russell 2000	NASDAQ	SB BIG (Bond)	EAFE (International Equity)	Money Market
	25%	20%	5%	20%	15%	15%

Figure IV.A-3

Sales Distribution Assumptions			
Gender	50% Male / 50% Female		
Election of GLWB	100%		
Issue age and GLWB deferral period	Issue Age	0-yr. Deferral	5-yr. Deferral	10-yr. Deferral
	55	0%	5%	20%
	65	5%	5%	30%
	75	10%	10%	10%
	85	5%	0%	0%

▊ Figure IV.A-4

Other Assumptions	
Initial premium	$50,000
Investment management fee	100 basis points
Revenue sharing	40 basis points
Acquisition expenses	1.5% of premium plus $125 per policy
Maintenance expenses	$75 per policy increasing by 3% per year
Lapse rate by policy year	1.5%, 2.5%, 3.0%, 3.0%, 4.0%, 5.0%, 8.0%, 40.0%, 10.0%, … Note the increased lapses occur when the surrender charge is zero.
Dynamic lapse multiple	When the GLWB is more in-the-money, the dynamic lapse multiple will be less than 100% and, therefore, will reduce lapses when applied to the lapse rate. Dynamic lapse multiple = Max [10%, 1 - 75% * (GLWB ITM% - 1.1)] If GLWB ITM% > 1.1, or 1 otherwise where GLWB ITM% = [PV of GLWB / AV]
Mortality	80% of Annuity 2000 Basic

▊ Figure IV.A-5

Economic Assumptions						
Correlation Matrix						
	S&P500	Russell 2000	NASDAQ	SBBIG	EAFE	Money Mkt.
S&P500	1	0.8	0.83	-0.07	0.68	0.02
Russell 2000	0.8	1	0.85	-0.12	0.62	-0.02
NASDAQ	0.83	0.85	1	-0.12	0.59	-0.01
SBBIG	-0.07	-0.12	-0.12	1	-0.12	0.05
EAFE	0.68	0.62	0.59	-0.12	1	-0.02
Money Mkt.	0.02	-0.02	-0.01	0.05	-0.02	1
Long-term volatility	0.171	0.208	0.281	0.038	0.157	0.01

Continuously compounded risk-free rate	4.50%

IV.A.3 Economic Scenarios

The GLWB effectively represents an embedded put option to the policyholders, because payments are made to them even if the account value is depleted. Assuming such a situation has occurred, the insurance company is liable for any future claims (withdrawals) that must be paid until the policyholder dies.

From an actuarial perspective, modeling the guarantee correctly will promote the subsequent analysis of the insurer's costs and pricing for the option. The modeler will need to make assumptions regarding future economic conditions and the number of scenarios to be used. In light of these assumptions, we now address the differences between choosing deterministic scenarios versus stochastic scenarios, including a more in-depth discussion of risk-neutral scenarios versus real-world scenarios.

IV.A.3.a Deterministic or Stochastic

Deterministic, usually constant path, scenarios, were used in early VA modeling to analyze VA guarantees; however, they are considered inadequate for capturing all the risks associated with these products. Any one single path is unlikely to result in a credible pattern of claims. Moreover, it is doubtful that a single path can encapsulate the appropriate level of risk when modeling in-force policies with varying degrees of in-the-moneyness. For these reasons, stochastically generated scenarios are appropriate to use in most situations.

IV.A.3.b Risk-neutral vs. Real-world

Using stochastic scenarios requires choosing whether they should be generated from real-world or risk-neutral parameters, which are discussed in some detail in Section I.B. The choice is closely related to the purpose of the modeling and the analysis at hand. For example, the pricing of VA with GLWB (or any other guarantees) can be divided into two major steps: For the first step – determining the cost of the GLWB, or similarly, the cost of the embedded option, depending on which is charged to the policyholder – risk-neutral scenarios are typically appropriate. But for the second step – a study of the profitability of the entire contract under the corresponding accounting jurisdiction – real-world scenarios are typically used, though there are exceptions. The real-world scenarios, however, are more likely to provide information for understanding the risk of the entire VA contract than risk-neutral scenarios.

Risk-free world

Some argue that, because a VA contract is a long-term liability that needs to be valued for that period, market assumptions ought to be used. This approach would not make the cost market-consistent, but it does generate a cost that is more stable over time by reflecting the long-term nature of the product.

Others favour the use of true market-consistent assumptions. Using this approach, implied volatilities with terms as long as possible are sought from investment banks. A grading technique is then applied to the bank-obtained long-term implied volatilities to extend the term to that of the insurer's longest term of implied volatilities. This approach arguably makes the results somewhat "market-consistent," but it could potentially lead to fluctuating costs of guarantees over time as the market moves.

In developing a product, it is worthwhile to study the costs of both approaches. But in this case study, we used the first approach to determine the cost of GLWB and then used the second method to perform the sensitivity tests.

Some additional comments need to be made about the assumptions used in this case study. The risk-neutral scenarios are equity-only scenarios. Future risk-free rates were not stochastically projected because they would require a stochastic interest rate model. Because the GLWB option by nature is an equity derivative, a claim is triggered when an account value – all of which is invested in managed equity funds – drops to zero. For cases in which the guarantee involves a minimum guaranteed interest rate, for example a GMIB, stochastic interest rate models such as the Hull-White model would be required to generate future risk-free rates for use in the equity model to generate future equity returns.

Real-world

A real-world measure considers the risk-return trade-off for bearing risk, over and above the risk-free rate associated with the concept of risk-neutrality, which provides no reward for bearing additional risk. In general, stochastic returns generated under a real-world parameterization are intended to be consistent with historical market returns, and as such, the drift interest rate and volatility assumptions used to generate these stochastic scenarios are typically calibrated using historical long-term averages. The drift interest rate implicitly assumes a certain equity risk premium that is distinct from the risk-neutral approach.

For this case study, we use the pre-packaged real-world scenarios prepared by the American Academy of Actuaries. These scenarios are generated from a stochastic volatility model and calibrated to historical U.S. market movements. For the purpose of risk-based capital calculation in the United States, companies could use real-world scenarios from either the pre-packaged scenarios or from an in-house economic model. In either case, the companies must provide evidence that the scenarios meet the calibration requirements prescribed by the Academy.

IV.A.4 Developing Mortality and Expense Fee

The largest revenue component of a bare-bones VA product with no guarantee option is usually the mortality and expense fee, which should be determined before consideration is given to guarantee features of the contract. The M&E fee should be large enough to generate a sufficient profit from the base VA. It would be appropriate to use a deterministic scenario for this purpose, since most revenues and expense items are either proportional to account value or constants. It might also be appropriate to use average results across a large number of real-world scenarios, because commissions and other up-front acquisition costs are fixed and must be recovered from future revenues. The case study M&E fee is set at 1.1% of account value to achieve a target after-tax return on assets of 20 basis points under regulatory (statutory) reporting criteria, based on a level equity growth rate of 7%.

IV.A.5 Developing GLWB Charge

An important step in the development of a VA product is determining the cost of the embedded guaranteed benefits, which forms the basis of the charge to policyholders. This charge can be expressed as a percentage of either the account value or the benefit base and is deducted from the policyholder's account value. In this case study, this charge is assumed to be a percentage of the benefit base.

IV.A.5.a Cost of GLWB

The cost of the GLWB is determined by constructing a model in a proprietary projection system that estimates the account value under multiple risk-neutral scenarios. For each scenario, the account value is projected over a 30-year horizon. When the account value falls to zero within the 30 years, the GLWB claim is calculated as the present value of annual guaranteed benefit over the policyholder's remaining lifetime. If the account value stays positive at the end of year 30, the present value is then compared with the account value. If the present value is higher, the difference is an approximation of the GLWB claim. Otherwise, the GLWB claim is zero. This approximation is made to reduce the projection horizon and lessen run time.

The GLWB claims, as well as the projected benefit base amounts, are then discounted to the present for each scenario. The ratio of the average present values of GLWB claims over the average present values of benefit base amounts was, therefore, the GLWB cost expressed as a percentage of the benefit base.

IV.A.5.b Charge of GLWB

Ignoring the competitive pressure that often drives the charge level, insurance companies can also set the charge to at least equal to the fair cost of the guarantees determined under risk-neutral scenarios. This process, however, requires some iterative calculations to eventually reach a charge that equals the cost of the benefits, because the charge is a reduction to the account value accumulation; thus, it increases the cost of the guaranteed benefits. In addition, insurance companies may commonly charge more than their cost to protect against unanticipated risks or to gain a profit. For this reason, companies will often start with an expected charge level and then assess the adequacy of the level based on various run results. For example, an expected charge level could be an input from the sales or marketing team.

Our study assumes that the expected charge level is 0.6% of the benefit base every year. The adequacy of this charge will be assessed by examining the cost of the GLWB under various sensitivity tests.

IV.A.5.c Adequacy of Charge

Number of scenarios

Before the results can be trusted, it should be determined how many risk-neutral scenarios are needed to generate accurate results. The answer usually results in a trade-off between accuracy and run time. Although it is common practice to use 1,000 scenarios in the United States, some type of convergence test is recommended to help determine the desired number of scenarios. The table in Figure IV.A-6 shows the costs of GLWB generated from running 10,000 risk-neutral scenarios compared to the costs generated from 1,000 and fewer risk-neutral scenarios.

The costs in Figure IV.A-6 are expressed as basis points instead of percentages. The table indicates that these GLWB costs, whether on an individual cell or a weighted average level, do not change significantly when the number of scenarios is reduced from 10,000 to 1,000, or even to 500, and that a large deviation occurs only when the number of scenarios is dropped to as few as 200.

A somewhat counterintuitive finding is that the results from 500 scenarios in fact match those of 10,000 scenarios, more so than the results from 1,000 scenarios. But it should be noted that the standard error increases when the number of scenarios is reduced (by roughly the square root of the reduction in the number of scenarios). A separate trial in which a different set of 500 scenarios – those of the last 500 of the 10,000 scenarios – shows the weighted average cost to be 44.16. To instil a relatively higher credibility in the case study results, remaining calculations are all based on 1,000 scenarios.

Figure IV.A-6

Comparison between Different Numbers of Scenarios

10,000 Scenarios

Female	Deferral Period		
Age	0	5	10
55	n/a	77.4	63.6
65	48.2	76.7	52.3
75	41.9	47.8	26.0
85	22.9	n/a	n/a

Male	Deferral Period		
Age	0	5	10
55	n/a	63.5	52.2
65	37.8	60.8	41.5
75	34.2	39.2	21.4
85	20.3	n/a	n/a
Weighted Average			46.4

1,000 Scenarios

Female	Deferral Period		
Age	0	5	10
55	n/a	78.2	64.4
65	49.3	77.9	53.0
75	43.2	48.7	26.4
85	23.7	n/a	n/a

Male	Deferral Period		
Age	0	5	10
55	n/a	64.1	52.9
65	38.7	61.7	42.1
75	35.2	39.9	21.7
85	21.0	n/a	n/a
Weighted Average			47.1

500 Scenarios

Female	Deferral Period		
Age	0	5	10
55	n/a	78.7	64.0
65	49.5	78.3	52.8
75	43.0	48.8	26.3
85	23.5	n/a	n/a

Male	Deferral Period		
Age	0	5	10
55	n/a	62.2	51.1
65	36.9	59.6	40.7
75	33.4	38.4	21.0
85	19.8	n/a	n/a
Weighted Average			46.3

200 Scenarios

Female	Deferral Period		
Age	0	5	10
55	n/a	84.5	68.5
65	53.9	83.7	56.9
75	46.6	52.5	28.9
85	25.4	n/a	n/a

Male	Deferral Period		
Age	0	5	10
55	n/a	64.1	52.8
65	38.5	61.3	42.0
75	34.8	39.5	21.7
85	20.6	n/a	n/a
Weighted Average			49.0

Figure IV.A-6 also shows that the expected charge level of 60 basis points is adequate to cover the weighted average costs of GLWB under our base pricing assumption. Some cells are more expensive than others, which implies that the weighted average cost would be different if the sales distribution were other than expected. The impact from different sales distributions, however, is beyond the scope of this case study.

Lapse sensitivity

A VA with minimum guaranteed benefits calls for a consideration of dynamic policyholder behaviour, particularly lapses. Because policyholders have to pay extra to obtain the guaranteed coverage, it would be rational to assume that they are more likely to maintain the coverage when they think the guarantee is valuable.

The table in Figure IV.A-7 compares the costs, expressed in basis points, of one GLWB with assumed dynamic lapses and one with no dynamic lapses. As the results indicate, the costs of GLWB can be significantly underestimated if dynamic lapses are ignored.

▌ **Figure IV.A-7**

Comparison of Assumed Dynamic Lapses vs. No Dynamic Lapses

Assumed Dynamic Lapses				No Dynamic Lapses			
Female	Deferral Period			**Female**	Deferral Period		
Age	0	5	10	Age	0	5	10
55	n/a	78.2	64.4	55	n/a	37.0	27.8
65	49.3	77.9	53.0	65	27.5	42.9	26.4
75	43.2	48.7	26.4	75	28.5	32.2	15.3
85	23.7	n/a	n/a	85	18.4	n/a	n/a
Male	Deferral Period			**Male**	Deferral Period		
Age	0	5	10	Age	0	5	10
55	n/a	64.1	52.9	55	n/a	31.9	23.6
65	38.7	61.7	42.1	65	22.7	35.7	21.6
75	35.2	39.9	21.7	75	24.0	27.1	12.7
85	21.0	n/a	n/a	85	16.4	n/a	n/a
Weighted Average			47.1	Weighted Average			25.1

Our model adopts a dynamic lapse factor in the form of Max [10%, 1 - 75%* (GLWB ITM% - 1.1)] when GLWB ITM% is greater than 110%. In other words, the policyholder is expected to behave as per base lapse rates when the GLWB is less than 10% in-the-money. But as the value of GLWB becomes increasingly in-the-money, the policyholder is expected to be more and more likely to retain the contract. When GLWB ITM% exceeds 130%, the policyholder becomes indifferent to any additional value from the guaranteed benefits. This form of dynamic lapse factor is rather arbitrary, and insurers should rely on their own experience or market intelligence to find an appropriate form. Most importantly, insurers should perform sensitivity tests on the lapse behaviour of their policyholders.

The sensitivity test assumes the factor is Max [0, 1 – 100% * (GLWB ITM% - 1)] if GLWB ITM% is greater than 100%. This approach implies that the reduction in base lapse rates is more significant than that of the case study's assumption, and it allows for the possibility of no lapses when the GLWB is significantly in-the-money. The graph in Figure IV.A-8 illustrates the difference in two dynamic lapse factors.

Figure IV.A-8

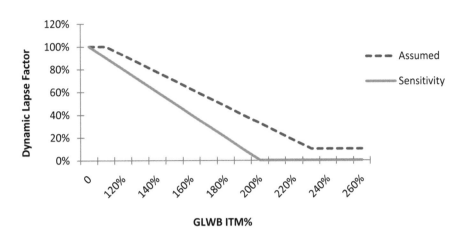

The table in Figure IV.A-9 compares the costs of GLWB under the assumed dynamic lapses and under the sensitivity assumption. The costs are expressed as basis points.

Figure IV.A-9

Comparison Between Assumed Dynamic Lapses and Sensitivity Dynamic Lapses

Assumed Dynamic Lapses				Sensitivity Dynamic Lapses			
Female	Deferral Period			**Female**	Deferral Period		
Age	0	5	10	Age	0	5	10
55	n/a	78.2	64.4	55	n/a	93.5	79.1
65	49.3	77.9	53.0	65	57.3	90.5	64.0
75	43.2	48.7	26.4	75	48.2	54.7	31.2
85	23.7	n/a	n/a	85	25.4	n/a	n/a
Male	Deferral Period			**Male**	Deferral Period		
Age	0	5	10	Age	0	5	10
55	n/a	64.1	52.9	55	n/a	76.3	64.9
65	38.7	61.7	42.1	65	44.5	71.2	50.7
75	35.2	39.9	21.7	75	39.0	44.5	25.6
85	21.0	n/a	n/a	85	22.5	n/a	n/a
Weighted Average			47.1	Weighted Average			55.8

The sensitivity dynamic lapse assumption increases the costs of GLWB up to 20%, but on average the expected charge of 60 basis points is still adequate.

Mortality sensitivity

The lifetime payment associated with the GLWM feature also poses a longevity risk. In this case study we use a sensitivity test to assess this risk by assuming mortality experience is to be 50% of the base pricing, i.e., mortality rates are 40% of Annuity 2000 Basic. The table in Figure IV.A-10 compares the costs between one GLWB option with assumed base mortality and one with the sensitivity assumption. The costs are expressed as basis points.

Figure IV.A-10

Comparison Between Base Mortality and Sensitivity Mortality

80% A2000 basic				40% A2000 basic			
Female	Deferral Period			**Female**	Deferral Period		
Age	0	5	10	Age	0	5	10
55	n/a	78.2	64.4	55	n/a	107.7	89.3
65	49.3	77.9	53.0	65	83.2	126.7	89.8
75	43.2	48.7	26.4	75	94.3	106.5	64.4
85	23.7	n/a	n/a	85	76.0	n/a	n/a
Male	Deferral Period			**Male**	Deferral Period		
Age	0	5	10	Age	0	5	10
55	n/a	64.1	52.9	55	n/a	95.9	79.8
65	38.7	61.7	42.1	65	72.3	111.0	79.0
75	35.2	39.9	21.7	75	84.0	95.1	57.9
85	21.0	n/a	n/a	85	70.4	n/a	n/a
Weighted Average			47.1	Weighted Average			85.9

Figure IV.A-10 indicates that the costs increase substantially with mortality at half the base assumption. The impact is most evident at older ages, which have increases more than double the base assumption. The much higher mortality rates at the oldest ages result in a life expectancy that is much more sensitive to changes in mortality rates than the younger ages.

Figure IV.A-10 also indicates that the expected charge of 60 basis points is not adequate in the event that mortality falls materially lower than expected. This possibility should prompt an insurer to review their mortality experience and consider whether the base assumption and their expected charge level need revising.

Fund allocation sensitivity

VA products would usually allow policyholders to invest in a combination of different managed funds with varying risk profiles, which thereby affect GLWB costs to varying degrees. For instance, a money market fund is expected to generate much less volatile returns than an equity fund; therefore, it would result in lower GLWB costs if selected as the predominant investment vehicle. Our base pricing, however, assumes that, on average, the fund allocations are as shown in Figure IV.A-11.

Figure IV.A-11

Fund Allocation	S&P 500	Russell 2000	NASDAQ	SB BIG (Bond)	EAFE (International Equity)	Money Market
	25%	20%	5%	20%	15%	15%

The allocation assumes that 65% of total investment is made in equity funds. We have also tested a more aggressive growth allocation and a more conservative growth allocation, shown in Figure IV.A-12.

Figure IV.A-12

	S&P 500	Russell 2000	NASDAQ	SB BIG (Bond)	EAFE (International Equity)	Money Market
Aggressive Growth	25%	20%	10%	10%	20%	15%
Conservative Growth	22%	15%	3%	30%	10%	20%

The aggressive growth allocation assumes that 75% of total investment is made in equity funds; the conservative growth allocation assumes 50%. The table in Figure IV.A-13 compares the costs, expressed as basis points, between one GLWB with the base fund allocation and one with the aggressive growth allocation.

Figure IV.A-13

Comparison between Assumed Fund Allocation and Aggressive Growth Allocation

Assumed Fund Allocation					Aggressive Growth Allocation			
Female	Deferral Period				**Female**	Deferral Period		
Age	0	5	10		Age	0	5	10
55	n/a	78.2	64.4		55	n/a	92.7	75.8
65	49.3	77.9	53.0		65	62.5	91.5	63.0
75	43.2	48.7	26.4		75	54.1	58.6	32.4
85	23.7	n/a	n/a		85	30.2	n/a	n/a
Male	Deferral Period				**Male**	Deferral Period		
Age	0	5	10		Age	0	5	10
55	n/a	64.1	52.9		55	n/a	77.3	63.2
65	38.7	61.7	42.1		65	49.8	73.5	50.7
75	35.2	39.9	21.7		75	44.5	48.3	26.9
85	21.0	n/a	n/a		85	26.9	n/a	n/a
Weighted Average			47.1		Weighted Average			56.8

Results indicate that a 10% increase in allocation to equity funds causes the cost of GLWB to climb some 20%. The expected level of 60 basis points is still adequate.

The table in Figure IV.A-14 compares the costs, expressed as basis points, between one GLWB with the base fund allocation and one with the conservative growth allocation.

▌ **Figure IV.A-14**

Comparison Between Assumed Fund Allocation and Conservative Growth Allocation

Assumed Fund Allocation				Conservative Growth Allocation			
Female	Deferral Period			**Female**	Deferral Period		
Age	0	5	10	Age	0	5	10
55	n/a	78.2	64.4	55	n/a	60.5	50.1
65	49.3	77.9	53.0	65	33.7	61.1	40.9
75	43.2	48.7	26.4	75	30.6	37.3	19.4
85	23.7	n/a	n/a	85	16.6	n/a	n/a
Male	Deferral Period			**Male**	Deferral Period		
Age	0	5	10	Age	0	5	10
55	n/a	64.1	52.9	55	n/a	48.4	40.1
65	38.7	61.7	42.1	65	25.9	47.5	31.8
75	35.2	39.9	21.7	75	24.7	30.3	15.8
85	21.0	n/a	n/a	85	14.5	n/a	n/a
Weighted Average			47.1	Weighted Average			35.5

With 15% less in equity funds, the GLWB cost decreases by about 25%.

These results clearly indicate the GLWB cost can be highly sensitive to different types of fund allocations. For this reason, fund allocation assumptions should be carefully considered when determining the charge level. An insurer might also consider setting restrictions on the fund allocation permitted, such as a maximum percentage allowed in equity funds.

Scenario sensitivity

All the results so far have been generated using risk-neutral scenarios generated from long-term economic assumptions. Both the long-term volatility assumptions and the correlation matrix are estimated from 10 years of weekly historical data. The risk-neutral rate is a long-term estimate of the U.S. risk-free rate.

Unlike most financial market derivatives, GLWB is an extremely long-term derivative easily spanning over 30 years. For this reason, a long-term economic assumption would be a more appropriate way to value the GLWB cost; however, sensitivity tests are usually performed using the market-consistent economic assumptions, and judgments about whether or not to revise the charge level are based on these test results.

The market-consistent assumptions in this case study have been developed according to the U.S. market data of December 31, 2007, and implied volatilities are used instead of long-term historical volatilities. Because implied volatilities for maturities greater than five years are illiquid, values exceeding five years are linearly interpolated using the long-term assumption to year 10. The continuous forward swap curve will be used as risk-free rates. The correlation matrix is unchanged. Appendix C shows the market-consistent assumptions.

The table in Figure IV.A-15 compares the costs, expressed as basis points, between one GLWB with the long-term economic assumptions and one with the market-consistent assumptions.

▌ **Figure IV.A-15**

Comparison Between Long-term Economic Assumption and Market-consistent Assumption

Long-term Economic Assumption				Market-consistent Assumption			
Female	Deferral Period			**Female**	Deferral Period		
Age	0	5	10	Age	0	5	10
55	n/a	78.2	64.4	55	n/a	106.1	82.0
65	49.3	77.9	53.0	65	76.8	106.5	69.0
75	43.2	48.7	26.4	75	67.9	70.1	36.5
85	23.7	n/a	n/a	85	39.5	n/a	n/a
Male	Deferral Period			**Male**	Deferral Period		
Age	0	5	10	Age	0	5	10
55	n/a	64.1	52.9	55	n/a	89.3	68.8
65	38.7	61.7	42.1	65	61.9	86.3	55.8
75	35.2	39.9	21.7	75	56.2	58.1	30.3
85	21.0	n/a	n/a	85	35.5	n/a	n/a
Weighted Average			47.1	Weighted Average			64.8

Results indicate the market-consistent assumption would increase the cost of GLWB as much as 70% for some cells, and, on aggregate, that the expected charge level would fall short of the cost. The implied volatilities increased quite remarkably in 2007, a roughly 15% increase from September 2007, and close to a 30% increase from June 2007. Costs generated with market-consistent data could vary significantly, depending on when data is collected. Long-term assumptions are perhaps more relevant to the determination of the charge level, but the use of market-consistent sensitivity could greatly inform an insurer about potential risks.

Decision of charge level

In this case study, the sensitivity tests have been useful in identifying the key drivers behind GLWB costs, and, with the exception of the mortality and market-consistent tests, have supported the adequacy of the expected charge level of 60 basis points. In reality, such decisions may not be so clear-cut. In addition to reviewing test assumptions, the insurer might also need to gather feedback from the marketing and sales teams to make a final decision on the charge level. But for the purpose of this case study, we have assumed that the test results are sufficient and we now proceed with a charge of 60 basis points. The next step is to assess the profitability of the base VA with the embedded GLWB guarantees.

Multiple stochastic variables

All runs so far are based on one stochastic variable, equity returns, and adjustments that are due to the sensitivity test were made on a deterministic basis, one factor at a time. A far more interesting and realistic approach is to determine the impact of multiple dynamic assumptions in the sensitivity test, which would be expected to be less than that for its individual parts.

IV.A.6 Assessing Profitability of the Entire Contract

This case study has so far focused on the base VA and the GLWB separately, thereby omitting consideration of the GMDB. The cost of the GMDB is much cheaper than that for the GLWB, so we expect it would be covered in the M&E fee. Having accounted for the cost of GMDB, we now turn to an assessment of the entire contract's profitability.

Unlike in Section IV.A.4, which relied on a deterministic scenario for developing the M&E fee, a study of the contract's profitability must employ stochastic scenarios, because neither the GLWB nor the GMDB claims are proportional to the account value. Moreover, nested stochastic modeling may be needed to capture the impact from liabilities and required capital.

The stochastic scenarios used in this section are real-world rather than risk-neutral. Real-world scenarios tend to reflect expected future profits and the tail risks associated with the product better than risk-neutral scenarios. The specific scenarios were 1,000 pre-packaged real-world scenarios developed by the American Academy of Actuaries.

Instead of focusing on liability and capital requirements, this case study generates results based on the following three different sets of liability and capital requirements:

- **Simple:** Liability is the cash surrender value, and capital is 1.5% of the liability.

- **U.S. Statutory:** Soon-to-be-adopted U.S. liability and capital requirements based on the tail loss from the product. Liability is set at the levels of the VA Commissioners' Annuity Reserve Valuation Method (VACARVM), based on the average of the worst 30% of the surpluses across all scenarios; capital is C3 Phase II, based on the average of the worst 10%. The details of each requirement are discussed in Section 7.

- **Economic:** Liability is the account value plus the economic liability of the GLWB, and capital is 1.5% of the liability.

The Economic requirements will be used to illustrate the impact of dynamic hedge simulation, which aims to offset change in the economic liability of the GLWB. For the Economic requirements, we chose the simple capital requirement because our focus is on the impact on profitability resulting from the change in economic liability before and after dynamic hedge. Also, using simple capital substantially decreases the run time.

The profit measure presented in the profitability runs is return on assets (ROA), defined as the ratio of present value of projected distributable earnings (that is, surpluses after tax and capital adjustments, discounted at the assumed required return of 12%) divided by present value of projected account values. ROA captures the levelized annual earned profit spread over the investments of the policyholders. It is a more preferred measure of VA performance than other common measures, such as premium margin or internal rate of return (IRR).

Distribution of profitability should be considered alongside average profitability, because potential losses could also result from extremely poor economic scenarios depending on their probability. Both the probability and potential magnitude of loss would need to be understood. The profit target of VA, unlike that with traditional products, should be established with respect to both the average and the tail events.

Various statistical measures or tools can be employed for determining this profit target. In this case study, the profitability across scenarios is evaluated using a box-whisker chart as well as a histogram chart. The box-whisker chart illustrates the spread of ROA around the median using a "box" and "whiskers" to break down data groups by percentile. The centerline within the box gives the median, and the top and bottom sides of the box define the 25th and 75th percentiles, respectively. The ends of a whisker represent the maximum and minimum ROA. The histogram, by contrast, breaks down the ROA into groups and populates the number of scenarios generating the ROA that falls within each group.

IV.A.6.a Profitability of Simple Requirements

The use of Simple requirements is not recommended for VA with guarantees, because they fail to capture the aggregated risk of the guarantees when an economic environment turns sour. For our case study, the Simple requirements are modeled as a way of comparing their results with those under more stringent requirements. The table in Figure IV.A-16 summarizes the average ROAs for each cell as well as the weighted average. The liability is the cash value, and capital is 1.5% of liability. The ROAs are expressed as basis points.

█ **Figure IV.A-16**

ROA of Simple Requirements

ROA			
Female	Deferral Period		
Age	0	5	10
55	n/a	49	55
65	28	43	52
75	13	35	45
85	-22	n/a	n/a
Male	Deferral Period		
Age	0	5	10
55	n/a	48	55
65	26	42	50
75	7	30	39
85	-30	n/a	n/a
Weighted Average			43

The ROA varies fairly significantly across cells and becomes negative at issue age 85. If the actual sales distribution shifts toward the older age cohorts, expected profitability would suffer. The weighted average ROA based on the expected sales distribution is 43 basis points, which is a healthy return considering the common ROA in the U.S. market probably hovers slightly above 20 basis points.

The chart in Figure IV.A-17 plots the spread of ROAs for each cell as well as weighted average in the box-whisker format.

█ **Figure IV.A-17**

Box-whisker of ROA

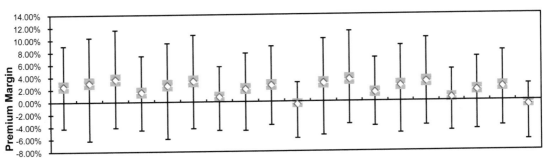

Some common features across all cells are indicated in Figure IV.A-17. For instance, the narrowness of the box reflects a relatively tight range of values between the 25th and 75th percentiles. The short upper whisker indicates relatively limited upside potential, while the long lower whisker indicates the existence of some extremely bad scenarios. Overall, these features imply a distribution that is skewed to the left, which is precisely the shape of the histogram of the weighted average ROAs shown Figure IV.A-18.

Figure IV.A-18

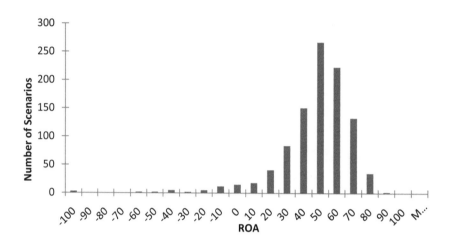

Distribution of Weighted Average Simple ROA

Each cell would be expected to have a shape similar to the distribution based on the box-whisker chart in Figure IV.A-17, which, indeed, occurs. Of 1,000 scenarios, 31 have negative ROAs, three of which have ROAs less than -100 basis points; the worst ROA is -113.8 basis points.

IV.A.6.b Profitability of U.S. Statutory Requirements

To capture the tail risk at each future projection date, U.S Statutory requirements for VACARVM liability and C3 Phase II risk-based capital (RBC) call for a nested stochastic modeling technique. From a practical standpoint, this means simulating a different set of stochastic paths at each projection year along each of the 1,000 real-world scenarios. (Note: The term "paths" is used to refer to inner loops, while "scenarios" indicates outer loops.) These stochastic real-world paths follow a regime-switching model calibrated to pass the requirements set by the American Academy of Actuaries for the purpose of C3 Phase II capital calculation.

Along the stochastic paths, account values, revenues, and expenses are projected independently of the 1,000 real-world scenarios projection. VACARVM is the 70th conditional tail expectation (CTE) level of the worst present value of pre-tax capital, and the C3 Phase II RBC is the 90th CTE level of the worst present value of after-tax capital under these stochastic paths. The CTE is the average of the results in the prescribed tail. It should be noted that in determining VACARVM and C3 Phase II RBC, both are subject to a floor level based on a "standard scenario" with predetermined economic and demographic assumptions as prescribed by the American Academy of Actuaries.

The more stochastic paths generated, the more accurate the results. But increased accuracy has its cost, one of which is run time. Determining the optimal number of paths then becomes a factor in the analysis. This issue can be resolved by performing some convergence runs on a sample cell, continually decreasing the number of stochastic paths until the financial results start to significantly deviate from the base run of 1,000 paths. In this case study model, 100 stochastic paths were used.

Figure IV.A-19

ROA of U.S. Statutory Requirements

ROA			
Female		Deferral Period	
Age	0	5	10
55	n/a	30	45
65	25	26	46
75	10	30	24
85	-24	n/a	n/a
Male		Deferral Period	
Age	0	5	10
55	n/a	38	49
65	26	32	48
75	6	27	39
85	-32	n/a	n/a
Weighted Average			36

The table in Figure IV.A-19 summarizes the average ROAs, expressed in basis points, for each cell along with the weighted average. The liability is VACARVM, and capital is C3 Phase II.

The ROAs are smaller than those based on the Simple requirements because more liability and capital are required.

The chart in Figure IV.A-20 plots the spread of ROAs for each cell, and the weighted average, in the box-whisker format.

Figure IV.A-20

Box-whisker of U.S. Statutory ROA

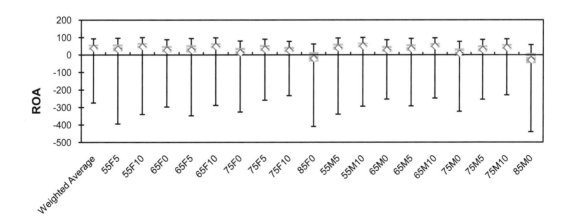

The boxes and whiskers in Figure IV.A-20 are similar to those in Figure IV.A-17 for the Simple requirements, except that the lower whiskers are much longer, indicating much worse results from bad scenarios. This exception is indeed significant. The Simple requirements, which base liability and capital on account value performance, call for lower liability and capital under extremely adverse scenarios, whereas the U.S. Statutory requirement seems to correct this miscalculation by requiring higher liability and capital under bad scenarios. Given U.S. Statutory requirements, the guaranteed benefits might be deep in-the-money and lead to worse profitability under those scenarios.

The chart in Figure IV.A-21 plots the histogram of the weighted average ROAs under the U.S. Statutory requirements.

Of 1,000 scenarios, 121 have negative ROAs, of which 16 have ROAs less than -100 basis points; the worst ROA is -274 basis points.

▌ Figure IV.A-21

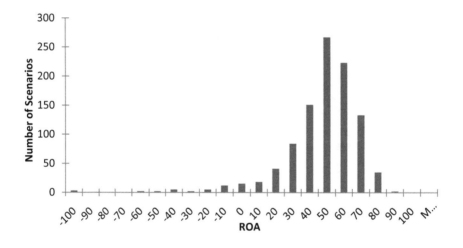

Distribution of Weighted Average U.S. Statutory ROA

IV.A.6.c Hedging Economic Liability

The economic liability, or market-consistent liability, approach recognizes the fair value of the GLWB, which is effectively a derivative whose value is based on the performance of the underlying managed funds. Under this approach, the liability is equal to the value of the guarantee less the value of the revenue averaged over multiple risk-neutral scenarios, and the revenue is calibrated such that the starting liability at policy issue is zero. In the United States, this approach is also known as the Financial Accounting Standards (FAS) 133 reserve, under U.S. GAAP requirements.

Economic liability, which immediately reflects the changes in market data, would result in more volatile financial results over time than the traditional U.S. Statutory results; however, the insurer can minimize the volatility in financial results by hedging the movement in economic liability with financial derivatives. Hedging essentially provides protection against bad scenarios by sacrificing a portion of the gains during good scenarios.

Like the U.S Statutory requirement calculation, the projection of economic liabilities calls for nested stochastic simulation. Each projection year uses a different set of stochastic paths along each of the 1,000 real-world scenarios. Unlike the U.S. Statutory requirement, the economic liability calls for risk-neutral paths with risk-free rates derived from the Treasury yield curves of the prevailing real-world scenarios. To simplify the model, we assume that both implied volatilities and the correlation matrix remain unchanged throughout the projection.

This approach, combined with the C3 Phase II capital projection, requires two layers of nested stochastic projection, which cause run time to become prohibitively long. To alleviate this issue, capital is assumed to be 1.5% of the liability. This assumption is a small concession in light of our present objective: to illustrate the impact from hedging the movement of economic liability.

Hedge modeling

The complexity of simulating dynamic hedging has prompted some to adopt an approach similar to that used in modeling reinsurance. A hedge effectiveness ratio of x% is assumed. An insurer's cash income as estimated by the hedge model would then be equal to x% of the GLWB claim amounts, and its cash outflow would be represented as the cost of hedging, equalling the basis point cost of GLWB (determined in Section IV.A.5) multiplied by the projected benefit base each projection year.

This is perhaps the simplest way to model hedges, and it might work reasonably well when analyzing the average result of multiple scenarios; however, when only one specific scenario is studied, it is likely to misstate the impact of hedging, because an average hedge effectiveness ratio of x% does not imply x% effectiveness for a particular scenario.

Let us now turn to a more realistic approach: the Delta/Rho dynamic hedging strategy. The Delta is the change in the economic liability when the starting equity indices move by 1%. The Rho is the change in the economic liability when the yield curve shifts in parallel by one basis point. To keep the already large model simple, Delta hedging is simulated using equity futures and Rho hedging with bond futures. The term of the futures corresponds to the projection cycle, which in this case study is one year.

The simulation can be described in four major steps:

1. At each projection year, summarize the hedge income or loss from the hedge position established in the last projection cycle.

2. Calculate Delta and Rho of the economic liability.

3. Calculate Delta of one unit of equity futures and Rho of one unit of bond futures.

4. Divide Delta of economic liability by Delta of one unit of equity futures to determine the number of units of equity futures to go long in the current projection cycle, and divide Rho of economic liability by Rho of one unit of bond futures to determine the number of units of bond futures to go long in the current projection cycle.

The dynamic hedge simulation is unlikely to reflect the real-life hedging, which rebalances the hedge position more frequently than annually, and trades derivatives of more variety and complexity. The simulation, however, does capture the movement of economic liability according to the specific scenario, and enables the insurer to understand the potential reduction in profit volatility resulting from this movement.

Hedge results on year-by-year basis

As described earlier, the main aim of hedge modeling is to minimize the impact of volatility on profitability resulting from the year-by-year change in economic liability. It is, thus, important to assess the effectiveness of hedge modeling by comparing the volatility of liability changes before and after the hedge on an annual basis. Results for this analysis are shown in the chart in Figure IV.A-22. The blue solid line captures the standard deviation of the change in economic liability for each future projection year, and the red dotted line depicts the standard deviation of the difference between change in economic liability and hedge income. The standard deviation is calculated across the 1,000 real-world scenarios. The chart reflects the average results of all pricing cells weighted by expected sales distribution.

Figure IV.A-22

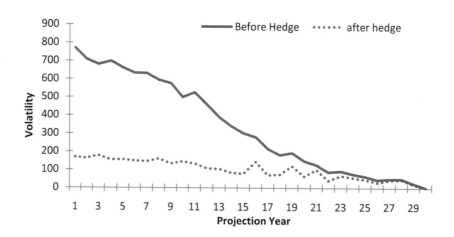

Before hedging in year one, the standard deviation of the change in economic liability is $769, assuming a single premium of $50,000. After the hedge, the change in economic liability is offset by a hedge income with the exact amount varying across the 1,000 scenarios. Consequently, the standard deviation in year one drops to $167, or a 78% reduction. The reduction is much less toward the end of the projection, where the absolute amount of standard deviation itself reduces to a much smaller number. Figure IV.A-22 shows the hedge model performing exactly as expected.

Hedge results on ROA basis

Given the reduced impact of year-by-year volatility on profitability, we would expect that the hedge would also reduce the volatility of ROA, or the profit measure itself. But is that the case?

The distribution of the ROAs shown in Figure IV.A-23 clearly illustrates that the ROA after the hedge (the red dotted line) is much more centered around the mean. Its far left tail lies below that of the before hedged ROA (the blue line), indicating fewer bad scenarios. In fact, 142 of the 1,000 scenarios before the hedge fall below -50 basis points, compared with only 72 scenarios after the hedge; 18 of 1,000 scenarios before the hedge fall below -150 basis points, while only one does after hedge. The standard deviation of the ROA falls by about 40% after the hedge. In the chart, average results were weighted by expected sales distribution.

■ **Figure IV.A-23**

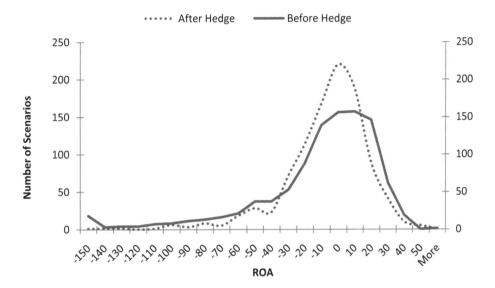

Distribution of Weighted Average ROA

IV.A.7 Financial Reporting of Variable Annuities in the United States

Variable annuity (VA) products are a relatively new market in many countries outside the United States, which may explain why few reporting authorities have developed specific reporting guidelines for them. The United States, however, has two financial reporting authorities with requirements for reporting modeling results. We now turn to a discussion of these financial reporting requirements and their implications on modeling results.

The United States has two financial reporting frameworks:

- **U.S. statutory – liability and capital**

- **U.S. GAAP**

It is important to note that the cash flows within each framework are the same; however, key timing differences exist for the recognition of profit and the means by which this profit recognition is achieved.

IV.A.7.a U.S. Statutory

State regulation requires all insurance companies across the United States to use statutory accounting, a balance sheet based reporting system. The primary purpose of this regulation is to conservatively measure insurer solvency as reflected in the preparation of financial statements. The use of "best estimate" assumptions in support of financial results is, therefore, not allowed.

Such U.S. regulatory conservatism is evidenced in the profit recognition for a newly issued policy, which typically shows a large negative stream of value followed by positive renewal profits. This pattern, referred to as "new business strain," has an up-front loss resulting from initial setup costs, which are slowly recouped as profit increases.

For VA, the standard valuation law prescribes use of VACARVM, as explained in Actuarial Guideline (AG) 33. The VACARVM liability is determined by first projecting the account value using a rate equal to the appropriate regulatory specified valuation interest rate minus any contract charges. The greatest present value of the resulting guaranteed benefit claims is then held as the VACARVM liability.

In addition to the VACARVM liability, the insurer is also required to hold additional liabilities to support any embedded guarantees in the contract. AG 34 covers GMDB while AG 43 covers living guarantees (GMWB, GMAB, and GMIB); both guidelines provide direction on calculating additional statutory liabilities above the VACARVM liability. AG 34 determines the additional liability by applying a "drop and recovery" scenario to the account value. The drop amount and the recovery rate vary depending on the type of assets in which the contract is invested and the fund allocation at the valuation date. AG 43 determines the additional liability by accumulating the associated "imputed charges" – that is, the portion of the overall charge attributed solely to the living guarantee. The accumulation need not consider any interest.

The above statutory guidelines are heavily formulaic; consequently, the guidelines are not always a good fit for the risk profiles of the contracts being valued, because they can result in required liabilities being too high or too low. For example, in bearish equity markets, an AG 34 liability may be too high, while the AG 43 liability may actually decrease. For this reason, these guidelines are primarily viewed as interim in nature.

IV.A.7.b U.S. GAAP

U.S. GAAP accounting is required by the U.S. Securities and Exchange Commission (SEC) for all companies listed on the U.S. stock exchange. This accounting method focuses on the preparation of realistic income statements using best estimate assumptions, particularly with regard to matching revenue and expenses over time as reflected in this accrual system.

Under U.S. GAAP, a VA with GLWB is viewed as having a host component (the base VA contract) and the GLWB. For the purposes of financial reporting, the host and the embedded derivative should be bifurcated and treated separately. The host is accounted for using FAS 97, which applies to contracts with mortality risks and non-guaranteed features, while the GLWB is valued using FAS 133. The GAAP liability for the total contract is considered to be the account value (the liability for the host), plus any additional liability required to cover the guarantee.

Under FAS 97, the insurer can defer a significant portion of the acquisition expense and up-front commissions through a deferred acquisition cost (DAC) asset that is then amortized over time. Decreases in the DAC asset are reflected on the income statement as bottom-line reductions. Thus, the new business strain that occurs under statutory accounting is usually eliminated in the GAAP framework.

A GAAP income statement for VA usually shows the revenues and expenses that were described in Section IV.A.1.c. Premium, which is usually considered revenue on statutory income statements, is handled as revenue for VA in GAAP, because it is invested in the policyholder's accounts and is not a source of profit. The change in the statutory liability line item found in a statutory income presentation is replaced by both a change in DAC and a change in the GAAP liabilities that are held to cover the guarantees.

To ensure that current best estimate assumptions are adopted over time, GAAP assumptions are typically unlocked periodically. The use of nested stochastic simulation is required to assess the expected change in DAC amortization resulting from these new economic assumptions.

Under FAS 133, the GAAP liability is calculated on a fair-value basis. The liability is treated essentially as a swap, with one side of the swap being the present value of expected claims stemming from the guarantee, and the other side being the present value of an attributed fee applied to future account value. The attributed fee is solved for such that the fair value of the swap at issue is equal to zero. Note that, over time, the value of the swap will change as economic conditions and the in-the-moneyness of the guarantee changes. It is also important to note that both sides of the swap are calculated under risk-neutral scenarios and discounted using path-wise risk-free spot rates. This approach ensures that the swap is valued using inputs calibrated to current market conditions.

IV.A.8 Risk Management of Variable Annuity

It is difficult to manage the various risks related to variable annuity (VA) products with embedded guarantees without an understanding of the fundamental characteristics. Insurers would do well to consider the following key risk factors when developing these VA products.

IV.A.8.a Product Design Risk

The embedded guarantee is essentially a put option written to policyholders against the insurer. The policyholder behaviour will affect the cost of the option and thus the profit to the company significantly. In designing the option, the insurer might consider ways to manage policyholder behaviour so as to minimize or control the insurer's loss exposure.

For example, withdrawals are typically designed to reduce GLWB/GMWB benefits on a dollar-for-dollar basis, which would contemplate a $1 reduction in benefit base for every $1 withdrawn. But they could also be designed to reduce GMDB/GMAB/GMIB on either a dollar-for-dollar or proportional basis, which, for a $1 withdrawal, would reduce the benefit base by $1 multiplied by the ratio of benefit base over account value, equivalently by the in-the-moneyness of the guarantee. With dollar-for-dollar, withdrawals would make the guarantees deeper in-the-money when account values tumble, potentially creating a large net amount at risk and exposing the insurer to greater risk. Therefore, when designing the product, careful consideration should be given as to which basis to choose for withdrawals.

Fund allocations offered to the policyholders could also be used to strike a balance between market appeal and risk management. Such allocations might consist of maximum limits on equity proportion or restrictions on funds that are difficult to hedge.

IV.A.8.b Market Risk

The cost of the guarantees as well as the profit from the entire VA contract is subject to significant market volatility. Section IV.A.6 shows that the distribution of the profit has a much longer left tail than right tail, indicating that the downside loss significantly outweighs the upside gain. Typically, the market risk can be hedged through either reinsurance or a dynamic hedge program; however, additional risks are associated with each of these options.

IV.A.8.c Risk with Reinsurance

Insurers have used reinsurance agreements that pay the insurer a percentage of the VA's guaranteed claims as a way of mitigating downside risk; however, as with any reinsurance agreement, these deals, known as share of loss, are subjected to counterparty risk. Some regulation might require capital to be held depending on the reinsurer's credit rating. In addition, reinsurance might involve caps on total benefits.

IV.A.8.d Risk with Dynamic Hedge

A dynamic hedge program can typically minimize fluctuations in the economic liability of the guarantee caused by market movement through a portfolio of financial instruments that behave opposite to that of the insurance guarantee. Basis risk could be incurred if the value of hedge instruments is dependent on underlying assets that are different from the insurance guarantee. In addition, the implementation and maintenance of the dynamic hedge program is extremely complicated. Significant operational risk could arise if the hedge program is mismanaged. It is advisable, therefore, to turn over the implementation and management of a hedging program to an outside specialist until the insurer gains the necessary skills and resources to manage it in-house.

IV.A.8.e Policyholder Behaviour Risk

Policyholder behaviour is perhaps the most difficult risk to hedge against. In developing a product, the insurer may assume policyholders behave rationally in terms of lapses, withdrawals, and annuitizations; in reality, however, some policyholders may not. Moreover, policyholder behaviour has not been studied in any great detail largely because of the lack of industry-wide data. Still, some risk may be mitigated by either introducing restrictive clauses in the product design or adding margins in the pricing assumption.

IV.A.9 Development on an International Platform

Much of the discussion in this section has focused on a typical U.S. product; however, many of the same issues could well apply to international products and situations. While product development considerations on an international platform are likely to vary from country to country, several of the more important considerations are worth discussing.

IV.A.9.a Market Needs and Product Design

One key issue is that a winning product in one country may not produce the same results in another country. Different markets have different needs driven by culture, economy, and living standards to name a few. In all likelihood, the product design would have to be modified to meet the specific needs of each target market.

In Asia, for example, product design varies by country, despite their geographical proximity. In Japan, most products tend to be single-premium, because Japanese consumers typically have large amounts of savings readily available for investment. In Korea, regular premium products are more popular among investors who prefer to finance the premium from their monthly wages. Prevailing low interest rates in Japan also could eliminate the possibility of offering very rich guarantees or any attractive guaranteed minimum incomes.

In Europe, differences are also observed across countries. For instance, the United Kingdom, Germany, and Belgium have seen greater emphasis on the development of VA products with guaranteed retirement income benefit, making contracts with GMIB and lifetime GMWB particularly popular in these countries. In continental Europe, especially in southern Europe, life insurance products are typically medium-term investment products, and capital guarantees like GMAB are considered more important.

Investment fund choices on VA products offered outside the United States are considerably fewer than those offered on VA products in the United States, where consumers typically select from among 30 to 40 funds. By contrast, fund choices in Asia or Europe are typically less than 10. This is largely due to different regulatory limitations and economic environments in each country.

Some innovation has also been witnessed in recent VA product developments outside the United States. Many European insurers are using a fund charge structure that is fund-specific rather than a generic flat rate, which is typical in the United States. This innovation, however, could pose a problem of having different fund allocations assumed in pricing.

IV.A.9.b Economic Model and Data

The pricing of VA products with embedded guarantees requires stochastic modeling, which then requires building economic models to generate stochastic interest rate and/or equity scenarios. The economic model would need to be calibrated to the economy in which products are developed. An interest rate model that works in the United States may not work well in Japan, where interest rates are close to 0%. This would necessitate advice from investment specialists to find the economic model, both risk-neutral and real-world, most appropriate to that particular economy.

Collecting market data may also be an issue in economies for which no sufficient credible historical records are maintained. Calibration to market price may also be a problem, if there is no liquid market for traded derivatives. In some countries, products might be available in both local currency and a foreign currency. This would necessitate development of an economic model that recognizes this exchange risk.

IV.A.9.c Liability and Capital Requirements

Precise liability and capital requirements have not been prescribed by regulators in most countries outside the United States, because most foreign VA products are still in their infancy. In Europe and Asia, insurance authorities typically rely on companies to set their own liability and capital rules. Japan has introduced liability and capital requirements, but their complexity has prompted some companies to reinsure business offshore to avoid having to adhere to these requirements.

At present, the United States is revising its current liability and capital requirements. The C3 Phase II capital requirement is expected to be replaced by a C3 Phase III requirement, and the liability is expected to follow a principles-based approach.

The rapid growth of the VA market seems to have stretched the resources of insurance authorities in recent years. Indeed, a good deal of work remains in determining appropriate liability and capital requirements.

IV.A.9.d Financial Reporting

Financial reporting requirements vary widely across countries. In the United States, both statutory and GAAP reporting requirements are in place for VA products. In other countries, financial reporting requirements for VA products are still evolving. In Europe, there is a trend toward IFRS and/or MCEV reporting. Both require financial results based on risk-neutral scenarios. This movement may indirectly affect the product design as well. A product showing profitability on a realistic reporting basis may not be on a risk-neutral reporting basis, and companies may, therefore, have to redesign the charge structure or guarantee benefits accordingly.

IV.B Economic Capital for a Multi-line Life Insurance Company

An economic capital (EC) model is one component of an insurance company's larger risk management framework. Through determination of an appropriate level of capital, it is designed to identify and manage the unique risks that threaten the solvency of an insurance company. In this sense, it is a powerful tool for actuaries and risk managers to guard against catastrophic risks (or "tail risks") facing a company.

As a way of demonstrating the strength of stochastic techniques discussed in this book and their application to a risk management setting, the following case study introduces the fundamental concepts of an EC framework, illustrates generation of stochastic scenarios for various risk factors, and presents EC results developed for a life and health insurance company using sophisticated stochastic models.

IV.B.1 The Case Study Company: Background on XYZ Life Insurance Company

This case study presents results for an EC analysis of XYZ Life Insurance Company, a large multi-line life and health insurance company writing primarily par individual life, variable annuity, and group health business. This generic company could be headquartered anywhere in the world. As such, the EC analysis discussed in the case study is not unique to any particular country, although certain references are made to U.S. stock market indices.

IV.B.2 Fundamental Concepts of an Economic Capital Framework

Economic capital is defined as the amount of capital required to cover losses at a given confidence level over a specified period of time. For example, a company may wish to be 99.5% confident that it will remain solvent over a 20-year time horizon. When implementing an EC framework, companies must first decide on:

- **A risk metric**

Companies must define how they will measure risk in terms of quantifying the variability of outcomes under a stochastic projection. Commonly used risk metrics are Value at Risk (VaR) or conditional tail expectation (CTE or Tail VaR), which are discussed in greater detail elsewhere in this book.

- **A confidence level to target**

Users of EC generally examine high levels of confidence. After all, EC models are intended to reveal catastrophic events that could materially, adversely affect operating results. To understand these catastrophic events, it is necessary to examine the tails of the risk factor distributions (e.g., extreme interest rate, default, or mortality events). Common confidence levels for users of EC are 99.5%, 99.9%, and 99.95%.

- **A time horizon**

For quick implementation, some companies will examine very short time horizons (e.g., one to five years). In this case, companies are looking for short-term shocks in risk factors that can have sudden, catastrophic consequences (e.g., what impact would a pandemic have on my term insurance block of business over the next year?). More commonly, companies perform longer-term projections with time horizons ranging from 20 to 60 years.

- **Projection techniques**

Given the objective of an EC analysis – to examine tail outcomes of company-specific risk factors – stochastic modeling is required. Alternative techniques, such as stress testing or scenario testing, are generally inadequate for EC work, although they may play a supporting role in helping to identify critical risk factors.

IV.B.3 Modeling Risks

After addressing the above issues, a company must analyze which risks are most relevant to its business. Intended to be company-specific tools, EC models aim to thoughtfully analyze which risks have the potential to materially impact the company's profitability.

Often, the materiality of a risk can be identified through the use of stress tests. If the present value of profits is sensitive to a particular assumption or risk factor, then it is a candidate for inclusion in the EC model. Alternatively, insight into relevant risk factors can often be obtained by interviewing the actuary with responsibility for a particular line of business.

Commonly modeled risk factors for an EC framework include:

- **Risk-free interest rates and credit spreads**
- **Asset defaults**
- **Liquidity**
- **Mortality**
- **Morbidity**
- **Lapses**
- **Currency exchange rates**
- **Mix of business (if future business is included in the model)**
- **Strategic risk (often modeled as a load to EC, rather than stochastically)**
- **Operational risk (often modeled as a load to EC, rather than stochastically)**

Risk analysis for XYZ Life revealed that the risks shown in Figure IV.B-1 are relevant and will be included in the EC model:

▌ Figure IV.B-1

Risks Modeled for XYZ Life Insurance Company Economic Capital

	Individual Life	Variable Annuity	Fixed Annuity	Asset Management	Individual Disability Income	Group Health	Capital / Surplus	Consolidated Corporate
Interest Rate	X	X	X		X		X	
Mortality	X							
Lapse	X					X		
Market/Equity Returns		X		X			X	
Morbidity					X	X		
Currency Exchange Rates							X	
Credit								X
Strategic								X
Operational								X

IV.B.4 General Methodology

IV.B.4.a Risk Metrics

This case study focuses on the following two risk metrics:

- **Present value of future profits (PVFP)**

PVFP is the discounted value of all future profits and losses over the entire projection period.

- **Greatest present value of accumulated loss (GPVL)**

GPVL is the present value of all net losses from the starting projection date to the end of the year, when the present value of the loss is greatest. If there are no losses (and, therefore, no accumulated losses), the GPVL is zero. GPVL does not allow future gains to mitigate the current need for capital.

IV.B.4.b Confidence Level

A CTE99 approach is for the business risks, and capital is set at the average of the worst 1% of losses over 30 years. For strategic and operational failure risks, the 99.5% probability of solvency is measured over five years.

IV.B.4.c Time Horizon

This case study also uses a long-term runoff approach with a 30-year projection horizon in determining required EC, consistent with developments in C3 Phase II, Variable Annuity Commissioners' Annuity Reserve Valuation Method, and a principles-based approach to liabilities and capital in the United States; and with European standards, such as Embedded Value (EV) and Solvency II. The long-term runoff approach for liabilities differs from the one-year economic balance sheet approach used by many European companies, which uses the fair value of assets and liabilities at the end of one year. To develop a fair value of liabilities, long-term modeling must be performed as in the long-term approach.

IV.B.4.d Projection Techniques

Our starting point for analysis was the company's deterministic Cash Flow Testing (CFT) or EV models (when such models exist). Note: if CFT or EV models did not already exist, new models would need to be developed. We proceeded with our analysis as follows:

1. Using best estimate assumptions, we developed a deterministic "baseline" 30-year profit projection for each line of business (LOB) and each risk factor.

2. For each risk to be modeled, we generated 1,000 stochastic scenarios. (The generation of these scenarios is discussed in greater detail later in this case study.)

3. The 1,000 scenarios for each risk were projected independently. For example, the 1,000 mortality scenarios were run separately from the 1,000 interest rate scenarios. This analysis tells us the amount of EC required for each risk factor, but does not reveal the required aggregate amount of EC because the correlation of risk factors is ignored. It is important to remember that total EC is not merely the sum of the indicated EC from each risk factor but rather an amount that reflects the interaction of all risk factors simultaneously. Running risk factors independently, however, provides the risk manager with insight into which individual risks pose the greatest threat to company profitability.

4. A decision then needed to be made regarding how to generate a large number of scenarios that would produce a meaningful number and reasonable result within the limits of projection run times. One of two approaches could have been taken. Every scenario with every risk could have been run, which would have required $1,000^6$ or 1,000,000,000,000,000,000 (one quintillion) runs if each of the 1,000 scenarios for each risk were run against the case study's six generators. This approach was clearly implausible. The case study instead used a "synthetic" scenario approach, which utilizes a PVFP measure (the difference between the present value of future profits for a scenario and the baseline) from each of the 1,000 scenarios for each independent risk. For each scenario, we assigned a number from one to 1,000. We then used Microsoft Excel to generate 1,500,000 random integers between one and 1,000 (inclusive), a process that generated 250,000 choices of scenarios from each risk (a grid of 250,000 by six). To verify the distribution, we reviewed each random number to determine whether it occurred roughly 1,500 times. Then, using a grid of scenarios, we performed a look-up of the present value, which was summed across all the risks. The sums were then ranked in ascending order so that the worst combined independent scenarios appeared first. It is felt that this approach produces a reasonable number of scenarios that showed poor results and would reflect an essential value of EC that could be used to determine how much capital needed to be put set aside to cover an extremely high level of possible outcomes.

5. To account for the interaction or correlation of various risk factors, we developed the "worst 2,500" scenarios from Step 4 and combined all risk factors (except for credit, operational, and strategic risks) into a single set of scenarios. Using these scenarios, which were originally generated stochastically, we ran a deterministic projection. These "worst 2,500" scenarios were believed to reasonably reflect the interaction of all risk factors that the company might simultaneously face in the real world, such that the company might now use the data to more realistically reflect on how it would respond to multiple occurring risks.

Scenario reduction techniques were used to aid in selecting the adverse scenarios, which drive the tail of the distribution of results and hence drive EC.

Credit defaults were projected at the aggregate company level. Gains and losses on assets, backing capital, and surplus were projected separately from LOB profits. As discussed above, strategic risk and operational risk were projected separately at the 99.5% confidence interval over five years.

IV.B.5 Scenario Generation

This section discusses how to generate 1,000 stochastic scenarios for the following risk factors included in the EC model:

- **Economic scenarios, including:**
    - Interest rates
    - Equity returns
    - Spot currency exchange rates
- **Credit/default**
- **Mortality**
- **Morbidity**
- **Lapses**
- **Operational risk**
- **Strategic risk**

IV.B.5.a Economic Scenario Generator

This section summarizes the economic scenario generator. The generator produces robust and internally consistent economic scenarios of equity index returns, yield curves, and spot exchange rates.

Equity model

The underlying model for the equity index is a stochastic volatility model, namely the model of Heston (1993). (The dynamics follow the equations below.)

$$d\begin{bmatrix} \ln(S_t) \\ \sigma_t^{\,2} \end{bmatrix} = \begin{bmatrix} f(t) - q - \dfrac{\sigma_t^{\,2}}{2} \\ \kappa(\beta - \sigma_t^{\,2}) \end{bmatrix} dt + \sigma_t \begin{bmatrix} \rho & \sqrt{1-\rho^2} \\ 0 & v \end{bmatrix} \begin{bmatrix} dz_1 \\ dz_2 \end{bmatrix} \qquad \text{(IV.B-1)}$$

where

$S(t)$ is the index level at time t

σ_t^2 is the underlying variance of the equity index process at time t

$f(t)$ is the expected return for the current period

q is the continuously compounded dividend yield over the same time interval

ρ is the correlation between return innovations and variance innovations

κ is strength of mean reversion of volatility

β is equilibrium variance

v is volatility of volatility

dz_1 and dz_2 are Brownian motion processes

The volatility of the equity index is itself a stochastic process with its own volatility and mean reversion.

The advantages of this form over the commonly used lognormal model is that stochastic volatility models allow generated scenarios to be consistent with the following stylized facts of the historical time series of the S&P 500 index:

- **The underlying volatility of the S&P 500 changes over time, but reverts to some long-term mean**
- **Changes in the underlying volatility are negatively related to index movements over time**
- **Distributions of equity price movements exhibit fatter tails and skew relative to lognormal distributions**

Interest rate model

The model for interest rates presents the yield curve as having three stochastic components: the level, the slope, and the curvature of the forward rate curve. This framework allows generated scenarios to reflect the following features of historical yield curve movements:

- **The points on the yield curve generally tend to move together**
- **Volatility of the short end of the yield curve is generally higher than the relative volatility of the long end of the yield curve**
- **Yield curves tend to flatten as they rise and steepen as rates drop**
- **Inversions may occur at a frequency of 5% to 20%**

Spot exchange rate model

The model for spot exchange rates is a lognormal model that maintains the principle of interest rate parity by using the difference between the domestic and foreign interest rate curves as the drift component.

Model parameterization

All model parameters and coefficients were estimated using historical data. We used 20 years of monthly data including S&P 500 index levels, risk-free yield curves, and the VIX index to estimate parameters.

We used the scenario generator, which was parameterized assuming a start date of September 30, 2006, to simulate 1,000 30-year scenarios projecting forward from that date.

The following sections present the parameters used in the model to produce the scenarios.

Starting interest rates (foreign and domestic)

The risk-free yield curves as of September 30, 2006, are shown in Figure IV.B-2.

Figure IV.B-2

Constant Maturity Risk-Free Rates					
Maturity (Years)	U.S.	Euro zone	Great Britain	Switzerland	Japan
1	4.91%	3.60%	5.02%	2.17%	0.33%
2	4.86%	3.59%	4.92%	2.17%	0.66%
3	4.80%	3.59%	4.84%	2.18%	0.76%
5	4.70%	3.63%	4.73%	2.28%	1.14%
7	4.60%	3.65%	4.63%	2.37%	1.37%
10	4.57%	3.71%	4.52%	2.38%	1.68%
20	4.84%	3.91%	4.34%	2.50%	2.18%
30	5.03%	3.90%	4.10%	2.53%	2.44%

This information translates to the starting forward rates in our three-factor model shown in Figure IV.B-3.

Figure IV.B-3

Maturity (Years)	Starting Rates				
	U.S.	Euro zone*	Great Britain*	Switzerland*	Japan*
1	4.85%	3.53%	4.96%	2.16%	0.33%
2	4.21%	3.66%	4.23%	2.65%	2.27%
30	5.80%	3.95%	3.41%	2.69%	3.16%

Only the domestic rate was simulated stochastically. The foreign interest rate curves were determined by adding (or subtracting) the starting spread to the domestic curves.

The domestic curve, which assumes a target slope and curvature of 1.52% and -2.30%, produces a target yield curve shape consistent with the historically observed average shape. If we assume the target one-year rate stays at 4.91% for this case study, our target long-term par semi-annual yield curve is as shown in Figure IV.B-4.

Figure IV.B-4

Constant Maturity Risk-free Rates	
Maturity (Years)	U.S.
1	4.91%
2	5.04%
3	5.16%
5	5.40%
7	5.63%
10	5.80%
20	5.87%
30	5.83%

Figure IV.B-5

	Interest Rate Parameters				
	Maturity	Starting Rate	Volatility (Monthly)	Mean Reversion Target	Mean Reversion Strength
Short Rate	1	4.85%	5.77%	3.97%	0.80%
Medium Rate (Slope Parameters)	7	4.21%	0.35%	1.52%	1.22%
Long Rate (Curvature Parameters)	30	5.80%	0.78%	-2.30%	2.75%

Duration parameters [for bond fund calculations]

We based the domestic bond duration parameter used in the bond fund calculations on the duration of the SBBIG bond index. For the foreign bond funds, we used market value weighted averages of XYZ's foreign bond funds as of September 30, 2006, as shown in Figure IV.B-6.

Figure IV.B-6

Market Weighted Duration Averages					
	U.S.	**Euro zone**	**Great Britain**	**Switzerland**	**Japan**
Duration	4.0 yrs	4.6 yrs	14.5 yrs	6.9 yrs	9.6 yrs

Figure IV.B-7

Correlation Matrix				
	Short Rate	**Yield Curve Slope**	**Yield Curve Curvature**	**S&P 500**
Short Rate	1.000	-0.730	0.537	-0.178
Yield Curve Slope	-0.730	1.000	-0.929	0.077
Yield Curve Curvature	0.537	-0.929	1.000	-0.035
S&P 500	-0.178	0.077	-0.035	1.000

Equity returns

The S&P 500 parameters are shown in Figure IV.B-8.

Figure IV.B-8

S&P 500 Parameters				
	Initial Total Return	Mean Reversion Strength	Target Total Return	Dividend Yield
Drift Process	8.50%	100.00%	8.50%	0.00%
	Initial Variance	Mean Reversion Strength	Target Variance	Volatility of Variance	Correlation (between underlying and variance)
Equity Volatility	2.96%	260.00%	2.96%	25.00%	-43.75%

We set the dividend yield assumption at zero to generate a total return index.

Other correlated indices are shown in Figure IV.B-9.

█ Figure IV.B-9

	Other Correlated Indices			
	S&P 500	**Russell 2000**	**NASDAQ 100**	**EAFE**
S&P 500	1.000	0.796	0.826	0.782
Russell 2000	0.796	1.000	0.873	0.784
NASDAQ 100	0.826	0.873	1.000	0.764
EAFE	0.782	0.784	0.764	1.000
Volatilities		25.0 %	21.3 %	21.3 %

Currency returns

Currency exchange rate correlations and volatilities were developed based on the historical correlations and volatilities observed in the foreign exchange rates. Figure IV.B-10 shows the correlations and volatilities of historical weekly data from January 1999 to September 2006.

To reflect currency hedging, the volatility of the currency return is reduced by a factor based on the proportion of currency hedged and the historical hedge effectiveness.

█ Figure IV.B-10

	Correlations and Volatilities, Jan. 1999-Sept. 2006			
	FX EUR/USD	FX GBP/USD	FX CHF/USD	FX JPY/USD
FX EUR/USD	1.000	0.708	0.940	0.379
FX GBP/USD	0.708	1.000	0.679	0.361
FX CHF/USD	0.940	0.679	1.000	0.401
FX JPY/USD	0.379	0.361	0.401	1.000
Volatilities	10.0 %	8.4 %	10.6 %	10.2 %

In addition to generating the four correlated equity index returns, the interest rates and currency returns were used to generate domestic money market returns and domestic and foreign bond returns.

Money market

We assumed the money market account would earn the one-year forward rate at the beginning of the period.

Domestic bond

We simulated the domestic bond fund, which has an assumed duration as a parameter, by purchasing a semi-annual coupon bond with the given duration, holding it for one period, and then rolling the position over into a new bond with the given duration parameter.

Foreign bond

We simulated the foreign bond fund, which also has an assumed duration as a parameter, by purchasing a semi-annual coupon bond with the given duration, holding it for one period, and then rolling the position over into a new bond with the given duration parameter; however, the par coupon at issue and the revaluation of the bond a week later are based on a set of foreign interest rate curves. The foreign interest rate curves are the stochastically generated domestic interest rate curves plus a given spread. The spread is the difference between the foreign and domestic term structures provided at time 0; it stays constant throughout the projection. This process gives the value of the foreign bond in the local currency. To calculate the value of the foreign bond in the domestic currency, we multiplied the value of the foreign bond in the local currency by the spot exchange rate.

The foreign bond fund value in the local currency for currency f and time t, $F_{f,t}$, is therefore

$$F_{f,t} = F_{f,t-1} * a)$$ (IV.B-2)

where $a)$ is the end-of-period bond value in local currency based on change in the foreign interest rate curve.

The spot exchange rate is calculated as

$$e_{f,T+\Delta t} = e_{f,T} \times \exp[(r_{d,T} - r_{f,T} - \sigma_f^2 / 2)(\Delta t) + \phi_f \sigma_f (\Delta t)^{1/2}]$$ (IV.B-3)

The foreign bond fund value in the domestic currency is

$$F_{d,t} = F_{f,t} * e_{f,t}$$ (IV.B-4)

IV.B.5.b Credit Risk Model

Valuation and risk management of corporate bond prices, which are largely driven by credit risk, and their derivatives require models that reflect the risk of the counterparty defaulting on a payment. There are many different ways to model credit risk.

This section describes a model for simulating default events to generate scenarios that represent the number of defaults in a certain year for a portfolio of credit-risky bonds. The model is similar to the model used for analyzing the EC requirement for Basel II. The first part of the section describes the dynamics of the model, and the second part presents key simplifications used to make the model more tractable. The section ends with a discussion of potential ways to further improve to the model.

Description of the model

We used the asymptotic single risk factor (ASRF; Vasicek, 1987) model to generate heavy-tailed credit loss distributions as a way of estimating the risk associated with a portfolio of bonds. The model assumes that the borrower's end-of-period state (default or no default) is driven by a normally distributed variable that describes the hypothetical firm's asset return. A default event, upgrade event, or downgrade event occurs if this variable $R_{i,t}$ falls below or rises above a specific level. Therefore, firm i defaults if, and only if,

$$R_{i,t} < C_{i,D};$$

downgrades if, and only if,

$$R_{i,t} < C_{i,DG};$$

and upgrades if, and only if,

$$R_{i,t} > C_{i,UG};$$

where C_i is the point on the standard normal distribution associated with the desired probability of a particular event. For example, if 50% is the desired probability of default, $C_{i,D}$ is set equal to zero, so that $N(C_{i,D}) = 50\%$.

The probability of upgrade, downgrade, or default for firm i can be given by

$$W_{i,E} = \Pr(R_i < C_{i,E}) = N(C_{i,E}) \qquad \text{(IV.B-5)}$$

where $N(.)$ is the cumulative standard normal distribution function.

This probability is approximated from the agency rating transition matrix for a given ratings class. To determine the value of C that results in a default, upgrade, or downgrade, the normal cumulative density function can be converted as follows:

$$C_{i,E} = N^{-1}(W_{i,E}) \qquad \text{(IV.B-6)}$$

To simulate the return for each period, we used the following equation:

$$R_{i,t} = \sqrt{\beta_i}\, X_t + \sqrt{1 - \beta_i}\, \varepsilon_{i,t} \qquad \text{(IV.B-7)}$$

This equation shows that the asset return on each firm can be described as a systematic factor X, and a firm-specific factor epsilon.

Potential simplifications to the model

In order to calculate the return for each firm in the above equations, we need to estimate the betas and also the correlations for each firm with the market parameter. However, if the portfolio is large enough and contains bonds from different ratings classes, the return and correlations can be approximated by the ratings class correlation with the market parameter. This information can be generated from the transition matrix, which describes the probability of a particular ratings class to default. The law of large numbers also allows us to conclude that every bond in a particular ratings class has the same correlation with the market parameter X_t. The corresponding beta for each firm, therefore, will be the same if the bonds are in the same ratings class. The formula for calculating the correlation coefficient for each ratings class is given by the Basel II risk-weight function:

$$\beta = 0.12\left(\frac{1 - e^{-50*PD}}{1 - e^{-50}}\right) + 0.24\left(1 - \frac{1 - e^{-50*PD}}{1 - e^{-50}}\right), PD = \text{probability of default} \qquad \text{(IV.B-8)}$$

The default probabilities for the ratings classes are taken from the Moody's transition matrices shown in Figures IV.B-11 and IV.B-12.

Figure IV.B-11

Public Transition Matrix (exhibit 24)
Taken from Moody's Public Bond Default Study

	Aaa	Aa	A	Baa	Ba	B	Caa-C	D
Aaa	89.90%	6.72%	0.54%	0.19%	0.01%	0.00%	0.00%	0.00%
Aa	1.04%	87.89%	6.92%	0.27%	0.05%	0.02%	0.00%	0.01%
A	0.06%	2.57%	88.12%	4.95%	0.52%	0.10%	0.02%	0.02%
Baa	0.05%	0.21%	4.92%	84.72%	4.44%	0.79%	0.25%	0.18%
Ba	0.01%	0.06%	0.48%	5.65%	76.68%	7.61%	0.62%	1.18%
B	0.01%	0.05%	0.17%	0.41%	5.55%	74.54%	5.44%	5.37%
CaaC	0.00%	0.04%	0.04%	0.20%	0.74%	7.17%	60.65%	19.52%

Figure IV.B-12

Private Transition Matrix (table 15)
Taken from the SOA Private Placement Study

	Aaa	Aa	A	Baa	Ba	B	Caa-C	D
Aaa	93.81%	2.99%	2.16%	0.84%	0.08%	0.07%	0.03%	0.01%
Aa	2.04%	88.78%	7.47%	1.25%	0.18%	0.18%	0.04%	0.08%
A	1.09%	1.74%	88.78%	7.37%	0.53%	0.25%	0.12%	0.12%
Baa	0.17%	0.75%	4.72%	89.12%	3.28%	0.85%	0.48%	0.63%
Ba	0.20%	0.34%	0.80%	9.22%	81.11%	3.81%	0.93%	3.59%
B	0.14%	0.31%	0.99%	4.87%	6.44%	79.19%	2.11%	5.96%
CaaC	0.62%	0.16%	1.87%	2.18%	3.35%	10.12%	75.49%	6.23%

The return thresholds and the rating-wise asset correlations can now be calculated as a way of simulating the return for each bond in the portfolio. The return at the end of the period is then compared to the return threshold, and a default event, upgrade event, or downgrade event is recorded, if the simulated return is more or less than the threshold for the corresponding event.

Calculating cost of a credit event

When calculating the cost of a particular upgrade or downgrade event, we can use the target duration of the portfolio and the change in the credit spread from the event. For example, if a bond rated AAA is downgraded to AA, the credit spread will widen by x basis points. The loss generated by this event is the portfolio duration times the change in the credit spread. For this analysis, the duration of XYZ Life's portfolio is assumed to be seven years.

To calculate the cost of a default event, we simply pay the inverse of the recovery rate. The tables in Figures IV.B-13 and IV.B-14 give example sets of credit spreads and recovery rates.

Figure IV.B-13

Public Spreads (market spreads as of Jan 5,
2007) and Recovery Rates (exhibit 14)
Taken from Moody's Public Bond Default Study

Rating	Recovery Rate	Credit Spread
AAA	100.00%	0.55%
AA	94.40%	0.62%
A	46.40%	0.69%
BBB	48.10%	0.98%
BB	40.10%	1.70%
B	36.60%	2.67%
CCC	30.40%	6.00%

Figure IV.B-14

Private Spreads (p. 138)
and Recovery Rates (p. 182)
Taken from the SOA Private Placement Study

Rating	Recovery Rate	Credit Spread
AAA	99.98%	2.10%
AA	99.55%	2.10%
A	99.78%	2.10%
BBB	99.43%	2.65%
BB	98.27%	4.85%
B	98.31%	7.70%
CCC	87.18%	7.70%

Results

The table in Figure IV.B-15 reports statistics when the model is applied to the company's portfolio of credit-risky bonds.

Figure IV.B-15

Default Costs

Default Costs Asset Book Value	Total Portfolio $23,134,742,000	Public total $14,713,695,912	Private PI $4,372,466,238	Public IG $13,742,036,748
Mean	(337,037,030)	(348,273,805)	11,236,774	(245,032,621)
Std Dev	160,597,325	148,995,351	57,576,405	111,491,777
Pct Rank				
0%	(992,296,673)	(993,856,730)	(160,794,768)	(878,724,306)
1%	(813,838,956)	(798,796,529)	(124,871,684)	(535,887,498)
5%	(630,155,806)	(621,287,441)	(83,171,480)	(440,604,228)
10%	(540,453,752)	(541,293,231)	(62,906,371)	(381,568,692)
15%	(490,512,886)	(497,860,302)	(47,820,458)	(353,159,947)
20%	(455,573,306)	(455,733,777)	(37,780,423)	(329,906,181)
25%	(431,157,732)	(429,045,515)	(28,268,226)	(311,554,238)
50%	(318,695,254)	(329,016,849)	10,192,706	(232,370,643)
75%	(233,001,008)	(246,116,664)	50,529,800	(162,232,191)
80%	(214,108,654)	(222,387,267)	59,346,554	(149,306,072)
85%	(181,353,285)	(200,371,434)	71,374,346	(133,437,155)
90%	(140,938,398)	(173,549,935)	83,661,549	(113,831,379)
95%	(98,727,220)	(140,797,629)	103,146,259	(86,993,860)
99%	(14,785,000)	(81,036,909)	142,276,413	(42,650,643)
100%	72,361,748	35,515,008	183,600,163	39,347,181

In situations in which items in the Public Total column are all publicly traded bonds, Private PI lists private placement bonds, and Public IG investment-grade bonds. Investment-grade bonds are typically bonds rated BBB or higher.

While the ASRF model has a relatively simple form, it is still a robust tool for simulating credit events for a portfolio of credit-risky bonds. Moreover, its assumptions hold well for large bond portfolios, and its inputs can be determined from published rating agency data, which includes the transition matrix published specifically for credit analysis.

IV.B.5.c Mortality

The mortality scenarios were developed using the mortality model described in Section II.B.1.

In this case study, we generated 30,000 random numbers to create 1,000 scenarios, each with a 30-year projection horizon. The results of the analysis generated mortality scaling factors that were applied to actual mortality. This process was used for all lines of business in which stochastic mortality was reflected.

Summary statistics for the first 10 years of the projection are summarized in the tables attached. Factors were generated for three risks: base mortality, pandemic mortality, and terrorism risk.

IV.B.5.d Morbidity

Our focus now turns to how claim costs can be developed for a stochastic projection model. The individual disability income LOB is used in this case study, but the discussion is general enough to apply to any health product.

Probability distributions for new claim costs and the runoff claim liability arising after September 30, 2006, were created using the company's September 30, 2006, policy in-force data and its September 30, 2006, disabled life data.

Probability distributions for new claim costs

We produced a probability distribution for the September 30, 2006, policy in-force data using proprietary software which is a Monte Carlo analytical tool. The following provides an overview of the process:

- **We used expected claim incidence and termination rates based on the company's cash flow testing assumptions.**

- **We created a table from the expected claim incidence and termination rates to reflect the probability of incurring a claim in a year (based on age, occupation class, and sex, among other factors) and staying on claim for one month, two months, or longer.**

- **We derived the probability distribution used in the stochastic liability model for 2006 claim costs by performing 10,000 risk simulation iterations over the full policy file. For each policy, and within each iteration, we chose a random number that determined whether the policy incurred a claim and, if so, how long it would remain on claim. We calculated the present value of paid benefits if the policy incurred a claim and accumulated over all in-force policies. Thus, one complete iteration through the policy in-force file represented one aggregate random claim cost scenario; 10,000 of these aggregate random claim cost scenarios were created and used as the basis for creating the probability distribution in the stochastic liability model.**

- **Because the projected in-force business will shrink because of policy lapses and expirations, the in-force file was aged every five years, and new probability distributions were created based on then-current data.**

The table in Figure IV.B-16 displays the probability distributions for years 2006, 2011, 2016, 2021, 2026, and 2031 for certain percentiles.

■ Figure IV.B-16

	Probability Distribution for Annual Claim Costs					
Percentile	Variances from Expected Annual Claim Costs by Year Incurred					
	2006	2011	2016	2021	2026	2031
0.010	-12.01%	-12.28%	-12.78%	-13.06%	-14.77%	-19.69%
0.050	-8.69%	-8.99%	-8.92%	-9.24%	-10.27%	-14.30%
0.100	-7.07%	-6.96%	-7.22%	-7.49%	-8.03%	-10.97%
0.150	-5.82%	-5.76%	-5.91%	-6.19%	-6.94%	-8.92%
0.200	-4.58%	-4.52%	-4.62%	-4.88%	-5.84%	-7.56%
0.250	-3.76%	-3.69%	-3.75%	-4.01%	-4.72%	-5.56%
0.300	-2.93%	-2.90%	-2.91%	-3.15%	-3.60%	-4.22%
0.350	-2.11%	-2.07%	-2.05%	-2.28%	-2.49%	-3.55%
0.400	-1.29%	-1.66%	-1.63%	-1.40%	-1.92%	-2.21%
0.450	-0.87%	-0.86%	-0.78%	-0.97%	-0.82%	-0.88%
0.500	-0.04%	-0.03%	0.07%	-0.09%	-0.25%	-0.21%
0.550	0.38%	0.78%	0.53%	0.78%	0.84%	1.15%
0.600	1.21%	1.19%	1.37%	1.21%	1.41%	1.81%
0.650	2.02%	2.01%	2.22%	2.08%	2.51%	3.16%
0.700	2.85%	2.82%	2.66%	2.95%	3.08%	4.50%
0.750	3.68%	3.63%	3.51%	3.83%	4.18%	5.85%
0.800	4.48%	4.85%	4.80%	4.69%	5.29%	7.16%
0.850	5.73%	5.67%	5.66%	6.00%	6.96%	9.20%
0.900	6.98%	6.91%	7.38%	7.30%	8.07%	11.21%
0.950	9.01%	9.34%	9.52%	9.47%	10.87%	14.55%
0.990	12.73%	13.05%	13.35%	13.83%	15.91%	21.34%

Using the table in the stochastic liability model is a rather straightforward process. For example, to determine the random annual claims for year 2006, if we selected the random number of 0.850, then the random annual claim cost would be 5.73% higher than the baseline claim cost in 2006.

Because the annual claim costs represent the present value of future paid claims, the 5.73% variance factor is applied to a vector of future paid claims (for which the present value is equal to the baseline annual claim cost) to produce variances in future aggregate paid claims arising from the variances in claim costs incurred in 2006. The 5.73% is also applied to the vectors of the various claim liabilities arising from claims incurred in 2006 to produce variances in future aggregate claim liabilities.

The results in Figure IV.B-16 show a general widening of the distributions as the policyholders age and numbers shrink.

Probability distribution of claim runoff

We also used Risk Simulator to produce a probability distribution of the September 30, 2006, claim runoff. The table in Figure IV.B-17 shows the resulting probability distribution at selected percentiles.

Figure IV.B-17

Probability Distribution for Claim Runoff	
Percentile	**Variance from Average Payout**
0.010	-2.41%
0.050	-1.67%
0.100	-1.29%
0.150	-1.07%
0.200	-0.84%
0.250	-0.69%
0.300	-0.55%
0.350	-0.40%
0.400	-0.25%
0.450	-0.10%
0.500	-0.02%
0.550	0.13%
0.600	0.27%
0.650	0.42%
0.700	0.50%
0.750	0.72%
0.800	0.88%
0.850	1.10%
0.900	1.32%
0.950	1.62%
0.990	2.36%

Because there is no claim incidence risk, the probability distribution in Figure IV.B-17 is much tighter around the mean for the annual claim costs than those in the table in Figure IV.B-16, which reflect both claim incidence and termination risks.

Pricing risk

The probability distributions for annual claim costs and runoff assume that the expected morbidity bases as defined by company's cash flow testing assumptions are correct; however, these morbidity bases represent estimates, and could differ from the current "true" expected basis. For this reason, we incorporated a pricing risk factor to these baseline claim projections as a way to reflect the pricing risk.

We used the probability distribution in the table in Figure IV.B-18 to represent the pricing risk for both annual claim costs and claim runoff.

■ **Figure IV.B-18**

Probability Distribution for the Pricing Risk	
Percentile	**Variance**
0.00	-5.0%
0.10	-2.5%
0.35	0.0%
0.65	2.5%
0.90	5.0%

IV.B.5.e Lapses

Lapse scenarios were developed based on historical company experience with an assumption that deviations from the expected rates would follow a normal distribution. The steps for developing the lapse scenarios are as follows:

1. Develop the expected lapse rates based on historical company experience. These rates constitute the best estimate assumptions and are used in the baseline projection. Any amount of company experience can be used in developing the lapse assumptions. But in order to ensure credible results, data for a minimum of five years, and typically 10 or more years, is used in the experience study.

2. Calculate the standard deviation of experience lapse rates based on the same historical company data used in Step 1.

3. Develop a string of random numbers using Excel's random number generator. The random numbers represent multiplicative scalars that will be applied to the best estimate lapse rates to generate the 1,000 scenarios.

In Step 3, the mean should always be equal to 1 (as was the value used in this case study) because, on average, the lapses are expected to equal the best estimate assumption; therefore, the average multiplicative scalar should also be 1. The standard deviation of 0.16 was based on XYZ Life company experience. The random number seed can be any value preferred by the user. We used a value of 1 for this case study.

A total of 30,000 random numbers were generated using the above process, allowing us to create 1,000 scenarios, each with a 30-year projection horizon.

Statistics for the first 10 years of the projection are summarized in the table in Figure IV.B-19.

■ Figure IV.B-19

Illustration of Stochastic Lapse Scenarios

					Projection Year					
	1	2	3	4	5	6	7	8	9	10
Mean	1.0045	1.0040	1.0032	0.9936	1.0018	0.9976	1.0018	0.9872	1.0005	0.9997
Std Dev	0.1606	0.1615	0.1552	0.1561	0.1580	0.1574	0.1567	0.1626	0.1617	0.1597
Percentile										
0.0%	0.4725	0.3585	0.5557	0.5334	0.4869	0.5298	0.4848	0.4664	0.5580	0.4558
0.5%	0.5879	0.5837	0.5987	0.5925	0.5970	0.6009	0.6134	0.5888	0.5892	0.6029
1.0%	0.6094	0.6165	0.6372	0.6250	0.6433	0.6219	0.6384	0.6129	0.6176	0.6349
5.0%	0.7498	0.7318	0.7408	0.7348	0.7483	0.7278	0.7532	0.7164	0.7364	0.7387
10.0%	0.8036	0.7926	0.8001	0.7981	0.8030	0.8010	0.8056	0.7759	0.8008	0.8015
25.0%	0.8998	0.8974	0.8973	0.8837	0.8885	0.8947	0.8892	0.8799	0.8874	0.8861
50.0%	1.0077	0.0087	0.0044	0.9891	1.0027	0.9962	1.0017	0.9890	0.9946	1.0001
75.0%	1.1101	1.1087	1.1120	1.1025	1.1047	1.1006	1.1112	1.0929	1.1060	1.1069
90.0%	1.2113	1.2079	1.1945	1.2045	1.2053	1.2024	1.2123	1.1973	1.2111	1.2046
95.0%	1.2701	1.2750	1.2440	1.2549	1.2598	1.2577	1.2584	1.2524	1.2665	1.2616
99.0%	1.3677	1.3483	1.3580	1.3460	1.3505	1.3608	1.3502	1.3627	1.3832	1.3692
99.5%	1.3793	1.4248	1.3824	1.3707	1.4022	1.3930	1.3625	1.4073	1.4218	1.4085
100.0%	1.4740	1.5275	0.5484	0.5131	1.8583	1.5484	1.4244	1.4693	1.5275	1.5198

Operational and strategic risks

In order to estimate the appropriate level of capital the company should hold for mitigating risks associated with operational or strategic sources, a series of scenarios have been developed to describe the company's risk exposure in these areas. Two pieces of analysis have been used to ensure that the scenarios are relevant to the company's business.

First, management conducted a data-gathering exercise of the profit centers to determine potential operational losses of both high-impact and low-frequency events. The business experts contributing to this exercise drew on their extensive knowledge of the organization's historical experience as well as knowledge of similar events occurring in other organizations.

In parallel with this process, the senior company team was engaged in a process to identify strategic risks facing the company using STRATrisk, a cutting-edge methodology to determine key sources of potentially high-impact risks of the company. The methodology is the result of a research program led by Neil Allan of Bath University in the UK and funded by the Department of Trade and Industry.

The two pieces of analysis are combined to identify scenarios that, in aggregate, suitably describe the company's exposure in these areas. These risks were not modeled stochastically, but were added as a load to the otherwise indicated EC.

IV.B.6 Presentation of Results

The results of an EC analysis conducted using the above methods discussed are presented using two risk metrics:

- **The 99% conditional tail expectation (CTE-99) on PVFP**
- **The CTE-99 on GPVL**

PVFP risk metric

The table in Figure IV.B-20 shows the PVFP for:

- **The baseline scenario (using best estimate assumptions)**
- **The "2,500 worst" scenarios by LOB**
- **The worst of the 1,000 scenarios run for each LOB and each risk factor**

■ Figure IV.B-20

Indicated Economic Capital Using CTE-99 Present Value of Future Profits

	Baseline	2,500 Worst	Difference from Baseline	Worst 1,000 for each risk factor
Individual Life	2,640	2,368	(273)	1,858
Individual Annuity	43	43	-	37
Disability Income	523	217	(306)	(482)
Group Health	773	393	(380)	48
Pensions	30	28	(2)	31
Variable Annuities	105	58	(47)	113
Subtotal	4,114	3,106	(1,007)	1,605
Credit Defaults	(380)	(668)	(289)	(1,170)
Total	3,734	2,438	(1,296)	436

The summary of the indicated required capital shown in Figure IV.B-21 indicates that the PVFP is greater than zero in all three scenarios. From this result, we can conclude that no EC is indicated, because EC is only required if the PVFP is less than zero under this matrix. The entire initial capital is redundant.

■ Figure IV.B-21

Summary of Indicated Economic Capital

	Baseline	2,500 Worst	Worst 1,000 for each risk factor
Insurance Risk in Lines of Business	4,114	3,106	1,605
Credit Defaults	(308)	(668)	(1,170)
Strategic and Operational Risk	(306)	(306)	(306)
Total Present Value of Profits	3,428	2,132	130
Indicated Economic Capital	-	-	-

GPVL risk metric

The table in Figure IV.B-22 shows the GPVL for:

- **The baseline scenario (using best estimate assumptions)**
- **The "2,500 worst" scenarios by LOB**

Figure IV.B-22

Indicated Economic Capital Using CTE-99
Greatest Present Value of Accumulated Losses

	Baseline	2,500 Worst
Individual Life	2,640	-
Individual Annuity	43	(3)
Disability Income	523	(60)
Group Health	773	(10)
Pensions	30	-
Variable Annuities	105	(39)
Subtotal	4,114	(113)
Credit Defaults	(380)	(960)
Total	3,734	(1,073)

The table in Figure IV.B-23 summarizes the indicated required capital when using this risk metric.

Figure IV.B-23

Summary of Indicated Economic Capital (GPVL Risk Metric)

	Baseline	2,500 Worst
Insurance Risk in Lines of Business	4,114	(113)
Credit Defaults	(308)	(960)
Strategic and Operational Risk	(306)	(306)
Total Present Value of Profits	3,428	(1,379)
Indicated Economic Capital	-	1,379

As with Figures IV.B-20 and IV.B-21, the results presented in the tables in Figures IV.B-22 and IV.B-23 assume each LOB is operated as a stand-alone company. Therefore, gains in one LOB cannot be used to offset losses in other LOBs. On a stand-alone basis, risk exists as indicated by the need for $1.4 billion in EC. But running the stochastic projections on an aggregate company basis yields a completely different result. Risks are completely mitigated by aggregation in this analysis as gains in some LOBs fully offset losses in other LOBs.

IV.B.6.a Calibration, Validation, and Review

As discussed in Section IV.B.3, we utilized a lengthy checking process. Existing projection models for each LOB were already established and validated. The purpose of this analysis was to add stochastic generators into the model to perform the EC analysis. For each LOB, we first completed a base case or best estimate projection using deterministic, fixed assumptions as our starting point. This projection was not allowed to vary. We then utilized the best estimate projection in each case to test and validate the stochastic generator.

Calibration

The stochastic models were calibrated based on historical experience as previously discussed. Nonetheless, it is important to note that while this analysis was a projection and the stochastic generators were only applied to the forecast, the initial projection and generators are tied to this experience. We performed one additional test to determine whether the projection trended forward from the valuation date as would be expected, thereby ensuring "dynamic" validation.

Validation

We validated the scenarios generated using expanded versions of the attached tables. In all cases, the means were compared to projected expected values based on deterministic projections. For equity and interest rate scenarios, we performed a review of the percentile distributions and individual scenarios by investment personnel at the company. Similar to Section IV.B.3, we graphed other scenarios to provide a visual representation of the projected scenarios and the projected variation from the mean over time.

For a specific generator, we compared the component of the projection affected by the generator to a base case. For example, projected best estimate death claims for Life LOB were compared to specific mortality scenarios, which were projected using the stochastic mortality generator. This comparison of death claims ensured that the projected death claims for the mortality scenario moved in a similar fashion to the base case death claims adjusted by the mortality for the specific scenario. We tested each component for the same reason.

As an additional test, we compared the mean projection across all 1,000 scenarios generated to the base case. We made this comparison for each independent risk assessment. Some variation was expected, but the deviation from the base was not material.

We performed additional tests, particularly on extreme scenarios, to ensure that results were plausible and appropriate for the scenario.

Peer review and checking

We implemented two kinds of review for the project. The first was a "bottom-up" approach in which individual inputs to the models and generators were reviewed and confirmed with the documentation prepared. The second "top-down" approach reviewed projected financial results and fluctuations in aggregate at various CTE levels for specific scenarios. The review occurred separately on the individual risk projections such as interest rate, mortality and morbidity, as well as for aggregated risk projections on scenarios with combined risks.

Table IV.B-1

				Summary of Stochastic Mortality Scenarios						
				Total Mortality Risk						
				Percentage Gross-up Applied to Mortality Input by Projection Year						
	Year 1	Year 2	Year 3	Year 4	Year 5	Year 6	Year 7	Year 8	Year 9	Year 10
Mean	0.49%	0.63%	0.77%	0.41%	0.98%	0.47%	0.46%	0.52%	0.63%	0.46%
Std Dev	2.65%	3.51%	9.49%	3.91%	11.88%	4.37%	4.67%	5.02%	8.13%	5.58%
Percentile Distribution										
0.0%	-4.39%	-7.10%	-8.47%	-10.82%	-11.21%	-12.81%	-14.49%	-15.49%	-16.48%	-17.95%
0.1%	-4.34%	-5.88%	-7.39%	-8.86%	-10.66%	-10.91%	-12.71%	-12.54%	-14.22%	-14.84%
0.5%	-3.94%	-5.48%	-6.60%	-7.95%	-7.93%	-9.61%	-10.48%	-10.85%	-12.50%	-12.91%
1.0%	-3.45%	-4.63%	-6.29%	-6.85%	-7.37%	-8.85%	-9.83%	-10.02%	-11.17%	-11.97%
5.0%	-2.26%	-3.24%	-4.12%	-4.61%	-5.36%	-6.01%	-6.54%	-7.11%	-7.79%	-8.22%
25.0%	-0.88%	-1.26%	-1.72%	-1.90%	-2.08%	-2.32%	-2.47%	-2.99%	-2.96%	-3.23%
50.0%	0.24%	0.27%	0.34%	0.10%	0.28%	0.30%	0.21%	0.48%	0.30%	0.42%
75.0%	1.38%	1.75%	2.14%	2.38%	2.57%	2.82%	3.07%	3.59%	3.85%	3.70%
90.0%	2.40%	3.36%	3.99%	4.45%	5.50%	5.71%	5.86%	6.35%	6.45%	7.32%
95.0%	3.47%	5.18%	5.27%	5.74%	7.48%	7.41%	8.03%	8.25%	8.66%	9.27%
99.0%	12.32%	14.00%	14.76%	9.35%	14.42%	13.50%	11.67%	12.12%	13.53%	13.61%
99.5%	18.71%	20.88%	19.67%	19.17%	28.45%	16.58%	18.68%	19.78%	20.19%	15.81%
99.9%	22.95%	32.64%	39.56%	35.10%	57.10%	22.00%	27.85%	30.95%	27.50%	30.51%
100.0%	25.04%	37.25%	277.67%	35.72%	345.37%	34.10%	29.12%	31.21%	197.77%	31.48%

Table IV.B-2

				Summary of Stochastic Mortality Scenarios						
				Base Mortality Risk						
				Percentage Gross-up Applied to Mortality Input by Projection Year						
	Year 1	Year 2	Year 3	Year 4	Year 5	Year 6	Year 7	Year 8	Year 9	Year 10
Mean	0.00%	0.00%	0.00%	0.00%	0.00%	0.00%	0.00%	0.00%	0.00%	0.00%
Std Dev	1.53%	2.09%	2.62%	3.03%	3.41%	3.77%	4.12%	4.47%	4.80%	5.14%
Percentile Distribution										
0.0%	-4.42%	-7.11%	-8.48%	-10.85%	-11.24%	-12.82%	-14.51%	-15.49%	-16.49%	-17.96%
0.1%	-4.40%	-6.02%	-7.40%	-8.86%	-10.88%	-10.93%	-12.76%	-12.67%	-14.27%	-14.86%
0.5%	-3.97%	-5.76%	-6.62%	-7.96%	-8.07%	-9.79%	-10.50%	-11.09%	-12.68%	-12.91%
1.0%	-3.49%	-5.07%	-6.31%	-7.13%	-7.46%	-8.86%	-9.86%	-10.23%	-11.64%	-11.99%
5.0%	-2.53%	-3.34%	-4.33%	-4.79%	-5.44%	-6.25%	-6.73%	-7.51%	-7.89%	-8.36%
25.0%	-1.03%	-1.38%	-1.86%	-2.02%	-2.34%	-2.43%	-2.68%	-3.15%	-3.12%	-3.46%
50.0%	0.04%	0.02%	0.09%	-0.06%	0.02%	-0.03%	-0.02%	0.13%	0.03%	0.17%
75.0%	0.99%	1.36%	1.76%	2.01%	2.11%	2.48%	2.79%	3.05%	3.32%	3.36%
90.0%	1.89%	2.74%	3.46%	4.01%	4.52%	4.94%	5.46%	5.52%	6.00%	6.40%
95.0%	2.47%	3.34%	4.33%	5.06%	6.03%	6.47%	6.94%	7.26%	7.62%	8.57%
99.0%	3.61%	4.81%	6.05%	6.88%	8.13%	8.91%	9.41%	10.38%	11.81%	11.79%
99.5%	4.13%	5.53%	6.52%	7.26%	8.82%	9.42%	10.37%	11.20%	12.38%	12.91%
99.9%	4.99%	6.59%	7.27%	8.17%	9.68%	10.59%	11.00%	12.09%	13.51%	13.77%
100.0%	5.77%	6.89%	8.37%	9.32%	9.80%	10.72%	11.47%	12.99%	14.21%	13.82%

Table IV.B-3

	Year 1	Year 2	Year 3	Year 4	Year 5	Year 6	Year 7	Year 8	Year 9	Year 10
Summary of Stochastic Mortality Scenarios										
Pandemic Mortality Risk										
Percentage Gross-up Applied to Mortality Input by Projection Year										
Mean	0.36%	0.47%	0.65%	0.35%	0.82%	0.37%	0.38%	0.38%	0.50%	0.33%
Std Dev	2.14%	2.33%	9.06%	2.39%	11.30%	1.84%	2.24%	1.99%	6.62%	2.00%
Percentile Distribution										
0.0%	0.00%	0.00%	0.00%	0.00%	0.00%	0.00%	0.00%	0.00%	0.00%	0.00%
0.1%	0.00%	0.00%	0.00%	0.00%	0.00%	0.00%	0.00%	0.00%	0.00%	0.00%
0.5%	0.00%	0.00%	0.00%	0.00%	0.00%	0.00%	0.00%	0.00%	0.00%	0.00%
1.0%	0.00%	0.00%	0.00%	0.00%	0.00%	0.00%	0.00%	0.00%	0.00%	0.00%
5.0%	0.00%	0.00%	0.00%	0.00%	0.00%	0.00%	0.00%	0.00%	0.00%	0.00%
25.0%	0.00%	0.00%	0.00%	0.00%	0.00%	0.00%	0.00%	0.00%	0.00%	0.00%
50.0%	0.00%	0.00%	0.00%	0.00%	0.00%	0.00%	0.00%	0.00%	0.00%	0.00%
75.0%	0.00%	0.00%	0.00%	0.00%	0.00%	0.00%	0.00%	0.00%	0.00%	0.00%
90.0%	0.00%	0.00%	0.00%	0.00%	0.00%	0.00%	0.00%	0.00%	0.00%	0.00%
95.0%	1.31%	2.07%	1.67%	1.16%	1.78%	1.76%	1.71%	1.94%	1.40%	1.25%
99.0%	8.72%	11.13%	11.15%	7.90%	10.76%	9.24%	10.37%	8.30%	6.80%	9.50%
99.5%	19.12%	14.46%	17.30%	13.00%	18.92%	13.32%	16.84%	12.55%	13.63%	15.44%
99.9%	24.89%	23.47%	36.23%	33.08%	55.07%	20.99%	32.17%	25.27%	30.79%	21.10%
100.0%	25.74%	38.08%	278.91%	33.15%	346.47%	21.11%	34.33%	27.30%	202.79%	33.40%

Table IV.B-4

	Year 1	Year 2	Year 3	Year 4	Year 5	Year 6	Year 7	Year 8	Year 9	Year 10
Summary of Stochastic Mortality Scenarios										
Terrorism Mortality Risk										
Percentage Gross-up Applied to Mortality Input by Projection Year										
Mean	0.13%	0.15%	0.12%	0.07%	0.16%	0.10%	0.09%	0.13%	0.12%	0.13%
Std Dev	0.92%	1.36%	1.35%	0.23%	1.55%	1.04%	0.45%	1.09%	0.87%	1.09%
Percentile Distribution										
0.0%	0.00%	0.00%	0.00%	0.00%	0.00%	0.00%	0.00%	0.00%	0.00%	0.00%
0.1%	0.00%	0.00%	0.00%	0.00%	0.00%	0.00%	0.00%	0.00%	0.00%	0.00%
0.5%	0.00%	0.00%	0.00%	0.00%	0.00%	0.00%	0.00%	0.00%	0.00%	0.00%
1.0%	0.00%	0.00%	0.00%	0.00%	0.00%	0.00%	0.00%	0.00%	0.00%	0.00%
5.0%	0.01%	0.00%	0.01%	0.00%	0.01%	0.01%	0.00%	0.01%	0.01%	0.01%
25.0%	0.01%	0.01%	0.01%	0.01%	0.01%	0.01%	0.01%	0.01%	0.01%	0.01%
50.0%	0.02%	0.02%	0.02%	0.02%	0.02%	0.02%	0.02%	0.02%	0.02%	0.02%
75.0%	0.04%	0.04%	0.03%	0.04%	0.04%	0.04%	0.04%	0.04%	0.03%	0.04%
90.0%	0.11%	0.11%	0.09%	0.10%	0.10%	0.11%	0.09%	0.10%	0.09%	0.10%
95.0%	0.30%	0.26%	0.21%	0.21%	0.21%	0.25%	0.18%	0.25%	0.21%	0.24%
99.0%	2.72%	2.01%	1.02%	1.11%	2.40%	1.03%	1.60%	2.27%	2.66%	1.96%
99.5%	3.86%	3.63%	2.70%	1.72%	5.22%	1.36%	3.25%	4.40%	3.03%	4.85%
99.9%	13.89%	19.93%	18.42%	2.73%	29.09%	10.92%	4.97%	9.81%	11.17%	11.49%
100.0%	19.76%	32.74%	37.47%	3.17%	35.17%	30.54%	8.74%	29.00%	21.46%	27.31%

IV.C Embedded Value for a Multi-national Multi-line Life Insurance Company

IV.C.1 Introduction

IV.C.1.a Brief History of Embedded Value Analysis

In the late '80s and early '90s, several companies started to disclose their traditional embedded value in addition to their annual financial accounts. Embedded value of a life insurance company is defined as the value of business in force (VIF) plus the adjusted net asset value (ANAV), where the VIF in the traditional embedded value (TEV) is equal to the present value of future profits (PVFP) minus the cost of solvency (COS).

The TEV figures of different companies were very hard to compare because every company used its own methods and assumptions and the disclosures were not sufficient to understand the differences. Also, the TEV was based on only one deterministic scenario where spreads on equity and bonds were capitalized. By using only one deterministic scenario the uncertainty of future market developments were not taken into account. Capitalizing spreads on equity leads to a higher embedded value when a company chooses a more aggressive asset mix without reflecting the actual risk.

To improve the quality of embedded value reports and to make them more comparable among different insurance companies, the European Insurance CFO Forum published European Embedded Value (EEV) principles and guidance in May 2004. According to the CFO Forum website, "The European Insurance CFO Forum ('CFO Forum') is a high-level discussion group formed and attended by the Chief Financial Officers of major European listed, and some non-listed, insurance companies. Its aim is to influence the development of financial reporting, value based reporting, and related regulatory developments for insurance enterprises on behalf of its members, who represent a significant part of the European insurance industry. The CFO Forum was created in 2002." CFO Forum documents related to Embedded Value can be found at the CFO Forum website (http://www.cfoforum.nl/embedded_value.html) and include:

- **MCEV Principles and Guidance**
- **MCEV Basis for Conclusions**
- **EEV Principles**
- **EEV Basis for Conclusions**
- **EEV Disclosures and Sensitivities**

The objective of the EEV principles was to provide greater guidance on embedded value methodologies for the members of the CFO Forum and other insurance companies. The guidance, which is subject to evolution over time, included definitions of the business covered, high-level descriptions of the methodology to be used, requirements for assumptions, and disclosure guidance. Very importantly, it prescribed that allowance should be made for the time value of options and guarantees (TVOG). In the EEV, the VIF is defined as:

- **Present value of future profits (PVFP)**
- **-/- cost of target capital (COC)**
- **-/- time value of options and guarantees (TVOG)**

As this definition shows, in the EEV the time value of options and guarantees is taken into account in the valuations. Another difference between TEV and EEV is that the required capital for EEV is based on internal targets for required capital, while in TEV the required capital according to Solvency I is used.

Early adopters of EEV generally used a "traditional" EEV methodology, which means that they were using "real world" assumptions that are not consistent with market prices. A number of the later EEV publishers used different economic assumptions that were stated to be "market-consistent." As the EEV principles were not written with market-consistent calculations in mind, there are gaps in a number of significant areas. Companies have adopted a range of different approaches, which has made the EEV disclosures still hard to compare.

On June 4, 2008, the CFO Forum presented a Market-consistent Embedded Value (MCEV) methodology in new MCEV guidelines. The CFO Forum believes that the adoption of the MCEV principles will deliver a shareholder's perspective on value, making the present value of future cash flows available to the shareholder, adjusted for the risks of those cash flows, consistent with valuations methods used in the financial markets. To value cash flows in a market-consistent way, two approaches are proposed. Either both asset returns and discount rates are equal to reference rates, gross of tax, and investment management expenses (certainty equivalent approach), or asset returns are based on real-world assumptions and discounted by using deflators reflecting the risk in the cash flows. Both methods have to result in a market-consistent valuation. In the MCEV principles, the VIF is defined as:

- **Present value of future profits (PVFP)**
- **-/- frictional cost of capital (FCOC)**
- **-/- time value of options and guarantees (TVOG)**
- **-/- cost of residual non-hedgeable risks (CNHR)**

In the TEV and the EEV, the cost of capital reflected the difference between the net return that the company expected to realize on the assets backing the required capital and the risk discount rate used for discounting. Because in the MCEV the investment returns and the risk discount rates are both based on the risk-free rate, the cost of capital only reflects the taxation and the investment expenses.

In MCEV an allowance should be made for the cost of non-hedgeable financial and non-financial risks not already allowed for in the TVOG or the PVFP. The cost of residual non-hedgeable risks (financial and non-financial) will be a result of asymmetries in the impact on the risks on shareholder value or risks that are not allowed for in the TVOG or PVFP – for example, operational risk. The CNHR should be presented as an equivalent cost of capital charge, such that the present value of charges on the residual non-hedgeable risk-based capital equals the cost of residual non-hedgeable risks. This means that a calculation should be made of the residual non-hedgeable risk-based capital. This risk-based capital should be calculated by using a model that projects the profits and losses arising from the residual non-hedgeable risks of using approximations based on appropriate shock scenarios. The risk-based capital should be consistent with a 99.5% confidence level over a one-year time horizon.

IV.C.1.b Time Value of Options and Guarantees

As described above, in the EEV and the MCEV an allowance should be made for the time value of options and guarantees. The PVFP calculation is based on a single (base) economic scenario. However, a single scenario cannot appropriately allow for the effect of certain product features. If an option or guarantee affects shareholder cash flows in the base scenario, the impact is included in the PVFP and is referred to as the intrinsic value of the option or guarantee. However, future investment returns are uncertain and the actual impact on shareholder profits may be higher or lower. The value of in-force business needs to be adjusted for the impact of the range of potential future outcomes, i.e., the time value of the option or guarantee. When cash flows do not develop linearly with market movements a product has an option or a guarantee with a time value. Examples of options and guarantees are:

- **Profit-sharing options**

- **Unit-linked guarantees**

- **Policyholder options (e.g., asymmetric lapse behaviour)**

- **Minimum interest rate guarantees**

Because of the complexity of options and guarantees in insurance liabilities it is very hard to define closed formulas for the calculation of the option or guarantee value. Therefore, most options and guarantees are valued by using stochastic modeling techniques. In EEV and MCEV, the time value of options or guarantees is defined as the difference between the intrinsic value (the value already taken into account in the PVFP) and the total stochastic value.

Stochastic modeling typically involves projecting the future cash flows of the business under thousands of economic scenarios that are representative of the possible future outcomes for market variables such as interest rates and equity returns. Under a market-consistent approach, the economic scenarios generated reflect the market's tendency towards risk aversion.

Allowance should also be made, where appropriate, for the effect of management and/or policyholder actions in different economic conditions on future assumptions such as asset mix, bonus rates, and surrender rates.

According to G15.3 of the MCEV principles, volatility assumptions should be based on the most recently available information as at the valuation date. Where there are concerns over the depth or liquidity of the market or if the market displayed unusual characteristics as at the valuation date then less recently observed measures and expert opinion should be considered.

IV.C.1.c Balance Sheet Approach

According to the MCEV principles, it is also allowed to use an approach to calculating MCEV based on a balance sheet presentation, where all components of the balance sheet are valued on a market-consistent basis, assets at market value and liabilities with market-consistent techniques. The assets exceeding the liabilities are equal to the MCEV. Companies that choose to use the balance sheet approach need to materially produce the same results and the MCEV should be subdivided into the required constituents, meaning the VIF, FCOC, TVOG, and CNHR. To calculate the MCEV in a balance sheet approach, the following steps have to be taken:

1. Split the asset side of the balance sheet in components where an observable market value is available and where no market value is observable. The majority of the assets have a market value. Analyze the remaining part of the assets and decide if a mark-to-market solution is available or if the book value is equal to the market value.

2. Split the liability side of the balance sheet into shareholder equity, technical provisions, and a remaining part. Analyze the remaining part of the liabilities and decide if a mark-to-market solution is available or if the book value is equal to the market value.

3. Calculate the certainty equivalent value of liabilities (CEVL).

4. Calculate the TVOG, CNHR, and FCOC.

5. Calculate the MCEV components as follows:

    VIF = Statutory technical liabilities – CNHR – TVOG – CEVL – FCOC
    Free capital = Stat cap – Required cap

Figure IV.C-1 gives a schematic presentation of the balance sheet approach.

Figure IV.C-1

Balance Sheet Approach

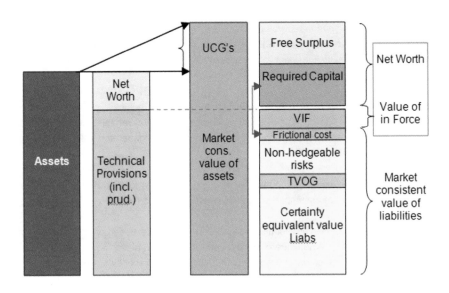

IV.C.2 Current Embedded Value Analysis

To get an impression of the different methods used in the market we studied the embedded value reports per end of year 2008 of the following four CFO Forum members:

- **Company A**
- **Company B**
- **Company C**
- **Company D**

Companies A and B reported on an MCEV basis; Companies C and D, reported on an EEV basis, where Company C already uses a market-consistent methodology. In this section, we will compare the stochastic models and assumptions that are used by the four companies. Also we will set out the embedded value results per company per end of year 2008.

IV.C.2.a Stochastic Models per Company

Company A
- In the UK, Europe, and North America, swap rates are generated by the LIBOR market model (LMM), which projects a full swap curve at monthly intervals. Forward rates are assumed to have a lognormal distribution that guarantees non-negative interest rates.
- In The Netherlands, yield curves are based on De Nederlandsche Bank (DNB) yield curve data. The interest rate model used is a short rate G2++ model.
- The equity model is a Heston model.
- Dynamic policyholder behaviour and management actions are taken into account.

Company B
- Stochastic economic scenarios are generated centrally by an application provided by Barrie & Hibbert.
- For modeling fixed-income stochastic scenarios, the extended two-factor Black-Karasinski model is used. For fixed-income instruments, parameters are fitted to at-the-money swaption implied volatilities.
- A range of equity indices is considered. For modeling equity and real estate returns, a short-rate excess model is used to generate returns from fixed-income dynamics of the economy.
- Dynamic policyholder behaviour and management actions are taken into account.

Company C
- The risk-neutral economic scenarios are constructed using a proprietary economic scenario generator developed by Barrie & Hibbert.
- A number of asset classes and economic assumptions are modeled stochastically. This includes equity, bond yields, credit spreads, credit defaults, property, foreign exchange, inflation, and GDP.
- Dynamic policyholder behaviour and management actions are taken into account.

Company D
- The Netherlands: vector autoregressive (VAR) with lagged variables for the interest rates, equity, and real estate returns.
- United States: modified lognormal model for interest.
- Japan: one-factor realistic interest rate generator in discrete time with mean reversion for interest rates and geometric Brownian motion for equity.
- South Korea: risk-neutral Hull-White model one-year forward rate.
- Dynamic policyholder behaviour and management actions are taken into account.

IV.C.2.b Economic Assumptions per Company

Company A
- The option volatilities are DJ Euro Stoxx 50 quotes taken from Bloomberg Analytics for the end of August 2008.
- The model considers an equity volatility surface in the market and covers strike levels between 0.8 and 1.2.
- For the UK and The Netherlands, model property implied volatility is 15% for Dec. 31, 2008.

Company B

- Assumptions for correlations among asset classes have been set based on historical data.

- Stochastic scenarios are based on swap rates as of Dec. 31, 2008.

- Implied volatilities are based on Sept. 30, 2008.

- Equity volatilities are taken from implied volatilities of long-term equity options at-the-money, targeted to the longest maturity option available (10 years).

- Real estate volatility is assumed to be 15% for all economies.

- To show the impact of asset mixes and inter-economy relations, correlation assumptions were estimated from historical market data.

Company C

- The economic scenarios have been calibrated using reference rates based on swaps yield curves plus a premium of 50bps and 100bps for, respectively, European and non-European entities (except Japan).

- For equity volatilities, the implied volatilities are the average daily at-the-money forward volatility observed over 2008.

- In the current market environment where there are some concerns over liquidity and unusual activity, Company C's swaption implied volatilities are the average daily at-the-money forward volatility observed during 2008.

- In addition, Company C also models credit spreads reflecting levels observed on credit defaults swaps (CDS) rather than on corporate bonds, also averaged over 12 months.

- The correlation of equity returns, inflation, bond yields, and economies has been set with reference to historical market data.

Company D

- The stochastic calculations of the time value of options and guarantees have been performed by business units using a range of real-world economic scenario generators.

- The returns have been calibrated to reflect on average the new money interest rate assumptions in the base calculation.

- Volatilities and correlations are derived from historical observations.

IV.C.2.c Results per Company

At end of year 2008 the four companies had the following embedded values. Both Company C and Company D are reporting not according to MCEV principles, but to EEV principles. Company D therefore does not calculate a cost of non-hedgeable risks. Company C, on the other hand, calculates a cost of non-financial risk as part of the cost of capital, which is comparable to the cost of non-hedgeable risks under MCEV.

The table in Figure IV.C-2 shows that the TVOG as a percentage of the PVFP differs very much among the different companies.

■ Figure IV.C-2

Company TVOG as Percentage of PVFP

	A	B	C	D
Present Value Future Profits	7.066	9.332	19.119	14.299
Frictional Cost of Capital	-726	-1.366	-2.395	-2.745
Cost of Non-hedgeable Risk	-681	-1.009		
Time Value of Options and Guarantees	-1.066	-4.296	-4.264	-741
VIF	**4.593**	**2.661**	**12.460**	**10.813**
Free Capital	1.348	-63	-1.053	1.966
Required Capital	8.148	9.946	15.803	10.304
MCEV / EEV	**14.089**	**12.544**	**27.210**	**23.083**
TVOG / PVFP	**15%**	**46%**	**22%**	**5%**

IV.C.3 Sample Embedded Value Analysis for a Single Product of a Life Insurance Company

IV.C.3.a Introduction

To get a good understanding of the impact of the time value of options and guarantees (TVOG) on the MCEV, we chose to work out a sample analysis of one single product of a life insurance company. By working out an example of one product, the sensitivity of the TVOG to changes in the market environment is easier to understand.

The product we chose is a universal life product with a guaranteed interest rate of 2.5% per year with profit-sharing based on the return of the assets that are allocated to this product. The profit-sharing for the product is defined as follows:

$$90\% * (\text{return for profit sharing} - 2.5\% - 0.75\%) \tag{IV.C-1}$$

The return for profit-sharing is based on the return on the assets that are allocated to this product, where the return on equity for profit-sharing is maximized to 20%. The management feels that outperformance of the company should not be paid out totally to the policyholder and therefore maximizes the return. At the end of each calendar year the liability increases with the profit-sharing percentage calculated using Equation IV.C-1. For this product, the company invests 92% of the liability in one-year bonds and the other 8% in equity (Euro Stoxx).

At the end of year 2008, the portfolio consists of 12,000 policies with:

- **An average annual premium of €900**
- **An average sum assured of €18K**
- **An average remaining term of 15 years**
- **A total liability of €592M**

IV.C.3.b Economic Scenario Generator and Assumptions

To generate the economic scenarios we used the Black-Scholes-Hull-White model. We used the following assumptions:

Equity volatilities	28.1% (Sept. 30, 2008)
Interest rate volatilities	0.6% (Sept. 30, 2008)
Risk-free rate	Swap yield curve Dec. 31, 2008, De Nederlandsche Bank
Spread on equity real-world	3%
Correlation one-year bond/Euro Stoxx	0.35
Mean reversion rate	1.81%

IV.C.3.c Certainty Equivalent Present Value of Future Profits

To calculate the MCEV of this product, we first calculated the certainty equivalent (CE) PVFP using the swap yield curve for asset returns as well as for discounting. This calculation led to the following CE PVFP (amounts in € millions):

PVF Mortality result	1.6
PVF Surrender result	1.0
PVF Expense result	-4.8
PVF Interest result	44.9
PVF Tax	10.9
CE PVF Profits	**31.8**

As mentioned above, the intrinsic value of the profit-sharing option is already taken into account in the CE PVFP, in this case in the PVF Interest result. The graph in Figure IV.C-3 shows the development of the interest result for the CE calculation as well as the swap forward rates used for this calculation. The graph shows that the forward rates are lower than 2.5% starting from 2030. As a result of this low interest rate, the impact on interest becomes negative, which means that the interest guarantee of 2.5% is in-the-money and therefore has an intrinsic value.

Figure IV.C-3

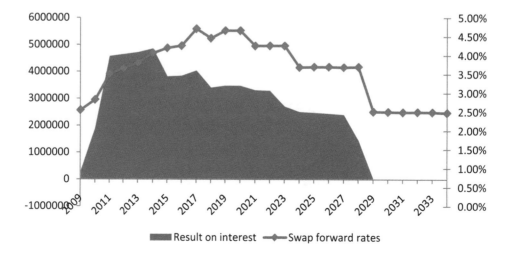

IV.C.3.d Time Value of Options and Guarantees

To calculate the time value of the profit-sharing option we calculated the PVFP for 1,000 real-world scenarios with deflators and for 1,000 risk-neutral scenarios. The graph in Figure IV.C-4 shows the distributions of both calculations. The TVOG should be calculated as the difference between the mean of the scenarios and the CE PVFP.

Figure IV.C-4

Distributions of Mean and CE PVFP

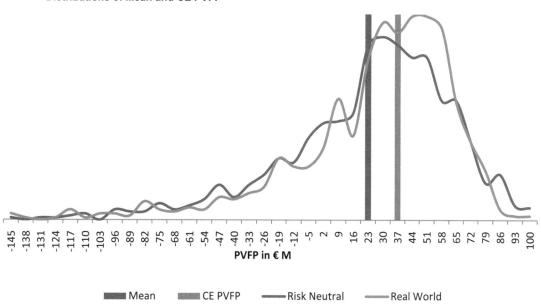

As can be seen from Figure IV.C-4, the means of both methods are equal to €21.7M and lead to a TVOG of (31.9 – 21.7 =) €10.2M.

IV.C.3.e Sensitivities

According to the MCEV principles, the following interest rates and asset sensitivities have to be disclosed in an MCEV report, and also have impact on the TVOG:

- **100 basis point pa change in the interest rate environment**
- **25% increase in equity/property implied volatilities at the valuation date**
- **25% increase in swaption implied volatilities at the valuation date**

The table in Figure IV.C-5 shows the CE PVFP and the TVOG for the mentioned sensitivities.

■ **Figure IV.C-5**

CE PVFP and TVOG for Sensitivities

	CE PVFP	TVOG
Base run	**31.8**	**10.2**
Swap yield curve + 100 Bp	41.9	-1.5
Swap yield curve - 100 Bp	7.5	16.5
25% increase in equity volatilities	31.8	8.8
25% increase in swaption implied volatilities	31.8	12.4

The table in Figure IV.C-5 shows that the MCEV results are very sensitive to changes in the swap yield curve. A parallel shift of the curve with 1% even results in a negative TVOG because the positive effect of high returns (10% of the extra return above the guarantee and equity return above 20% is for the insurer) outweighs the cost of the 2.5% interest guarantee. The graph in Figure IV.C-6 shows the distributions of the sensitivities for a parallel shift in the swap yield curve of 1%.

■ **Figure IV.C-6**

Distribution of Sensitivities

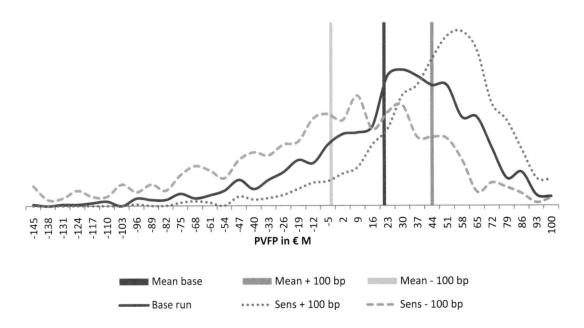

To see how sensitive the TVOG is to more extreme changes in the market environment, we calculated the TVOG for more possible shifts in the swap curve.

Figure IV.C-7

TVOG at different swap curves

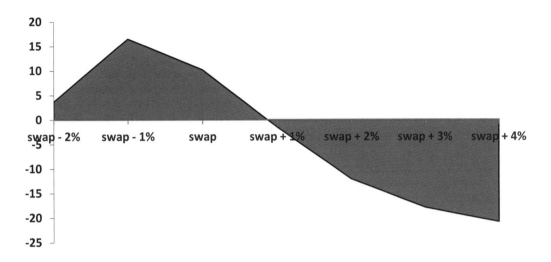

Because in this example we did not take into account any policyholder actions or management actions, except for the maximization of the return on equity, the TVOG is very sensitive to changes in the market and will become very negative in markets with a high swap curve. This negative value shows the upwards potential for the insurer that is due to the maximization of the equity return to 20%. Actually, the insurer has an option now, instead of the policyholder. In reality, management will change the product in a changing economic environment, because no policyholder will buy this product when the swap rates increase significantly. Possible management actions are:

- **Make guaranteed interest rate for future premiums dependent on market interest rates**

- **Increase or remove the maximum on equity return for profit-sharing**

The graph in Figure IV.C-7 also shows that the time value is at its maximum value when the swap curve decreases with 1%. In this scenario, the average swap forward rate is very near to the interest rate guarantee of 2.5%, which results in a high time value. The time value is at its maximum when the swap forward rates are equal to the interest rate guarantee.

IV.C.3.f Review

For the auditor, reviewing the TVOG of the MCEV is quite difficult. As the graph in Figure IV.C-7 shows, the TVOG is very sensitive to changes in the interest rates. For the sample product in this case study, the movement of the TVOG is more or less predictable based on the level of the guaranteed interest rates and the market rates. If, as in reality, more products have an option or a guarantee, with different methods of profit-sharing and different levels of guaranteed interest rates, the TVOG becomes much less predictable.

Reviewers tend to use the sensitivity calculations of the year before to judge the plausibility of the outcomes of the TVOG of the reporting year.

IV.C.4 Future Embedded Value Analyses: Non-financial Stochastic Calculations?

As mentioned above, a part of the VIF in the MCEV consists of the cost for residual non-hedgeable risks (CNHR). The MCEV principles prescribe that the risk-based capital that is the basis for this CNHR should be based on a 99.5% confidence level. For the calculation of this 99.5% confidence interval one can choose to do single stress tests or stochastic calculations. Companies that have an internal risk-based capital model will calculate the non-hedgeable risk-based capital using stochastic techniques also for non-financial risks.

For the calculation of the other items of the VIF, we do not expect any additional stochastic calculations to be done. The only development that can be made is in the level of management actions that will be modeled dependent on the market interest rates. For example, in a very bad economic environment, insurers tend to cut back on their expenses. Taking these management actions into account in the calculations will also make the expenses stochastic, but only as a result of the dependency on the economic environment.

Other stochastic calculations, such as mortality or lapses, will not lead to different outcomes, because the average will be equal to the outcome of the average scenario and will therefore not lead to a TVOG.

IV.D Unpaid Claim Variability for a Multi-line Non-life Insurance Company

IV.D.1 Introduction

In many countries, the financial impact of previously written insurance policies is split among the estimated cost of fulfilling the unexpired portion of the insurance contracts (the unearned premium), the estimated value of the claims, and the estimated costs associated with settling those claims on the balance sheet. Accompanying exhibits show how the estimates relate to historical time periods in their development of loss.

Loss liabilities and claim provisions are among the many terms used in different countries to describe the claim cost liabilities in the financial statements. This case study, however, will use the more generic term of "unpaid claim estimates," which includes both the value of the claims and the associated settlement costs, unless noted otherwise.

While the best estimate of the historical liability can be a huge amount, it is generally only shown as a single point or deterministic estimate in financial statements. In order to use this value in an EC model, it is necessary to estimate the distribution of possible outcomes, which will be referred to as claim variability. The process of estimating the variability of the historical claims also allows us to estimate the variability of the future claims and cash flows, and from this analysis, we will be able to quantify the three major components of insurance risk:

- **Unpaid claim risk (for claims that have already occurred)**

- **Pricing risk (for claims that will occur in upcoming financial periods)**

- **Cash flow risk (for the loss of investment income when actual cash flows exceed expectations)**

The variations in the projected cash flows can also be used to analyze one of the major financial risks – asset/liability matching risk – or, more precisely, the effects of mismatching cash inflows and outflows.

The distributions of possible outcomes estimated can then be used to quantify insurance and financial risk components directly. The simulated outputs can also be used as inputs to a larger EC model or to parameterize an EC model that will simulate possible outcomes within the model. As part of this case study, we will illustrate the calculation of some insurance risk components. The next case study will then illustrate the use of the distributions as part of a larger EC model.

IV.D.1.a Model Selection

As discussed in Sections II.C and II.D, there are a wide variety of non-life models that can be used to estimate the claim variability, ranging from individual claim to aggregate claim models. The specific type of claim variability model to be used as building block of an EC model will depend on the types of data available, user familiarity, and available software, among other factors. As important as these criteria are for model selection, they are secondary to the way in which the model output will be used in the EC model.

For example, if the EC model is to be used to analyze excess of loss or facultative reinsurance, then models based on individual claim data will be preferred. The level of detail required in the EC model will determine the types of models to consider for analyzing claim variability. For example, changes in the estimate of remaining unpaid claims, given possible future outcomes, is critical for determining whether a company can remain technically solvent (and be allowed to stay in business) at various points in the interim, even if it is expected to stay solvent in the long run.

In turn, the types of models and the level of detail being considered will usually cause the modeler to seek data sources other than published financial data in order to build the type of claim variability model needed.[34]

Once the model selection process is completed, the data will then need to be analyzed and parameterized to ensure that the distributions of possible outcomes are reasonable. A variety of criteria can be used to test underlying model assumptions against the data and to test the model output to determine whether the model assumptions and results are reasonable. One of the key goals in the process is to make sure each model iteration is a plausible outcome. If any outcome seems implausible, then it must be determined whether the outcome should be removed, i.e., constrained from the model, or if refitting the model would provide better results. Care must be exercised not to remove improbable (plausible but unlikely) outcomes, because these tail events are a critical part of the distribution of possible outcomes.[35]

Model parameterization often involves multiple steps, because the modeler will generally want to use components of more than one model in an attempt to overcome the oversimplification inherent in any one model and to more accurately reflect the complex reality under analysis. Actuarial (and statistical) theory has long recognized that blending the best features of multiple models will generally result in a better overall model and helps to address model risk.

Once the results from multiple models have been combined or credibility weighted into a single distribution of possible outcomes for each business segment, the modeler will then correlate the results in an aggregate distribution for the entire business unit. This step may also involve sub-units based on management or legal organizations within the entire business unit. The calculation of the correlation coefficients may vary depending on which models are used, but there are three general areas in which correlation can be applied.

First, correlation may occur among variables of different business segments. For example, inflation parameters may be correlated in different segments, or claims in multiple business segments may be affected by contagion effects, such as a new legal precedence or a catastrophe. Since we are ignoring catastrophes and have not correlated parameters in this case study we are not focusing on this type of correlation.

Correlation can also occur among the random incremental payments for claims that have previously occurred by business segment. For this type of correlation, we are concerned with whether the historical incremental claims payments for each business segment are correlated with each of the other business segments. This is relatively easy to measure and is illustrated when we discuss aggregation later in this case study.

Finally, correlation may occur among the ultimate loss ratios by business segment. This phenomenon can also be thought of as price adequacy correlation related to underwriting cycles. As with the estimation of model parameters, the estimation of correlation coefficients is not an exact science, so testing different correlation assumption scenarios is prudent in order to gain insight into the sensitivity of these assumptions.

---

[34] The other data sources are likely to be the raw data underlying the financial statements or subgroups of the financial data aligned with the EC modeling goals rather than the financial reporting goals. No matter the source, the data should still tie to the financial statements.

[35] For some models the most likely implausible outcomes are negative amounts when only positive amounts are possible (e.g., no recoveries).

IV.D.1.b Bootstrap Modeling

While there are many models from which to choose, this case study uses the bootstrap model for the following three reasons:

First, setting up the model involves aggregate loss triangles of both paid and incurred losses and volume weighted age-to-age factors (i.e., the chain ladder method), which should be familiar to most people.[36] The use of aggregate triangle data means the required data should be readily available in most cases and perhaps even readily tied to published financial statements.

Second, while the bootstrap model has commonly understood components, it also has components sophisticated enough to produce robust distribution estimates of possible outcomes. Even for users with a modest mathematical background, the sophisticated components are straightforward and easy to learn. A more advanced understanding of the theory behind the model requires a high level of statistics and is, therefore, beyond the scope of this case study.[37]

Third, even though the framework of the bootstrap model is based on the chain ladder method, other methods can also be used with this model, thus giving us multiple models that can be credibly weighed into a more robust distribution, rather than one model derived from another approach.

Our discussion of the mechanics will focus only on the paid "chain ladder" model, but this case study also illustrates the results from both paid and incurred Chain Ladder, Bornhuetter-Ferguson, and Cape Cod methods for a total of six different models. The basic chain ladder model is illustrated in Appendix D.1.b; and the Excel file "Section IV.D - Bootstrap Model.xls" (which can be found on the IAA website www.actuaries.org/stochastic) may also be referenced for a more comprehensive understanding of the model.

Our goal in using an approach both familiar and sophisticated is to illustrate the concepts in the underlying model in enough detail so that the techniques in this example may not only be understood, but also applied to other types of models as needed.

IV.D.2 Building a Model

Sample Insurance Company (SIC) is a non-life insurer that writes coverage in three primary segments: property, casualty one, and casualty two lines.[38] SIC has been operating with a stable underwriting and claim handling staff for many years and has had only modest growth in exposures over the past 10 years. While the property exposures are subject to weather-related claims, the exposures are geographically diverse and not subject to major catastrophes.

The financial data includes paid and incurred loss development triangles by accident year, as well as earned premiums and earned exposures by calendar year. For simplicity, the loss data contains all claim handling expenses in addition to the value of the claims. The data for all three segments is contained in Exhibit IV.D-1, but the remainder of this section will focus only on the casualty one business.

---

[36] The volume weighted age-to-age factors are derived from a generalized linear model (GLM) using the Over-dispersed Poisson (ODP) assumption, but understanding that the theoretical background is not a prerequisite for using the factors. Many papers refer to this as the ODP Bootstrap model.

[37] The references contain several papers that provide a deeper understanding of the theory.

[38] The fundamental process of modeling a business segment only requires one segment to illustrate, but three are used to illustrate the correlation concepts later in the case study. We will only focus on the non-life one segment for most of the model building discussion, but these processes can be extended to any number of segments in practice.

IV.D.2.a Diagnostic Testing

Like all models and methods, the quality of a bootstrap model depends on the quality of the assumptions. This point cannot be overemphasized because the results of any simulation model are only as good as the model used in the simulation process. If the model does not "fit" the data, then the results of the simulation may not be a good estimate of the distribution of possible outcomes.

Another advantage of the bootstrap model is that it can be "tailored" to some of the statistical features found in the data under analysis. Thus, a variety of diagnostic tools can be used to help us judge the quality of those assumptions and to change or adjust the parameters of the model, depending on the statistical features we find in the data. In this sense, the diagnostic tools are used to find the model(s) providing the best fit to the data.

The diagnostic tests are designed to either test various assumptions in the model, to gauge the quality of the model fit, or to help guide the adjustment of model parameters. Moreover, these tests are relative in nature in that test results from one set of model parameters can be compared to those of another. From this comparison, a modeler may then be able to "improve" the fit of the model.

The model will generally provide a distribution with any set of parameters. The immediate question is: Which set of model parameters will yield simulations that are most realistic and most consistent with the statistical features found in the data (or believed to be in the data)?

Some diagnostic measures also include statistical tests, which can be viewed as a type of pass/fail test for some aspects of the model assumptions. It is important to keep in mind that a "fail" result for a given test does not generally invalidate the entire model, but rather, it signals the possibility that improvements can be made to the model (or the model parameterization).

Residual graphs

The bootstrap model relies on fitting a model to the company's data triangle. The residuals – the differences between the fitted and actual data – are used to create sample triangles. While the bootstrap model does not require a specific type of distribution for the residuals, it is nevertheless important that all residuals are independent and identically distributed. At a minimum, they must share a common mean and standard deviation. This requirement is important, because residuals will be sampled and used to replace data during the simulations.

Graphs of the residuals are a useful diagnostic test when reviewing the data to ensure that they are, indeed, independent and identically distributed. Residuals can be compared to the predicted or actual values by development period, accident period, and calendar period.[39] Let us turn to the residual data plotted in the graphs in Figure IV.D-1, which include a trend line (pink line) linking the averages for each period in addition to the plotted residual points (blue dots) in the development, accident, and calendar graphs.

At first glance, the residuals in the graphs appear reasonably random, indicating that the model is a reasonably good fit of the data. But the graphs may also reveal potential features in the data that, once analyzed, may be used to improve model fit.

---

[39] Note that for each of these four graphs the same residuals are being plotted. In other words, this is four different views of the same data.

■ Figure IV.D-1

Residual Graphs Prior to Heteroscedasticity Adjustment

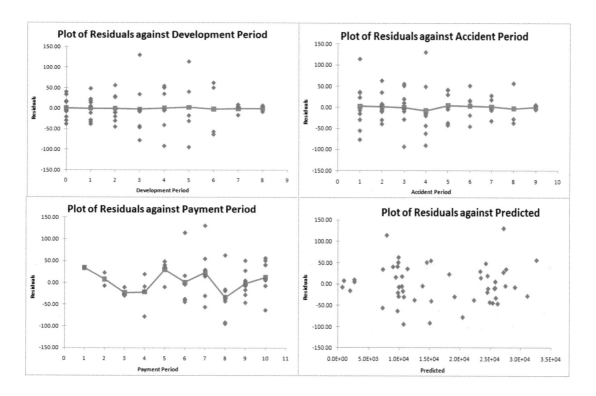

The graphs do not indicate any issues with the trends, but the development period graph reveals a common issue associated with insurance triangle data. From the upper left graph it can be observed that the range of the residuals in the first three periods differs from that of the middle four or the last two periods. This finding indicates that the residuals in the three different subgroups may have three separate standard deviations. If this were the case, it would statistically be referred to as *heteroscedasticity*.[40]

Adjustments for this heteroscedasticity can be made with the bootstrap model that allow us to identify groups of development periods and then adjust the residuals to a common standard deviation value. While a set of tools for adding parameters for the groups of development periods is beyond the scope of this case study, graphs of the standard deviation and range relativities can be used to help visualize the proper groupings of periods. Pre-adjusted relativities are displayed in Figure IV.D-2 for the residuals shown in Figure IV.D-1.

---

[40] While some papers on bootstrap modeling have discussed whether the mean of the residuals should be zero or not, this requirement is usually not as important a consideration as the standard deviations and adjustment for heteroscedasticity. Even after adjusting for heteroscedasticity, the mean of the residuals will usually not equal zero.

▌ **Figure IV.D-2**

Residual Relativities Prior to Heteroscedasticity Adjustment

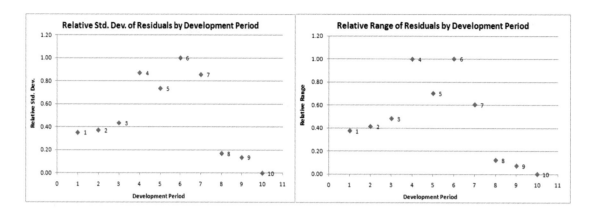

The relativities illustrated in Figure IV.D-2 appear to confirm that the residuals in the first three periods are not the same as those in the middle four or the last two, but further testing is required to determine the optimal groups. It can be performed using the other diagnostic tests noted below.[41]

The residual plots in Figure IV.D-3 are developed from the same data model after the first three groups and the seventh and last two development periods, respectively, were separately adjusted. This grouping led to better results in the other tests described below versus the results of other tested groupings.[42]

A comparison of the residual plots in Figures IV.D-1 and IV.D-3 shows that the general "shape" of the residuals has not changed and the "randomness" is still consistent. Now, however, the residuals appear to exhibit the same standard deviation (or homoscedasticity).[43] A comparison of the residual relativities in Figures IV.D-2 and IV.D-4 illustrates that the relativities are also more consistent.

---

[41] As a technical note, the later development periods have fewer observations so it is not clear whether the apparently lower standard deviation is statistically relevant.

[42] The results of adjusting for and testing different heteroscedasticity groups are illustrated here, but they are beyond the scope of the companion Excel files.

[43] While not illustrated in the companion Excel file, during the simulation process the residuals would actually need to reflect their original heteroscedastic groups to ensure that the simulation process produces sample triangles that exhibit the same statistical properties as the original data. This could be done by sampling only within each group or by adjusting all residuals back to the relative standard deviation within each group (i.e., unwinding the adjustment during the simulation process).

■ Figure IV.D-3

Residual Graphs After Heteroscedasticity Adjustment

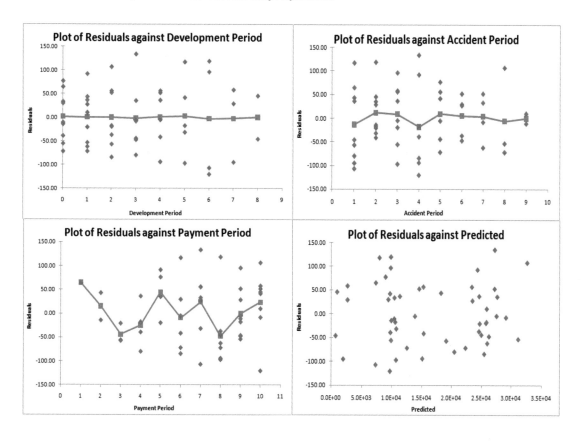

■ Figure IV.D-4

Residual Relativities After Heteroscedasticity Adjustment

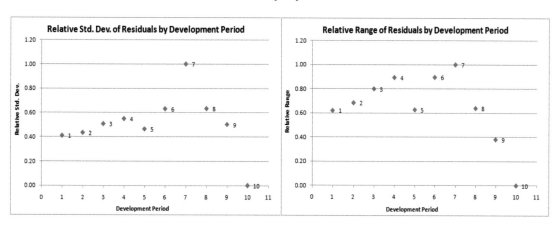

Normality test

While the bootstrap model does not depend on the residuals being normally distributed, determining whether residuals are derived from a normal distribution is still a useful test for comparing parameter sets and for gauging the skewness of the residuals. This test uses both graphs and calculated test values. Let us start with the graphs in Figure IV.D-5 for the same heteroscedasticity groups used earlier.

▌ **Figure IV.D-5**

Normality Plots Prior to and After Heteroscedasticity Adjustment

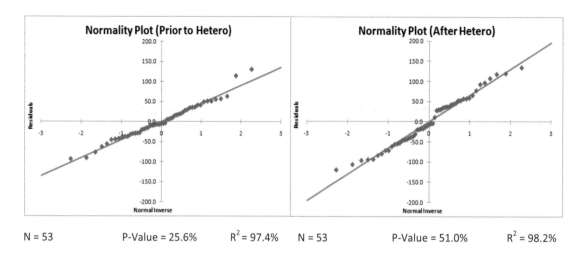

| N = 53 | P-Value = 25.6% | R^2 = 97.4% | N = 53 | P-Value = 51.0% | R^2 = 98.2% |

Even before the heteroscedasticity (hetero) adjustment, the normality plot looks quite good in that the data points are tightly distributed around the diagonal line. The $p\text{-}value$, which can be thought of as a statistical pass-fail test for normality, came in at 25.6%, far exceeding the value of 5.0%, generally considered a "passing" score of the normality test. It does not, however, indicate whether the bootstrap model passes or fails.[44] Also shown with the graphs in Figure IV.D-5 are N (the number of data points) and the R^2 test.[45] After the hetero adjustment, the values improve, and a data plot indicates an improvement in model fit.

While the $p\text{-}value$ and R^2 tests are straightforward and easy to apply, they have one limitation: neither adjusts for the additional parameters used in the model. For this reason two other tests, the Akaike Information Criteria (AIC) and the Bayesian Information Criteria (BIC), are performed. A smaller value calculation for either test, however, indicates a better model fit (see [2], Section 3.1.3., pp. 48-51 for a more complete discussion of these goodness-of-fit measures).[46] Thus, even though both the $p\text{-}value$ and R^2 tests improved, the AIC and BIC may not, indicating that the model improvement may be due to over-parameterization.

---

[44] This is known as the Shapiro-Francia test. The null hypothesis is typically considered to be invalid if the value is less than 5.0%, but as noted earlier failing this test does not generally invalidate the bootstrap model.

[45] The value of R^2, also known as the coefficient of determination, is simply the square of the sample correlation coefficient between the outcomes and their predicted values.

[46] Note that the AIC and BIC are relative to the model being tested and cannot be compared from one model to the next.

Outliers

Another useful test is to check for outliers in the data, or values outside of the "typical" range. These outliers can be represented graphically as a box-whisker plot, which uses a box to show the inter-quartile range (the 25th to 75th percentiles) and the median (50th percentile) of the residuals. The whiskers then extend to the largest values that are less than three times the inter-quartile range. Any values beyond the whiskers are generally considered outliers and are identified individually with a point.

An example is shown in Figure IV.D-6 of the same residuals with the same hetero groups as previously used. A pre-hetero adjustment plot shows four outliers (the red dots) in the data model, corresponding to the two highest and two lowest values in all the previous graphs.

█ **Figure IV.D-6**

Box-whisker Plots Prior to and After Heteroscedasticity Adjustment

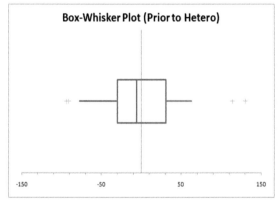
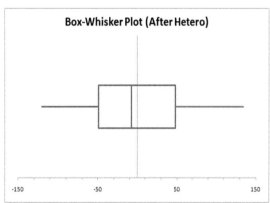

Interquartile Range = [-29.90, 30.96] Median = -5.54   Interquartile Range = [-49.13, 47.74] Median = -7.67

After the hetero adjustment, the residuals do not contain any outliers. If the data were to continue to contain outliers – for example, a cell in the data triangle that includes an unusual event – the outliers could be removed from the model by giving them zero weight in the calculations and not being used in the sampling with replacement. This step, however, should not be taken if there are still a lot of outliers, a result that would typically mean the model isn't yet sufficiently "optimized" or the residuals are not normally distributed. In this circumstance, some other aspect of the model would need to be adjusted first, or else significant skewness could occur in the data that would be replicated in the bootstrap simulations. Caution should be taken even when the removal of outliers is warranted, because there is always the possibility that they may represent realistic "extreme" or "skewed" values in the simulations.

The outlier issue also highlights a potential weakness of the bootstrap model that should be considered when assessing both the model assumptions and results. Because the number of data points used to parameterize the model are limited (in this case study to 53 residuals in our 10x10 triangle), it is hard to determine whether the most extreme observation is a one-in-100 or a one-in-1,000 event (or simply, in this example, a one-in-53 event).[47]

---

[47] One way to overcome a lack of extreme residuals for the bootstrap model would be to parameterize a distribution for the residuals and resample using the distribution (e.g., use a normal distribution if the residuals are normally distributed). This option for "sampling residuals" is beyond the scope of this case study and was not included in the companion Excel files.

Of course, the nature of the extreme observations in the data will also affect the level of extreme simulations in the results. For purposes of this case study, it is assumed that the modeler is satisfied with the level of extreme simulations in the results that follow.

While the three diagnostic tests shown above demonstrate techniques commonly used with most types of models, they are not the only tests available. But rather than catalogue an exhaustive set of tests here, we refer interested readers to CAS Working Party (2005). For the following examples, these tests were applied to both the paid and incurred data for all three business segments.

IV.D.2.b Model Results

After the diagnostics have been reviewed, simulations for the segment under review should be run for each model. In many ways, simulation results serve as an additional diagnostic tool for evaluating the quality of the model. To illustrate the diagnostic elements of the simulation output, let us turn to the results for the casualty one data. The estimated unpaid results shown in FigureIV.D-7 were simulated using 2,500 iterations with the hetero adjustments noted above.

▌ **Figure IV.D-7**

Estimated Unpaid Model Results

Casualty One
Accident Year Unpaid
Paid Chain Ladder Model

Accident Year	Mean Unpaid	Standard Error	Coefficient of Variation	Minimum	Maximum	50.0% Percentile	75.0% Percentile	95.0% Percentile	99.0% Percentile
1999	-	-	0.0%	-	-	-	-	-	-
2000	-	-	0.0%	-	-	-	-	-	-
2001	976	454	46.5%	61	3,281	916	1,246	1,819	2,225
2002	3,596	993	27.6%	1,029	8,937	3,505	4,197	5,400	6,235
2003	12,187	4,270	35.0%	2,913	39,429	11,645	14,707	19,850	23,782
2004	22,792	8,796	38.6%	5,230	62,407	21,546	27,858	39,518	48,890
2005	41,378	14,172	34.3%	6,231	101,480	39,797	50,516	66,463	80,247
2006	84,576	22,276	26.3%	33,391	173,224	82,471	98,243	124,937	143,191
2007	97,687	26,188	26.8%	23,024	192,785	95,807	114,852	144,415	164,088
2008	112,068	45,828	40.9%	17,001	294,564	108,003	143,382	190,353	233,141
Totals	375,258	65,906	17.6%	178,745	642,724	370,784	419,399	486,903	545,865
Normal Dist.	375,258	65,906	17.6%			375,258	419,711	483,664	528,579
logNormal Dist.	375,318	65,906	17.8%			369,493	416,310	494,260	557,576
Gamma Dist	375,258	65,906	17.6%			371,407	417,364	489,835	545,348
TVaR						427,997	461,990	523,880	575,418
Normal TVaR						427,843	459,032	511,203	550,912
logNormal TVaR						428,009	464,459	533,362	592,941
Gamma TVaR						427,618	462,007	523,994	574,816

Estimated unpaid results

The best place to start a diagnostic review of the estimated unpaid table[48] in this case study is with standard error and coefficient of variation, shown in Figure IV.D-7.

As a general rule, the standard error should go up when moving from the oldest years to the most recent years. This increase occurs because the standard errors (value scale) tend to follow the magnitude of the mean of unpaid estimates. In the table in Figure IV.D-7, the standard errors follow this general rule.

At the same time, the standard error for the total of all years should be larger than any individual year. For the coefficients of variation (standard error divided by the mean), they should decrease when moving from the oldest years to the more recent years and the coefficient of variation for all years combined should be less than for any individual year.[49] With the exception of the 2008 accident year, the coefficients of variation in the table in Figure IV.D-7 seem to follow this general rule, although some random fluctuations also exist.

The reason that the coefficients of variation (percent scale) tend to go down is largely related to the independence in the incremental claim payment stream. Because the oldest accident year typically has only one (or a few) incremental payment(s) remaining, the variability is nearly all reflected in the coefficient. For the more current accident years, the "up and down" variations in the future incremental payment stream can offset one another, thereby causing the total variation to be a function of the correlation among incremental payments, which are assumed to be independent for that accident year.

While the coefficients of variation should go down, they could start to go back up in the most recent year(s), as illustrated in the result for 2008 shown in Figure IV.D-7. Such a reversal could be the result of the following issues:

- **The parameter uncertainty tends to increase when moving from the oldest years to the more recent years as more and more parameters are used in the model. In the most recent years, the parameter uncertainty could be "overpowering" the process uncertainty, causing the coefficient of variation to start going back up. At a minimum, the increasing parameter uncertainty will cause the rate of decrease in the coefficient of variation to slow down.**

- **If the increase in the most recent years is significant, then it could indicate the model is overestimating the uncertainty in those years. In this situation, the model parameters for incremental payments may need to be limited to zero, or a Bornhuetter-Ferguson or Cape Cod model may need to be used instead of a chain ladder model.[50]**

In addition to the correlation within each accident year, the rules for the standard error and coefficient of variation also include the impact of the correlation across accident years for all years. In its simplest form, the rule states all accident years would not be expected to be "bad" if one or more accident years develop bad results. This phenomenon can be observed mathematically by adding the accident year standard errors. Their total will not sum to the standard error for all years combined.

---

[48]   The output tables from a bootstrap model could include any number of percentiles, but we are only showing four percentiles to keep the table more manageable.

[49]   These standard error and coefficient of variation rules are based on the independence of the incremental process risk and assume that the underlying exposures are relatively stable from year to year – i.e., no radical changes. In practice, random changes do occur from one year to the next that could cause the actual standard errors to deviate from these rules somewhat. In other words, these rules should generally hold true, but are not considered hard and fast in every case. Strictly speaking, the rules for the total of all years assume that the individual years are not positively correlated.

[50]   Caution should be exercised in the interpretation and adjustments for increases in the coefficient of variation in recent years. While keeping the theory in mind is appropriate, this must be balanced with the need to keep from underestimating the uncertainty of the more recent years.

The next diagnostic elements in our analysis of the estimated unpaid claims model in Figure IV.D-7 are minimum and maximum results, which represent the smallest and largest values from among all iterations of the simulation. These values need to be reviewed to determine whether any fall outside the "realm of possibility." If any do, the model assumptions would need reviewing. [51] For example, the presence of negative numbers might require that a limitation of zero be placed on incremental values. Sometimes "extreme" outliers in the results will show up in these values and may also distort the histogram, which will be discussed later in this case study.

For example, in Figure IV.D-7 the minimum and maximum for 2008 might be considered a bit outside the "realm of possibility," while the totals for all accident years may be reasonable. The purpose or use of the model can affect the need to refit the model or to use another model.

Some final observations regarding the table in Figure IV.D-7 are appropriate at this time. Shown at the bottom of the table are three rows of percentile numbers for the normal, lognormal, and gamma distributions that have been fitted to the total unpaid claim distribution. These fitted mean, standard deviation, and selected percentiles are shown under the columns labelled Mean, Standard Error, and Percentile, respectively, so the smoothed results can be used to assess the quality of fit, parameterize a larger EC model, or for estimates of the extreme values, [52] among other applications.

Also shown at the bottom of the table are four rows of numbers for the Tail Value at Risk (TVaR), defined as the average of all of the simulated values equal to or greater than the percentile value. For example, in the table in Figure IV.D-7, the 95th percentile value for the total unpaid claims for all accident years combined is 486,903, and the average of all simulated values that are greater than or equal to 486,903 is 523,880. The results in the normal, lognormal, and gamma TVaR rows are calculated the same way, except that instead of using the actual simulated values from the model, the respective fitted distributions are used in the calculations.

An analysis of the TVaR values will ideally help to answer one fundamental question: If the actual outcome exceeds the X percentile value, how much will it exceed that value on average? Such an assessment has important implications related to risk-based capital calculations and other technical aspects of enterprise risk management. It is worth noting, however, that the purpose of the normal, lognormal, and gamma TVaR numbers is to provide "smoothed" values in the sense that some of the random noise is kept from distorting the calculations.

Estimated cash flow results

The model's output can also be reviewed by calendar year (or by future diagonal) as shown in the Estimated Cash Flow table in Figure IV.D-8. A comparison of the values in Figures IV.D-7 and IV.D-8 reveals that the Totals rows are identical, such that summing the parts horizontally or diagonally produces the same total. Similar diagnostic issues can be reviewed in the table in Figure IV.D-8, except that the relative values of the standard errors and coefficients of variation move in the opposite direction for calendar years compared to accident years. This phenomenon intuitively makes sense when one considers that "final" payments when projected to the furthest point in the future should be the smallest, yet relatively most uncertain.

---

[51] To some degree the implausibility of the minimum or maximum values may be consistent with the coefficient of variation issues so refitting model assumptions for one issue may impact the other.

[52] Of course, the use of the extreme values assumes that the models are reliable.

Figure IV.D-8

Estimated Cash Flow Model Results

Casualty One
Calendar Year Unpaid
Paid Chain Ladder Model

Calendar Year	Mean Unpaid	Standard Error	Coefficient of Variation	Minimum	Maximum	50.0% Percentile	75.0% Percentile	95.0% Percentile	99.0% Percentile
2009	123,393	22,538	18.3%	58,136	214,264	121,375	138,524	161,982	182,711
2010	96,444	22,279	23.1%	35,774	202,000	94,991	110,223	135,394	155,003
2011	70,278	20,395	29.0%	21,655	168,722	67,897	82,934	106,885	126,542
2012	42,389	14,170	33.4%	9,869	98,242	40,420	51,107	68,369	83,108
2013	24,833	9,366	37.7%	5,629	74,666	23,330	29,853	42,065	52,794
2014	13,409	5,411	40.4%	3,066	39,488	12,590	16,571	23,587	28,784
2015	3,577	1,312	36.7%	853	9,144	3,428	4,429	5,896	7,094
2016	934	558	59.8%	23	3,563	828	1,263	2,003	2,507
2017	-	-	0.0%	-	-	-	-	-	-
2018	-	-	0.0%	-	-	-	-	-	-
Totals	375,258	65,906	17.6%	178,745	642,724	370,784	419,399	486,903	545,865

Estimated ultimate loss ratio results

Another output table, Figure IV.D-9, shows the estimated ultimate loss ratios by accident year. Unlike the estimated unpaid and estimated cash flow tables, the values in the estimated ultimate loss ratios table are all calculated from simulated values, not just the values beyond the end of the historical triangle. Because the simulated sample triangles represent additional possibilities of what could have happened in the past, and the "squaring of the triangle" and process variance represent what could happen as those same past values are played out into the future, we have enough information to estimate the complete variability in the loss ratio from day one until all claims are completely paid and settled for each accident year.[53]

Figure IV.D-9

Estimated Loss Ratio Model Results

Casualty One
Accident Year Ultimate Loss Ratios
Paid Chain Ladder Model

Calendar Year	Mean Loss Ratio	Standard Error	Coefficient of Variation	Minimum	Maximum	50.0% Percentile	75.0% Percentile	95.0% Percentile	99.0% Percentile
1999	59.5%	9.4%	15.7%	29.0%	89.8%	59.5%	66.0%	75.1%	80.6%
2000	74.3%	10.3%	13.8%	44.7%	110.0%	74.1%	81.3%	91.6%	98.3%
2001	68.2%	9.4%	13.8%	34.3%	96.8%	68.1%	74.6%	83.6%	89.3%
2002	65.7%	9.5%	14.4%	37.2%	96.1%	65.4%	72.3%	81.8%	87.5%
2003	60.2%	9.8%	16.2%	30.8%	96.4%	60.2%	66.6%	76.6%	83.6%
2004	61.1%	10.6%	17.3%	27.3%	103.7%	60.7%	68.1%	78.8%	87.0%
2005	61.8%	11.2%	18.1%	27.4%	109.9%	61.3%	69.2%	81.2%	89.4%
2006	65.6%	11.6%	17.6%	36.1%	109.2%	64.8%	72.9%	86.2%	94.3%
2007	48.1%	11.2%	23.2%	16.0%	86.4%	47.4%	55.6%	67.5%	75.5%
2008	40.8%	16.4%	40.1%	6.7%	104.1%	39.5%	52.0%	68.8%	83.4%
Totals	59.0%	4.3%	7.3%	47.0%	75.6%	58.9%	61.9%	66.3%	69.7%

---

[53] If we are only interested in the "remaining" volatility in the loss ratio, then the values in the estimated unpaid table (Figure IV.D-7) can be added to the cumulative paid values by year and divided by the premiums.

The use of all simulated values indicates that the standard errors in Figure IV.D-9 should be proportionate to the means, while the coefficients of variation should be relatively constant by accident year. Diagnostically, the increases in standard error and coefficient of variation for the most recent years are consistent with the reasons cited earlier for the estimated unpaid tables. In addition, the drop-off in the mean loss ratio over the last two years could indicate the need to switch to another model like the Bornhuetter-Ferguson.[54]

Estimated incremental results

The information in the next two output result tables, which show the mean and standard errors by accident year by incremental period[55], is aimed at promoting a deeper review of the simulations and an understanding of the reasons for increases in the coefficients of variation shown in the tables in Figures IV.D-7 and IV.D-9. Irregularities in expected patterns can be identified by scanning down each column or across each row of the mean values by incremental period in Figure IV.D-10. The standard errors can similarly be reviewed in Figure IV.D-11.

Based on the data in the columns for 24 and 36 months shown in Figures IV.D-10 and IV.D-11, it appears as though the means have dropped off to some extent in 2007 and 2008 compared to the exposures. The values also indicate that there might be "too much" variability in future incremental values for 2007 and 2008—an observation based on the fact that the values below the diagonal line do not appear consistent with the values above the line. This pattern, however, does not imply that the values above the diagonal line are correct and the values below are overstated; only that they are not always consistent. These inconsistencies appear to be affecting both the unpaid and loss ratio results for 2007 and 2008.

Figure IV.D-10

Estimated Means by Accident Year by Incremental Period

Casualty One
Accident Year Incremental Values by Development Period
Paid Chain Ladder Model

Accident Year	Mean Values										
	12	24	36	48	60	72	84	96	108	120	120+
1999	7,278	18,357	19,080	20,562	11,629	8,027	7,161	1,974	723	-	-
2000	9,874	24,855	25,677	27,491	15,255	10,476	9,942	2,663	969	-	-
2001	9,797	24,417	25,614	27,153	15,164	10,729	9,660	2,636	976	-	-
2002	9,758	24,331	25,305	27,215	14,969	10,401	9,592	2,634	962	-	-
2003	9,064	22,469	23,150	25,018	14,096	9,786	8,857	2,430	900	-	-
2004	9,261	23,423	24,616	26,384	14,417	9,862	9,430	2,561	938	-	-
2005	10,366	26,004	27,007	28,932	16,231	11,116	10,157	2,829	1,045	-	-
2006	12,429	31,083	32,689	34,468	19,198	13,671	12,589	3,399	1,252	-	-
2007	10,401	25,788	27,053	28,643	16,451	11,395	10,294	2,812	1,038	-	-
2008	9,300	23,314	24,665	26,537	14,639	10,095	9,345	2,538	934	-	-

---

[54] The decrease in mean loss ratios (and the increase in coefficient of variation) is consistent with what one might find in a similar deterministic analysis—i.e., a lower-than-average paid to date could project to an ultimate that is too low.

[55] Since the bootstrap model is simulating a random value for each incremental value in the historical data triangle and each projected future incremental value, we can summarize the mean and standard deviation for each of those random values.

█ Figure IV.D-11

Estimated Standard Errors by Accident Year by Incremental Period

Casualty One
Accident Year Incremental Values by Development Period
Paid Chain Ladder Model

Accident Year	Standard Error Values										
	12	24	36	48	60	72	84	96	108	120	120+
1999	2,952	4,774	4,766	9,238	6,836	5,660	2,890	470	291	-	-
2000	3,486	5,303	5,481	10,669	7,766	6,606	3,413	556	342	-	-
2001	3,444	5,432	5,457	10,497	8,008	6,567	3,366	564	454	-	-
2002	3,324	5,410	5,437	10,464	7,872	6,616	3,353	795	465	-	-
2003	3,283	5,236	5,272	10,136	7,594	6,309	3,916	779	436	-	-
2004	3,406	5,228	5,384	10,407	7,742	6,949	4,245	807	459	-	-
2005	3,528	5,485	5,662	10,982	9,146	7,652	4,248	868	500	-	-
2006	3,893	6,003	6,211	13,622	10,376	8,763	4,934	916	559	-	-
2007	3,508	5,617	8,239	12,940	9,529	8,209	4,501	899	510	-	-
2008	3,330	10,232	10,796	15,279	10,237	8,070	5,249	1,175	558	-	-

Taken together, the tables show that the mean incremental values below the diagonal line in Figure IV.D-10 will sum to the mean unpaid values in Figures IV.D-7 and IV.D-8. A couple of individual standard error incremental values in Figure IV.D-11 will match the corresponding value in Figures IV.D-7 or IV.D-8, respectively, but the total standard error for a row or diagonal can only be summed because of the independence of the values.[56]

Distribution graph

The final model output to be discussed is a histogram of the estimated unpaid amounts for the total of all accident years combined, as shown in the graph in Figure IV.D-12. We created the total unpaid distribution graph or histogram shown in Figure IV.D-12 by dividing the range of all values (for the maximum and minimum values) generated from the simulation into 100 "buckets" of equal size and then counting the number of simulations that fall within each "bucket." Dividing the number of simulations in each bucket by the total number of simulations (2,500 in this case) yields the frequency or probability for each "bucket" in the graph.

---

[56] The total standard error for a row or diagonal is roughly equivalent to the square root of the sum of the squares of the individual values.

■ Figure IV.D-12

Total Unpaid Claims Distribution

Casualty One
Total Unpaid Distribution
Paid Chain Ladder Model

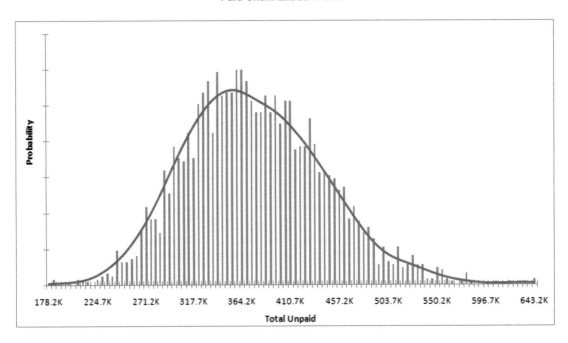

Because the simulation results often appear "jagged," as they do in Figure IV.D-12, a Kernel density function is also used to calculate a "smoothed" distribution fit to the histogram values.[57] The Kernel density distribution is represented by the blue line in Figure IV.D-12. In simple terms, a Kernel density function can be thought of as a weighted average of values "close" to each point in the "jagged" distribution with progressively less weight being given to values furthest from the point being evaluated.[58]

IV.D.2.c Combining Model Results

Once the results for each model have been reviewed and "finalized" according to the iterative process involving the diagnostic testing and model output, they can be "combined" by assigning a weight to the results of each model.[59, 60] Similar to the process of weighting the results of different deterministic methods to arrive at an actuarial "best

---

[57] Essentially, a Kernel density function will estimate each point in the distribution by weighting all of the values near that point, with less weight given the further the other points are from each respective point.

[58] For a more detailed discussion of Kernel density functions, see Wand & Jones (1995).

[59] In order to weight the results of the incurred models with the paid models, the results of the incurred models in the remainder of the case study were adjusted to include stochastic results for case reserves – i.e., both paid and incurred results are for total unpaid claims. This adjustment is beyond the scope of the companion Excel files.

[60] The weighting process illustrated here is beyond the scope of the companion Excel files.

estimate," the process of weighting the results of different stochastic models produces an actuarial "best estimate of a distribution."

Figure IV.D-13

Accident Year	Model Weights by Accident Year						
	Chain Ladder		Bornhuetter-Ferguson		Cape Cod		
	Paid	Incurred	Paid	Incurred	Paid	Incurred	Total
1999	50.0%	50.0%					100.0%
2000	50.0%	50.0%					100.0%
2001	50.0%	50.0%					100.0%
2002	50.0%	50.0%					100.0%
2003	50.0%	50.0%					100.0%
2004	50.0%	50.0%					100.0%
2005	50.0%	50.0%					100.0%
2006			25.0%	25.0%	25.0%	25.0%	100.0%
2007			25.0%	25.0%	25.0%	25.0%	100.0%
2008			25.0%	25.0%	25.0%	25.0%	100.0%

By comparing the results for up to all six models,[61] a qualitative assessment of the relative merits of each model can be determined. Bayesian methods can be used to inform the selection of weights based on the quality of each model's forecasts. The weights can be determined separately for each year so that different weights can be used for each year. The table in Figure IV.D-13 shows an example of weights for the casulaty one data.[62] The weighted results are displayed in the "Best Estimate" column of Figure IV.D-14.

Figure IV.D-14

Casualty One
Summary of Results by Model

Accident Year	Mean Estimated Unpaid						
	Chain Ladder		Bornhuetter-Ferguson		Cape Cod		Best Est.
	Paid	Incurred	Paid	Incurred	Paid	Incurred	(Weighted)
1999	-	-	-	-	-	-	-
2000	-	-	-	-	-	-	-
2001	976	1,207	1,032	1,240	907	1,145	1,090
2002	3,596	4,656	3,871	4,817	3,518	4,646	4,105
2003	12,187	16,438	13,330	20,228	13,127	17,868	14,231
2004	22,792	30,589	24,157	37,519	24,588	32,670	26,673
2005	41,378	55,528	41,710	59,644	45,017	58,288	48,336
2006	84,576	110,101	100,078	109,110	88,926	110,051	101,536
2007	97,687	121,158	137,189	146,400	143,199	157,838	145,932
2008	112,068	142,762	185,269	172,251	201,321	202,841	189,555
Totals	375,258	482,439	506,636	551,208	520,603	585,346	531,458

---

[61] Other models in addition to a bootstrap model could also be included in the weighting process.
[62] For simplicity, the weights are judgmental and not derived using Bayesian methods.

Because our focus is now on the entire distribution and not on just a single point estimate, the weights by year are used to randomly sample the specified percentage of iterations from each model. An example of "weighted" results is shown in the table in Figure IV.D-15.

▌ **Figure IV.D-15**

Estimated Unpaid Model Results (Best Estimate)

Casualty One
Accident Year Unpaid
Best Estimate (Weighted)

Accident Year	Mean Unpaid	Standard Error	Coefficient of Variation	Minimum	Maximum	50.0% Percentile	75.0% Percentile	95.0% Percentile	99.0% Percentile
1999	-	-	0.0%	-	-	-	-	-	-
2000	-	-	0.0%	-	-	-	-	-	-
2001	1,090	561	51.5%	92	4,011	986	1,400	2,138	2,907
2002	4,105	1,446	35.2%	1,027	12,262	3,850	4,873	6,840	8,694
2003	14,231	5,952	41.8%	3,270	43,752	13,248	17,399	25,426	33,551
2004	26,673	12,366	46.4%	5,512	117,480	24,462	32,539	49,433	68,566
2005	48,336	20,344	42.1%	6,231	159,440	45,136	58,707	88,891	111,742
2006	101,536	29,029	28.6%	34,484	267,750	97,546	117,790	156,226	189,465
2007	145,932	36,889	25.3%	47,377	415,623	141,425	163,623	215,319	263,222
2008	189,555	47,174	24.9%	68,217	470,041	187,980	212,051	273,525	327,577
Totals	531,458	72,925	13.7%	325,354	878,155	527,167	575,720	658,026	722,120
Normal Dist.	531,458	72,925	13.7%			531,458	580,645	651,409	701,106
logNormal Dist.	531,470	73,048	13.7%			526,520	577,415	659,386	723,818
Gamma Dist	531,458	72,925	13.7%			528,126	578,661	656,823	715,657
TVaR						588,000	626,587	703,503	772,366
Normal TVaR						589,644	624,153	681,881	725,818
logNormal TVaR						589,301	627,978	699,103	758,866
Gamma TVaR						589,491	626,789	692,999	746,498

Using these weighted results, it should be possible to populate tables of estimated cash flow, estimated ultimate loss ratios, mean incremental values, and standard deviation incremental, along with a graph of the total unpaid distribution, similar to those shown in Figures IV.D-8, IV.D-9, IV.D-10, IV.D-11, and IV.D-12, respectively. An additional graph for the weighted results could also be created to summarize the distribution graphs for all models. An example of this graph is shown in Figure IV.D-16.

Additional graphs and tables for the property, casualty one, and casualty two segments are shown in Exhibits IV.D-2, IV.D-3, and IV.D-4 at the end of this section. This information includes the estimated unpaid, estimated cash flow, estimated ultimate loss ratios, mean incremental, and standard deviation incremental tables. Graphs of the total unpaid distribution and of a summary of model distributions are also included.

▌ Figure IV.D-16

Summary of Model Distributions

Casualty One
Summary of Model Distributions
(Using Kernel Densities)

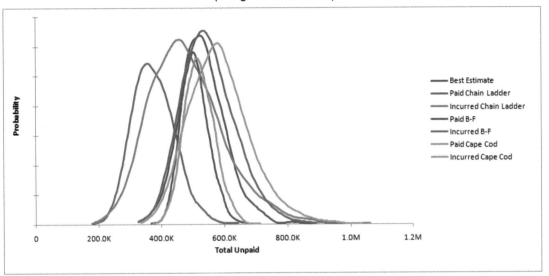

IV.D.3 Aggregation of Results

Results for the entire business unit can now be aggregated. The procedure, however, is not a simple matter of "adding up" the distributions for each segment in order to estimate the distribution of possible outcomes for the company as a whole, but rather a process that incorporates the correlation of results among segments.[63]

Correlations can be both positive and negative. Personal property claims are usually not related to automobile claims, but catastrophes, for example, would likely result in a positive correlation of claims, because multiple lines of business could experience increases in claims at the same time. On the other hand, claims could move in opposite directions, resulting in a negative correlation. For example, rising unemployment causes an increase in unemployment claims, but it is also associated with a decrease in workers' compensation claims because there are fewer employed people. Both of these examples can impact both the estimation of unpaid claims and the pricing of future business, but the relative impact is different as unpaid claims are more influenced by the correlation of the incremental payments for claims that have already occurred while future business is more influenced by the correlation of rate adequacy between business segments.

As such, correlations among multiple segments will have an effect on the distribution of possible outcomes for all segments combined, and therefore eliminate the possibility of merely summing the results for each segment to arrive

---

[63] The remainder of the case study assumes the reader is familiar with correlation. See also Appendix E: Correlation, which provides some background on correlation.

at an aggregate value. Perhaps the only two exceptions in which summing results would be appropriate are when the mean or expected value for the aggregate distribution is determined, or when all segments are 100% correlated with each other—a highly unlikely situation. Determining other values such as the 75th percentile would require a different approach.

Figure IV.D-17 graphically illustrates the impact of correlation on the aggregate distribution of three identical business segments. To start, let us assume all three segments are 100% correlated. Summing the segments produces the same identical distribution, but all numbers along the value axis (estimated liability) are three times as large.

■ Figure IV.D-17

Impact of Correlation on Aggregate Distributions

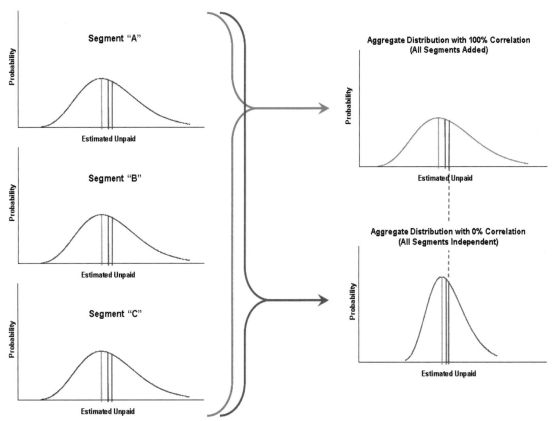

Now let us assume that the three segments are completely independent with 0% correlation among segments. The expected value (or mean) would be the same as the sum, but the resulting aggregate distribution is narrower, because some positive outcomes are offset by some negative outcomes and vice versa. Other than the mean, the values of the distribution will not be the same as the sum, as was the case in which the segments were 100% correlated.

The degree to which the segments are correlated will influence the shape of the aggregate distribution. How significant will this impact be? That primarily depends on three factors: the volatility or width of the distributions for the individual segments, the relative values of the amounts, and the strength of the correlations among segments. All else being equal, low volatility would indicate that the strength of the correlation would not much matter. If, however, there is considerable volatility, the strength of correlations (or lack thereof) will produce differences that could be significant.

It is important to note that the correlation among individual segments does not affect the distribution of any individual segment, but only influences the aggregate distribution of all segments combined.

IV.D.3.a Calculating Correlation

There are several ways to measure correlation using either parametric tests, such as Pearson's R, or non-parametric tests, such as Spearman's Rank Order, or Kendall's Tau, which tend to be more useful than Pearson's correlation coefficient when distributions are not normal.

For the bootstrap model, Spearman's Rank Order calculation is often used to assess the correlation between each pair of segments. In this case study, residuals are used as the basis for assessment, because they directly reflect the movements of incremental payments between pairs of segments, which are now the focus of our analysis. Rather than calculating the correlation of the residuals, Spearman's formula calculates the correlation of the ranks of those residuals. [64]

IV.D.3.b Correlation Process

Simulating correlated variables is frequently done using a multivariate distribution whose parameters and correlations have been specified for each variable in the distribution. This type of simulation is most easily applied when all distributions are the same, are known in advance (e.g., they are all derived from a multivariate normal distribution). These conditions, however, do not exist in our present case study, in which we estimated the distributions with bootstrapping. This process does not allow us to know the characteristics of distributions in advance. If their shapes are, indeed, different, another approach is needed.

Two useful correlation processes for the bootstrap model are location mapping and re-sorting. [65] For location mapping, we note that the residuals for each pair of segments represent the correlation between the segments as the location of each residual are compared cell by cell. We can use this to our advantage in the simulation process. For each iteration in the simulation process, the residuals for the first segment are sampled and the location in the original residual triangle of each sampled residual is noted. Each of the other segments is sampled using the residuals at the same locations for their respective residual triangles. Thus, the correlation of the residuals is preserved in the sampling process for each iteration.

The location mapping process is easily implemented in Excel and does not require the need to calculate a correlation matrix; [66] however, there are two drawbacks to this process. First, it requires all of the business segments to have data triangles that are precisely the same size with no missing values or outliers when comparing each location of the

---

[64]   See Appendix E for an example of the calculation.

[65]   For a useful reference see Kirschner, et al (2008).

[66]   For example, in the companion Excel files the locations of the sampled residuals are shown in Step 11, which could be replicated iteration by iteration for each business segment.

residuals. [67] Second, the correlation of the residuals is used in the model, and no other correlation assumptions can be used for stress testing the aggregate results.

The re-sorting process can be accomplished using algorithms such as Iman-Conover or copulas, among others. The primary advantages of the re-sorting option include:

- **The triangles for each segment can have different shapes and sizes;**

- **Different correlation assumptions can be used; and**

- **The different algorithms can have other beneficial impacts on the aggregate distribution.**

For example, using a t-distribution copula with low degrees of freedom, instead of a normal distribution copula will effectively "strengthen" the focus of the correlation in the tail of the distribution. This type of consideration is important for risk-based capital and other EC modeling issues.

To induce correlation among different segments in the bootstrap model, we will calculate the correlation matrix using Spearman's Rank Order and use re-sorting based on the ranks of the total unpaid claims for all accident years combined. The companion "Section IV.D – Correlations Ranks.xls" Excel file (which can be found on the IAA website www.actuaries.org/stochastic) demonstrates the Spearman Rank Order re-sorting method of inducing correlation among segments. The calculated correlations based on the paid residuals after hetero adjustments are displayed in the table in Figure IV.D-18. [68]

Figure IV.D-18

Estimated Correlation and P-values

Bank Correlation of Residuals after Hetero Adjustment – Paid

LOB	1	2	3
1	1.00	-0.22	0.22
2	-0.22	1.00	-0.20
3	0.22	-0.20	1.00

P-Values of Rank Correlation of Residuals after Hetero Adjustment – Paid

LOB	1	2	3
1	0.00	0.12	0.12
2	0.12	0.00	0.14
3	0.12	0.14	0.00

Using these correlation coefficients and the simulation data used from Exhibits IV.D-2, IV.D-3, and IV.D-4, the aggregate results for the three business segments are summarized in the table in Figure IV.D-19. The complete set of tables for the aggregate results is shown in Exhibit IV.D-5. The calculation of the aggregate results is shown in the companion Excel file "Section IV.D – Aggregate Estimate.xls" (which can be found on the IAA website www.actuaries.org/stochastic).

---

[67] It is possible to fill in "missing" residuals in another segment using a randomly selected residual from elsewhere in the triangle, but in order to maintain the same amount of correlation the selection of the other residual would need to account for the correlation between the residuals, which complicates the process considerably.

[68] The companion Excel files only illustrate estimated correlation prior to hetero adjustment since these adjustments are beyond the scope of the companion files.

▌ Figure IV.D-19

Aggregate Estimated Unpaid

Aggregate All Lines of Business
Accident Year Unpaid

Accident Year	Mean Unpaid	Standard Error	Coefficient of Variation	Minimum	Maximum	50.0% Percentile	75.0% Percentile	95.0% Percentile	99.0% Percentile
1999	16,435	9,051	55.1%	-	58,465	15,486	21,569	33,056	42,454
2000	16,831	9,141	54.3%	-	58,719	15,986	22,173	33,077	41,801
2001	19,358	9,461	48.9%	473	59,797	18,449	24,986	36,711	46,414
2002	30,685	12,420	40.5%	3,627	83,178	29,864	38,764	52,499	61,836
2003	40,009	12,788	32.0%	8,705	93,308	38,907	47,989	62,282	73,247
2004	62,956	18,184	28.9%	16,743	173,665	61,589	73,761	93,988	112,889
2005	123,202	30,348	24.6%	49,952	256,752	121,242	142,119	174,216	204,499
2006	210,465	39,193	18.6%	88,361	358,102	208,243	234,493	278,841	313,267
2007	303,949	45,030	14.8%	190,743	568,321	299,581	330,647	382,138	437,422
2008	560,718	61,724	11.0%	362,079	826,297	556,150	599,796	666,590	719,999
Totals	1,384,609	144,806	10.5%	988,951	1,942,710	1,381,216	1,478,766	1,632,970	1,725,027
Normal Dist.	1,384,609	144,806	10.5%			1,384,609	1,482,279	1,622,793	1,721,477
logNormal Dist.	1,384,636	145,544	10.5%			1,377,049	1,477,936	1,636,181	1,757,343
Gamma Dist	1,384,609	144,806	10.5%			1,379,564	1,479,335	1,631,087	1,743,565
TVaR						1,501,022	1,573,271	1,696,921	1,790,845
Normal TVaR						1,500,147	1,568,672	1,683,301	1,770,547
logNormal TVaR						1,500,233	1,575,453	1,710,765	1,821,875
Gamma TVaR						1,499,971	1,572,743	1,700,205	1,801,856

IV.D.4 Communication

The communication of results should start with an internal peer review to ensure quality of work and consistency of analysis. All tables and graphs in Section IV.D.3, including the assumptions, diagnostic tests, and results, should be reviewed for each segment. In addition, comparisons among segments could also reveal inconsistencies or key issues that might need further review.

Once the analysis has passed peer review, communication to management and designated external audiences may begin. In general, the goal is to communicate the depth and breadth of the risk profile that has been calculated. This can be achieved with visual slides, printed exhibits, and written reports, or other media. The form of the communication will likely depend on its specific purpose. The discussion in Section IV.D.3 can serve as a useful road map for the peer review and communication process, because it is applicable to a broad range of analyses.

IV.D.5 Components of the Capital Model

The results of a stochastic unpaid claims analysis can be leveraged into various applications using a complete EC model, including but not limited to, the insurance risk component of economic capital, the allocation of required capital, the related underwriting profit targets by business segment and return on equity targets, various reinsurance options, mergers and acquisitions, strategic planning, performance management, and rating agency discussions. As noted earlier, the simulated outputs can be used as inputs to a larger EC model or to parameterize an EC model that will simulate possible outcomes within the model.

The next case study illustrates the use of the distributions as part of a larger EC model, so we will complete this case study by discussing the calculation of some of the insurance risk components of required capital. [69]

IV.D.5.a Required Capital

The required capital can be viewed as a "shared asset" in that each segment can "tap into" and in fact "use all' the capital as needed. Thus, the calculation of required capital is based on the aggregate distribution of all segments combined. Because one of the primary purposes of capital is to guard against potentially adverse outcomes, the difference between a relatively unlikely, but possible, outcome and the booked liability is a quantifiable measure of required capital. For example, the difference between the 99th percentile and the mean estimate would signify the amount of capital required to cover 99.0% of the possible outcomes. This situation is illustrated in the graph in Figure IV.D-20.

While each business segment can "tap into" the total capital for a firm, we would not expect every segment to "go bad" (or need capital) at the same time. Quite the contrary, a more likely scenario would be that better-than-expected results from some segments would offset worse-than-expected results from other segments. In practice, events such as catastrophes, unanticipated major changes in inflation, or major changes in interest rates and industry underwriting cycles will simultaneously affect multiple segments, so the "better" and "worse" results by segment will typically not balance out. In general, however, the effects of certain correlation issues will result in a significant reduction in total required capital for the firm. This phenomenon, known as the diversification benefit, is illustrated in Figure IV.D-20.

▌ Figure IV.D-20

Required Capital

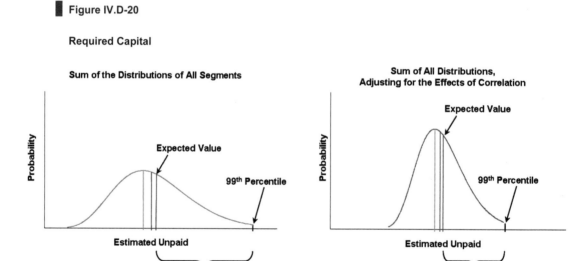

The impact of two key issues – discounting and risk measure – also need to be considered in a discussion related to quantifying a firm's required capital. Discounting of liabilities is generally an accounting issue by country, but it can also be thought of as a statutory (non-discounting, risk-based capital, conservative) issue versus an economic

---

[69] The determination of required capital is not limited to insurance-risk components, so the remainder of the case study should only be viewed as an example of how this process can be undertaken.

(discounting, economic capital, going concern) issue. And Value at Risk (VaR), discussed earlier, is only one type of the risk measure. Two other possible measurements are Tail Value at Risk and expected policyholder deficit (see Section I.E for more discussion of risk measures).

Finally, the required capital illustrated in Figure IV.D-20 assumes the mean of the distribution is used as the booked liability held on the balance sheet. In this case study, if management decides to book a liability different than the mean estimate, then the required capital would change by the difference between the calculated mean and the selected liability.[70]

Figure IV.D-21

Required Capital from Unpaid Claims Risk

	Indicated Unpaid-claims-risk Portion of Required Capital as of December 31, 2008 (No Discounting, Modeled Correlation, in 000s)					
	(1) 2008 Premium	(2) Mean Unpaid	(3) 99.0% Unpaid	(4) (3) – (2) Indicated VaR Risk Capital	(5) Allocated [71] Unpaid Claim Risk Capital	(6) (5) / (1) Ratio
Property	1,716	136	199	63	36	2.1%
Casualty One	298	531	722	191	111	37.1%
Casualty Two	374	717	1,050	334	193	51.7%
Sum	2,387	1,385	1,972	587		
SIC Aggregate [72]	2,387	1,385	1,725	340	340	14.3%

Based on the unpaid claim estimates in Figures IV.D-2, IV.D-3, IV.D-4, and IV.D-5, we calculated the unpaid claims risk portion of required capital using the 99th percentile and summarized the results in the table shown in Figure IV.D-21. According to Figure IV.D-21, the unpaid claims risk capital, calculated by summing the required capital for the segments, is 587,000, but after the impact of correlation, the required capital becomes 340,000. The "savings" of 247,000 in required capital is the benefit from diversification. The total required capital is then allocated to the segments in proportion to the required capital by segment.[73]

The distributions of ultimate loss ratios and future cash flows could have also been used in a similar fashion to quantify other insurance risk components of required capital to the unpaid claims risk. Figure IV.D-22 shows the summarized results of calculating the pricing risk portion of required capital for the 99th percentile using the ultimate

---

[70] Rather than illustrate various combinations of these options, we will only use undiscounted results and VaR in the quantification of required capital.

[71] The allocated unpaid-claims-risk capital amounts, shown in Column (5) in Figure IV.D-21, are based on shares for each segment, which sum to the aggregate unpaid-claims-risk capital and the proportionate share of indicated capital, shown in Column (4) by segment.

[72] The SIC aggregate VaR is less than the sum of the segment VaRs due to the impact of correlation between the three segments, as illustrated in Figures IV.D-17 and IV.D-20.

[73] Other methods of allocating capital by segment may be preferred (e.g., based on coherent measures) but are more complex. For a more complete discussion of the different methods of allocating capital, see Ruhm and Mango (2003) and Venter (2003).

loss ratio distributions for 2008 by segment.[74] Rather than use the calculated correlation matrix, we assumed the future pricing correlation among segments to be stronger than that indicated by the calculations that were due to contagion risk and underwriting cycles. Thus, the correlation coefficients for pricing risk were assumed to be 50%.

▌ **Figure IV.D-22**

Required Capital from Pricing Risk

	Indicated Pricing Risk Portion of Required Capital as of December 31, 2008 (No Discounting, 50% Correlation, in 000s)					
	(1) 2008 Premium	(2) Mean Ultimate	(3) 99.0% Ultimate	(4) (3) – (2) Indicated VaR Risk Capital	(5) Allocated Pricing Risk Capital	(6) (5) / (1) Ratio
Property	1,716	1,221	1,366	145	95	5.5%
Casualty One	298	199	340	142	92	31.1%
Casualty Two	374	304	412	108	71	18.9%
Sum	2,387	1,723	2,118	395		
SIC Aggregate	2,387	1,723	1,981	258	258	10.8%

In practice, the pricing risk analysis can be extended for future years and would add future values to the cash flow analysis. Finally, complete required capital calculation would call for additional inputs for other risks, such as credit risk, market risk, and operational risk.

---

[74] For illustration purposes, we simply used 2008 as a proxy for 2009. In practice, consideration of actual rate level changes and underwriting cycle information could lead to a better estimate of the expected ultimate loss ratio for 2009 and beyond.

References for IV.D

Brender, A. (2002). The use of internal models for determining liabilities and capital requirements. *North American Actuarial Journal* Vol. 6, No. 2: 1-10.

Casualty Actuarial Society (CAS), Working Party on Quantifying Variability in Reserve Estimates (2005). The analysis and estimation of loss & ALAE variability: A summary report. *CAS Fall Forum:* 29-146.

England, Peter D. & Verrall, Richard J. (1999). Analytic and bootstrap estimates of prediction errors in claims reserving. *Insurance: Mathematics and Economics* 25: 281-293.

England, Peter D. & Verrall, Richard J. (2001). A flexible framework for stochastic claims reserving. *PCAS* Vol. LXXXVIII: 1-38.

England, Peter D. & Verrall, Richard J. (2002). Stochastic claims reserving in general insurance. *British Actuarial Journal* 8: 443-544.

Kirschner, Gerald S., Kerley, Colin & Isaacs, Belinda (2008). Two approaches to calculating correlated reserve indications across multiple lines of business. *Variance* Vol. 2-1: 15-38.

Mack, Thomas (1993). Distribution-free calculation of the standard error of chain ladder reserve estimates. *ASTIN Bulletin* 23:2: 213-25.

Mildenhall, Stephen (1999). Minimum bias and generalized linear models. *PCAS* Vol. LXXVI: 393-487.

Milliman P&C Insurance Software Team (2009). Using the Milliman Reserve Variability Model: An overview of the Milliman bootstrap modeling system. *Version 1.4.*

Pinheiro, Paulo J. R., Silva, João Manuel Andrade e, & Centeno, Maria de Lourdes (2001). Bootstrap methodology in claim reserving. *ASTIN Colloquium.*

Ruhm, David L. & Mango, Donald F. (2003). A method of implementing Myers-Read capital allocation in simulation. *CAS Fall Forum:* 451-458.

Shapland, Mark R. (2007). Loss reserve estimates: A statistical approach for determining "reasonableness." *Variance* Vol.1-1: 121-148.

Venter, Gary G. (1998). Testing the assumptions of age-to-age factors. *PCAS* Vol. LXXXV: 807-47.

Venter, Gary G. (2003). A survey of capital allocation methods with commentary: Topic 3: Risk control. *ASTIN Colloquium.*

Verrall, Richard J. (2004). A Bayesian generalized linear model for the Bornhuetter-Ferguson Method of claims reserving. *North American Actuarial Journal* Vol. 8, No. 3: 67-89.

Wand & Jones (1995). *Kernel smoothing.* Chapman & Hall.

Exhibit IV.D-1: Raw Data by Segment

▌ **Property Business**

Cumulative Paid Loss Triangle

Accident Year	12	24	36	48	60	72	84	96	108	120
1998	633,138	702,081	702,776	702,597	702,582	702,574	702,600	702,603	702,603	702,606
1999	690,044	753,278	753,974	753,728	753,699	753,755	753,759	753,776	753,740	
2000	715,149	788,987	789,751	789,417	789,483	789,454	789,458	789,459		
2001	776,683	869,154	869,418	869,503	869,526	869,443	869,453			
2002	835,881	969,913	970,431	970,570	970,667	970,687				
2003	852,298	962,409	962,621	962,724	962,791					
2004	925,163	1,043,937	1,044,530	1,044,580						
2005	996,162	1,111,148	1,111,666							
2006	1,037,082	1,146,098								
2007	1,097,779									

Cumulative Incurred Loss Triangle

Accident Year	12	24	36	48	60	72	84	96	108	120
1998	676,785	702,528	702,863	702,637	702,602	702,578	702,600	702,603	702,603	702,606
1999	735,945	753,820	754,069	753,769	753,719	753,762	753,766	753,776	753,740	
2000	771,742	789,568	789,908	789,482	789,515	789,462	789,458	789,459		
2001	843,292	869,893	869,524	869,548	869,544	869,450	869,453			
2002	934,776	970,853	970,647	970,630	970,685	970,691				
2003	928,419	963,823	962,801	962,755	962,794					
2004	1,008,315	1,044,810	1,044,644	1,044,612						
2005	1,073,005	1,111,893	1,111,787							
2006	1,100,650	1,146,641								
2007	1,166,903									

Calendar Year	Earned Premium	Earned Exposures		Calendar Year	Earned Premium	Earned Exposures
1998	691,456	4,526		2003	1,291,574	6,019
1999	810,079	4,905		2004	1,458,613	6,420
2000	952,501	5,278		2005	1,646,366	6,907
2001	1,087,494	5,582		2006	1,721,347	7,265
2002	1,189,652	5,846		2007	1,715,950	7,504

▌ **Casualty One Business**

Cumulative Paid Loss Triangle

Accident Year	12	24	36	48	60	72	84	96	108	120
1998	9,517	29,915	46,152	58,997	73,021	88,298	92,190	93,679	94,269	94,269
1999	9,365	32,876	57,714	89,184	101,039	109,576	123,613	126,445	127,539	
2000	7,726	34,370	59,003	86,042	106,011	109,918	123,109	126,092		
2001	8,261	37,736	58,379	99,932	107,179	116,542	122,028			
2002	11,786	30,222	56,605	77,070	90,497	103,014				
2003	10,535	35,458	57,998	79,408	98,184					
2004	11,724	34,268	64,358	92,636						
2005	9,561	37,796	76,183							
2006	10,018	36,258								
2007	9,149									

Cumulative Incurred Loss Triangle

Accident Year	12	24	36	48	60	72	84	96	108	120
1998	61,031	62,004	82,200	74,078	79,713	103,520	100,403	97,249	94,269	94,269
1999	47,864	61,938	101,627	121,076	147,448	144,723	135,012	130,060	127,539	
2000	27,940	69,617	108,167	104,884	133,231	125,720	125,973	127,563		
2001	40,334	76,821	95,402	129,831	147,298	159,224	136,515			
2002	61,777	57,617	93,842	102,773	115,469	140,689				
2003	74,724	68,238	105,243	97,981	136,617					
2004	60,430	69,929	111,746	126,229						
2005	48,068	76,242	135,332							
2006	48,261	67,012								
2007	48,873									

Calendar Year	Earned Premium	Earned Exposures		Calendar Year	Earned Premium	Earned Exposures
1998	159,259	1,665		2003	197,982	2,127
1999	171,133	1,782		2004	216,206	2,267
2000	184,964	1,903		2005	245,144	2,446
2001	190,587	1,999		2006	278,137	2,583
2002	192,215	2,078		2007	297,604	2,667

▌ Casualty Two Business

Cumulative Paid Loss Triangle

Accident Year	12	24	36	48	60	72	84	96	108	120
1998	26,453	50,795	60,576	64,988	68,047	69,557	71,158	71,603	73,120	73,321
1999	24,968	47,880	56,324	62,265	65,595	68,776	70,277	71,230	71,843	
2000	26,426	47,491	58,548	63,709	67,454	71,041	72,546	73,327		
2001	26,922	55,991	68,865	76,951	85,351	90,432	94,551			
2002	27,727	57,487	67,796	77,489	81,584	83,946				
2003	32,901	68,559	84,330	94,676	102,470					
2004	49,268	109,278	140,617	163,074						
2005	66,695	137,801	171,684							
2006	65,820	148,036								
2007	68,147									

Cumulative Incurred Loss Triangle

Accident Year	12	24	36	48	60	72	84	96	108	120
1998	50,947	65,810	69,642	70,593	70,926	71,267	73,263	75,084	74,068	73,434
1999	46,488	60,277	65,964	69,713	71,788	72,780	73,396	73,619	75,324	
2000	49,839	63,077	68,256	69,440	71,718	74,568	74,448	75,646		
2001	61,884	80,397	86,551	94,218	102,053	101,615	113,513			
2002	53,356	71,295	77,395	86,863	89,656	91,356				
2003	66,344	88,119	101,862	105,915	111,328					
2004	101,272	154,280	176,998	192,595						
2005	149,776	190,519	213,007							
2006	153,855	236,113								
2007	151,973									

Calendar Year	Earned Premium	Earned Exposures
1998	182,934	530
1999	162,791	536
2000	150,917	541
2001	145,400	563
2002	160,840	597

Calendar Year	Earned Premium	Earned Exposures
2003	181,833	629
2004	264,025	700
2005	326,343	747
2006	360,235	752
2007	373,839	758

Exhibit IV.D-2: Property Results

Property
Summary of Results by Model

Accident Year	Mean Estimated Unpaid						Best Est. (Weighted)
	Chain Ladder		Bornhuetter-Ferguson		Cape Cod		
	Paid	Incurred	Paid	Incurred	Paid	Incurred	
1999	-	-	-	-	-	-	-
2000	7	7	7	7	6	6	7
2001	2	12	12	12	11	11	12
2002	22	22	23	23	21	21	22
2003	38	38	38	38	36	36	38
2004	73	73	72	72	73	74	73
2005	124	124	132	132	130	131	124
2006	194	193	199	198	214	214	194
2007	879	880	874	878	1,020	1,024	879
2008	130,912	127,976	126,710	124,583	146,736	142,644	135,073
Totals	132,261	129,325	128,066	125,945	148,247	144,161	136,421

Property
Accident Year Ultimate Loss Ratios
Best Estimate (Weighted)

Accident Year	Mean Loss Ratio	Standard Error	Coefficient of Variation	Minimum	Maximum	50.0% Percentile	75.0% Percentile	95.0% Percentile	99.0% Percentile
1999	101.9%	7.4%	7.2%	80.1%	120.9%	101.6%	107.8%	113.3%	117.1%
2000	93.4%	6.6%	7.1%	75.5%	111.9%	93.4%	98.8%	103.5%	108.3%
2001	82.9%	5.7%	6.9%	66.4%	99.3%	82.8%	87.5%	91.8%	94.7%
2002	80.1%	5.2%	6.6%	64.8%	95.0%	79.8%	84.3%	88.4%	90.6%
2003	81.7%	5.0%	6.1%	68.7%	96.2%	81.5%	85.7%	89.7%	92.0%
2004	74.6%	4.6%	6.2%	61.8%	87.9%	74.3%	78.2%	81.8%	84.5%
2005	71.7%	4.3%	6.0%	60.2%	82.8%	71.3%	75.3%	78.4%	81.0%
2006	67.5%	4.0%	5.9%	56.2%	77.7%	67.4%	70.7%	73.7%	75.8%
2007	66.5%	3.8%	5.7%	56.2%	76.5%	66.3%	69.5%	72.6%	74.5%
2008	71.1%	3.5%	4.9%	61.1%	83.7%	71.0%	73.5%	77.0%	79.6%
Totals	76.2%	1.5%	2.0%	71.0%	81.1%	76.2%	77.2%	78.7%	79.6%

Property
Accident Year Unpaid
Best Estimate (Weighted)

Accident Year	Mean Unpaid	Standard Error	Coefficient of Variation	Minimum	Maximum	50.0% Percentile	75.0% Percentile	95.0% Percentile	99.0% Percentile
1999	-	-	0.0%	-	-	-	-	-	-
2000	7	16	222.7%	-	192	0	6	38	77
2001	12	21	178.9%	-	249	2	15	54	103
2002	22	28	126.2%	-	186	12	32	80	127
2003	38	36	95.5%	-	236	27	55	111	159
2004	73	205	282.7%	-	3,296	29	65	204	974
2005	124	220	177.6%	0	3,336	67	131	395	1,119
2006	194	368	189.9%	0	4,648	84	192	714	1,983
2007	879	503	57.2%	83	4,627	776	1,075	1,816	2,748
2008	135,073	24,979	18.5%	69,538	256,611	133,256	150,445	179,231	198,213
Totals	136,421	24,986	18.3%	69,992	259,900	134,787	151,657	180,659	199,324
Normal Dist.	136,421	24,986	18.3%			136,421	153,274	177,520	194,548
logNormal Dist.	136,444	25,358	18.6%			134,147	151,901	181,642	205,947
Gamma Dist	136,421	24,986	18.3%			134,899	152,342	179,953	201,173
TVaR						156,248	169,587	192,841	211,341
Normal TVaR						156,357	168,181	187,961	203,015
logNormal TVaR						156,392	170,277	196,657	219,589
Gamma TVaR						156,265	169,352	193,012	212,464

Property
Calendar Year Unpaid
Best Estimate (Weighted)

Calendar Year	Mean Unpaid	Standard Error	Coefficient of Variation	Minimum	Maximum	50.0% Percentile	75.0% Percentile	95.0% Percentile	99.0% Percentile
2009	134,964	24,939	18.5%	68,375	258,963	133,033	150,357	178,784	197,698
2010	943	518	54.9%	82	4,861	852	1,172	1,879	2,756
2011	194	378	194.4%	0	6,357	75	186	780	1,864
2012	137	224	163.1%	0	3,439	72	154	472	1,079
2013	84	189	225.5%	0	2,433	37	74	325	968
2014	45	40	89.2%	0	265	35	64	129	176
2015	29	32	110.6%	0	223	18	42	95	143
2016	20	28	136.8%	0	223	10	27	73	116
2017	18	25	137.8%	0	241	9	26	67	117
2018	-	-	0.0%	-	-	-	-	-	-
Totals	136,421	24,986	18.3%	69,992	259,900	134,787	151,657	180,659	199,324

Property
Total Unpaid Distribution
Best Estimate (Weighted)

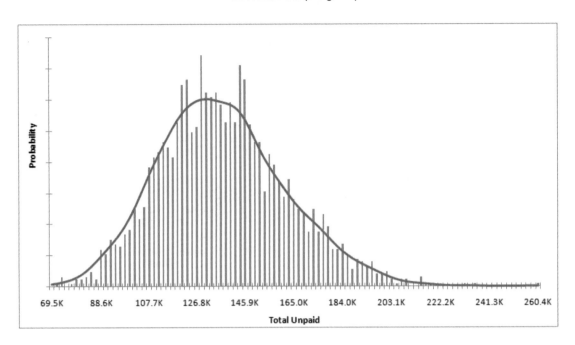

Property
Summary of Model Distributions
(Using Kernel Densities)

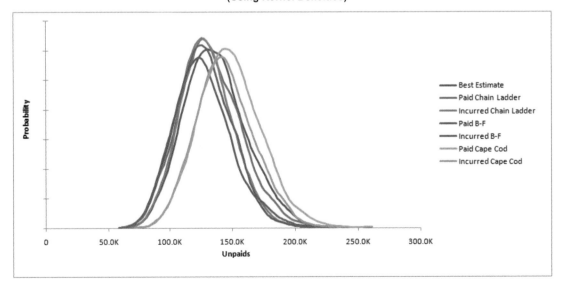

Exhibit IV.D-3: Casualty One Results

Casualty One
Summary of Results by Model

| Accident Year | Mean Estimated Unpaid | | | | | | Best Est. (Weighted) |
| | Chain Ladder | | Bornhuetter-Ferguson | | Cape Cod | | |
	Paid	Incurred	Paid	Incurred	Paid	Incurred	
1999	-	-	-	-	-	-	-
2000	-	-	-	-	-	-	-
2001	976	1,207	1,032	1,240	907	1,145	1,090
2002	3,596	4,656	3,871	4,817	3,518	4,646	4,105
2003	12,187	16,438	13,330	20,228	13,127	17,868	14,231
2004	22,792	30,589	24,157	37,519	24,588	32,670	26,673
2005	41,378	55,528	41,710	59,644	45,017	58,288	48,336
2006	84,576	110,101	100,078	109,110	88,926	110,051	101,536
2007	97,687	121,158	137,189	146,400	143,199	157,838	145,932
2008	112,068	142,762	185,269	172,251	201,321	202,841	189,555
Totals	375,258	482,439	506,636	551,208	520,603	585,346	531,458

Casualty One
Accident Year Unpaid
Best Estimate (Weighted)

Accident Year	Mean Unpaid	Standard Error	Coefficient of Variation	Minimum	Maximum	50.0% Percentile	75.0% Percentile	95.0% Percentile	99.0% Percentile
1999	-	-	0.0%	-	-				
2000	-	-	0.0%	-	-				
2001	1,090	561	51.5%	92	4,011	986	1,400	2,138	2,907
2002	4,105	1,446	35.2%	1,027	12,262	3,850	4,873	6,840	8,694
2003	14,231	5,952	41.8%	3,270	43,752	13,248	17,399	25,426	33,551
2004	26,673	12,366	46.4%	5,512	117,480	24,462	32,539	49,433	68,566
2005	48,336	20,344	42.1%	6,231	159,440	45,136	58,707	88,891	111,742
2006	101,536	29,029	28.6%	34,484	267,750	97,546	117,790	156,226	189,465
2007	145,932	36,889	25.3%	47,377	415,623	141,425	163,623	215,319	263,222
2008	189,555	47,174	24.9%	68,217	470,041	187,980	212,051	273,525	327,577
Totals	531,458	79,925	13.7%	325,354	878,155	527,167	575,720	658,026	722,120
Normal Dist.	531,458	79,925	13.7%			531,458	580,645	651,409	701,106
logNormal Dist.	531,470	73,048	13.7%			526,520	577,415	659,386	723,818
Gamma Dist	531,458	72,925	13.7%			528,126	578,661	656,823	715,657
TVaR						588,000	626,587	703,503	772,366
Normal TVaR						589,644	624,153	681,881	725,818
logNormal TVaR						589,301	627,978	699,103	758,866
Gamma TVaR						589,491	626,789	692,999	746,498

Casualty One
Calendar Year Unpaid
Best Estimate (Weighted)

Calendar Year	Mean Unpaid	Standard Error	Coefficient of Variation	Minimum	Maximum	50.0% Percentile	75.0% Percentile	95.0% Percentile	99.0% Percentile
2009	166,592	28,143	16.9%	89,278	316,269	164,670	183,838	216,605	240,162
2010	135,242	26,181	19.4%	61,060	256,781	133,509	151,547	181,699	205,003
2011	101,188	24,406	24.1%	39,744	213,715	99,007	115,970	144,667	172,658
2012	61,142	17,332	28.3%	22,362	159,500	59,434	71,001	92,278	111,828
2013	38,160	11,992	31.4%	11,986	95,577	36,481	45,340	59,766	73,650
2014	21,651	6,655	30.7%	6,950	72,594	20,878	25,616	33,130	41,042
2015	5,897	1,688	28.6%	1,726	14,740	5,685	6,834	8,927	11,038
2016	1,585	776	48.9%	144	6,918	1,487	1,984	2,978	3,881
2017	-	-	0.0%	-	-	-	-	-	-
2018	-	-	0.0%	-	-	-	-	-	-
Totals	531,458	72,925	13.7%	325,354	878,155	527,167	575,720	658,026	722,120

Casualty One
Accident Year Ultimate Loss Ratios
Best Estimate (Weighted)

Accident Year	Mean Loss Ratio	Standard Error	Coefficient of Variation	Minimum	Maximum	50.0% Percentile	75.0% Percentile	95.0% Percentile	99.0% Percentile
1999	67.0%	18.8%	28.0%	15.1%	159.9%	63.4%	75.5%	104.6%	122.7%
2000	82.4%	20.8%	25.2%	16.3%	183.8%	78.3%	91.9%	122.9%	144.6%
2001	76.5%	19.6%	25.6%	19.9%	173.4%	72.7%	86.1%	114.3%	135.4%
2002	75.1%	19.9%	26.5%	27.7%	165.2%	71.4%	85.2%	115.2%	132.3%
2003	70.7%	20.7%	29.3%	20.3%	158.4%	65.8%	82.6%	111.3%	132.0%
2004	72.1%	23.8%	32.9%	22.1%	260.3%	67.1%	81.2%	118.4%	151.7%
2005	73.0%	24.7%	33.8%	15.8%	200.2%	67.4%	83.2%	124.1%	152.4%
2006	75.5%	19.0%	25.1%	28.0%	180.6%	72.1%	83.4%	112.6%	138.3%
2007	65.9%	15.8%	23.9%	19.8%	167.5%	64.1%	73.0%	95.4%	117.4%
2008	66.8%	16.5%	24.6%	23.9%	167.6%	66.4%	74.3%	96.3%	114.4%
Totals	72.0%	6.5%	9.1%	52.6%	99.3%	71.6%	76.1%	83.6%	88.5%

Casualty One
Total Unpaid Distributions
Best Estimate (Weighted)

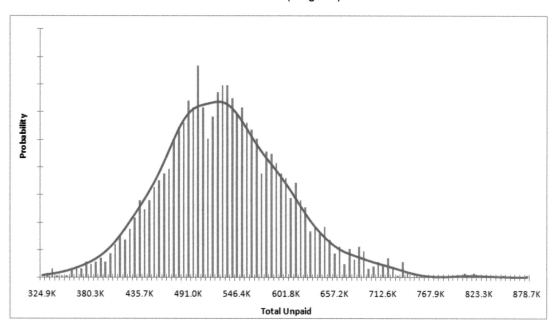

Casualty One
Summary of Model Distributions
(Using Kernel Densities)

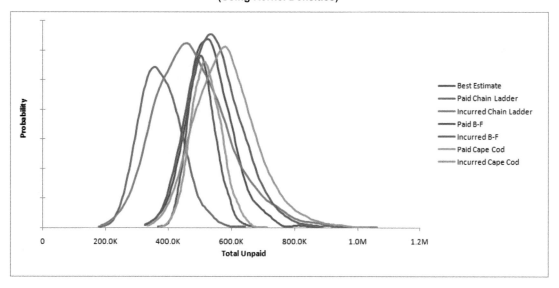

Exhibit IV.D-4: Casualty Two Results

Casualty Two
Summary of Results by Model

Accident Year	Chain Ladder		Bornhuetter-Ferguson		Cape Cod		Best Est. (Weighted)
	Paid	Incurred	Paid	Incurred	Paid	Incurred	
1999	18,361	14,437	14,511	12,160	21,314	16,486	16,435
2000	18,204	15,298	15,158	13,458	20,245	16,859	16,824
2001	20,009	16,481	17,338	15,066	21,097	17,445	18,257
2002	27,116	26,056	21,341	21,664	22,274	22,104	26,557
2003	27,156	24,303	21,772	20,646	28,544	25,566	25,740
2004	38,659	33,913	32,079	29,840	38,071	33,843	36,211
2005	77,313	71,545	70,934	68,361	68,298	64,746	74,742
2006	112,490	104,909	95,585	94,383	108,846	102,607	108,736
2007	154,041	166,808	143,911	156,903	162,114	167,586	157,138
2008	221,184	224,523	213,306	220,217	263,632	248,271	236,091
Totals	714,533	698,273	645,937	652,698	754,436	715,514	716,730

Casualty Two
Accident Year Unpaid
Best Estimate (Weighted)

Accident Year	Mean Unpaid	Standard Error	Coefficient of Variation	Minimum	Maximum	50.0% Percentile	75.0% Percentile	95.0% Percentile	99.0% Percentile
1999	16,435	9,051	55.1%	-	58,465	15,486	21,569	33,056	42,454
2000	16,824	9,141	54.3%	-	58,719	15,963	22,168	33,077	41,801
2001	18,257	9,428	51.6%	34	57,320	17,322	23,83	35,904	44,993
2002	26,557	12,278	46.2%	598	80,676	25,856	34,207	48,029	57,945
2003	25,740	11,301	43.9%	1,318	76,697	24,747	32,865	46,250	55,459
2004	36,211	14,096	38.9%	6,109	100,047	34,900	45,148	60,836	74,920
2005	74,742	24,133	32.3%	15,871	161,666	72,977	89,632	117,908	136,670
2006	108,736	29,029	26.7%	37,309	232,830	105,774	127,441	160,386	182,009
2007	157,138	28,523	18.2%	90,090	260,815	154,047	175,134	207,948	232,219
2008	236,091	37,338	15.8%	145,206	383,716	229,886	260,076	305,443	335,669
Totals	716,730	136,695	19.1%	355,975	1,279,276	713,601	808,327	947,050	1,050,407
Normal Dist.	716,730	136,695	19.1%			716,730	808,929	941,573	1,034,730
logNormal Dist.	717,014	141,217	19.7%			703,499	802,432	969,661	1,107,536
Gamma Dist	716,730	136,695	19.1%			708,058	803,596	955,392	1,072,443
TVaR						826,181	894,209	1,011,448	1,109,657
Normal TVaR						825,796	890,484	998,692	1,081,051
logNormal TVaR						827,915	905,801	1,054,885	1,185,481
Gamma TVaR						825,246	897,120	1,027,436	1,134,872

Casualty Two
Calendar Year Unpaid
Best Estimate (Weighted)

Calendar Year	Mean Unpaid	Standard Error	Coefficient of Variation	Minimum	Maximum	50.0% Percentile	75.0% Percentile	95.0% Percentile	99.0% Percentile
2009	171,971	17,145	10.0%	117,337	250,746	171,184	183,775	200,280	215,344
2010	100,901	11,801	11.7%	62,989	144,455	100,875	108,020	121,364	130,786
2011	71,049	10,934	15.4%	42,026	115,416	70,398	78,138	90,070	98,426
2012	57,849	12,032	20.8%	26,259	117,280	57,215	65,435	78,790	89,215
2013	42,577	10,592	24.9%	14,251	89,105	41,552	49,129	61,247	69,716
2014	39,271	13,267	33.8%	8,088	98,349	38,204	47,574	62,410	76,129
2015	52,945	22,719	42.9%	1,905	137,821	51,393	67,419	93,297	111,598
2016	58,911	26,670	45.3%	716	183,030	56,953	76,669	104,443	126,115
2017	61,229	27,262	44.5%	0	162,216	61,060	78,467	108,836	130,517
2018	61,101	27,529	45.1%	67	180,740	59,308	78,469	107,538	135,281
Totals	716,730	136,695	19.1%	355,975	1,279,276	713,601	808,327	947,050	1,050,407

Casualty Two
Accident Year Ultimate Loss Ratios
Best Estimate (Weighted)

Calendar Year	Mean Loss Ratio	Standard Error	Coefficient of Variation	Minimum	Maximum	50.0% Percentile	75.0% Percentile	95.0% Percentile	99.0% Percentile
1999	45.6%	10.6%	23.3%	13.5%	78.1%	46.2%	52.4%	62.4%	69.75
2000	51.9%	11.7%	22.5%	15.2%	91.6%	51.9%	59.3%	71.3%	79.3%
2001	57.2%	13.2%	23.1%	13.8%	105.8%	57.6%	65.8%	78.2%	87.9%
2002	83.5%	16.0%	19.2%	34.6%	159.7%	82.8%	93.0%	111.6%	124.5%
2003	66.4%	13.7%	20.6%	24.1%	117.5%	66.7%	75.1%	88.5%	101.7%
2004	73.6%	14.3%	19.4%	32.1%	131.9%	73.6%	82.9%	96.7%	108.2%
2005	88.8%	14.0%	15.8%	48.3%	143.4%	88.6%	97.9%	112.5%	123.2%
2006	84.8%	13.3%	15.7%	47.9%	142.4%	84.2%	93.6%	107.1%	118.6%
2007	86.1%	11.0%	12.7%	59.0%	139.6%	84.8%	92.9%	106.3%	114.8%
2008	81.3%	11.0%	13.6%	49.4%	120.8%	79.8%	88.3%	101.1%	110.2%
Totals	75.4%	5.4%	7.1%	55.7%	96.8%	75.2%	78.9%	84.5%	89.2%

Casualty Two
Total Unpaid Distribution
Best Estimate (Weighte3d)

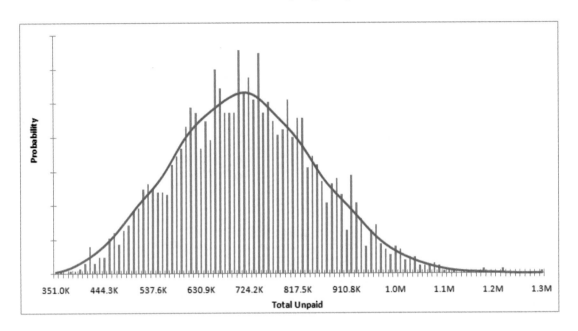

Casualty Two
Summary of Model Distributions
(Using Kernel Densities)

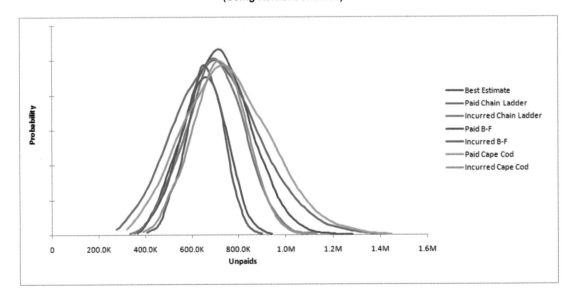

Exhibit IV.D-5: Aggregate Results
(Using Model Correlations)

Aggregate All Lines of Business
Calendar Year Unpaid

Calendar Year	Mean Unpaid	Standard Error	Coefficient of Variation	Minimum	Maximum	50.0% Percentile	75.0% Percentile	95.0% Percentile	99.0% Percentile
2009	473,528	38,439	8.1%	363,468	623,870	472,222	498,972	538,176	570,565
2010	237,086	28,098	11.9%	156,716	382,161	234,938	254,752	283,991	310,427
2011	172,431	25,990	15.1%	100,899	284,663	170,464	188,277	218,322	243,693
2012	119,129	19,981	16.8%	63,245	214,867	117,809	131,502	153,406	172,045
2013	80,821	15,034	18.6%	33,159	141,781	79,421	89,985	108,218	120,261
2014	60,967	14,411	23.6%	21,329	127,311	59,903	69,515	86,765	99,384
2015	58,870	22,634	38.4%	6,264	150,479	57,301	73,579	98,857	116,661
2016	60,511	26,654	44.0%	1,572	183,821	58,557	78,246	105,757	127,699
2017	61,118	27,371	44.8%	0	162,216	60,988	78,404	108,787	130,517
2018	61,101	27,529	45.1%	67	180,740	59,308	78,469	107,538	135,281
Totals	1,384,609	144,806	10.5%	988,951	1,942,710	1,381,216	1,478,766	1,632,970	1,725,027

Aggregate All Lines of Business
Accident Year Ultimate Loss Ratios

Accident Year	Mean Loss Ratio	Standard Error	Coefficient of Variation	Minimum	Maximum	50.0% Percentile	75.0% Percentile	95.0% Percentile	99.0% Percentile
1999	86.5%	6.1%	7.1%	68.1%	106.7%	86.4%	90.8%	96.7%	100.6%
2000	85.8%	5.8%	6.8%	69.8%	106.3%	85.8%	89.9%	95.6%	99.2%
2001	79.0%	5.3%	6.7%	62.4%	97.2%	79.0%	82.5%	88.0%	91.3%
2002	79.7%	5.1%	6.4%	64.2%	98.1%	79.6%	83.1%	88.4%	91.9%
2003	78.7%	4.9%	6.2%	62.5%	97.4%	78.5%	82.1%	87.1%	90.6%
2004	74.2%	4.7%	6.4%	59.6%	95.7%	73.9%	77.2%	82.2%	86.5%
2005	74.2%	4.6%	6.2%	61.1%	90.7%	73.9%	77.1%	82.3%	85.6%
2006	70.9%	4.0%	5.6%	58.6%	86.1%	70.9%	73.6%	77.6%	80.6%
2007	69.4%	3.7%	5.4%	58.4%	84.1%	69.3%	71.8%	75.7%	78.8%
2008	72.2%	3.5%	4.8%	60.7%	85.5%	72.1%	74.4%	78.0%	80.8%
Totals	75.6%	1.5%	2.0%	70.8%	81.3%	75.6%	76.6%	78.1%	79.2%

Aggregate All Lines of Business
Total Unpaid Distribution

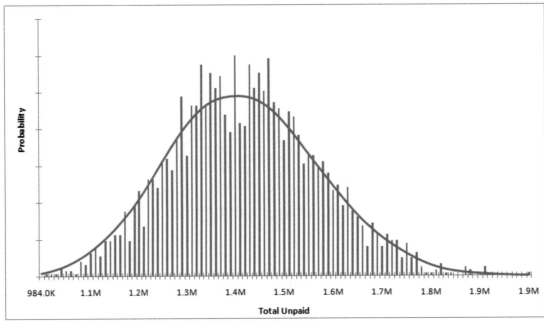

(Using 50% Correlation)

Aggregate All Lines of Business
Accident Year Ultimate Loss Ratios

Accident Year	Mean Loss Ratio	Standard Error	Coefficient of Variation	Minimum	Maximum	50.0% Percentile	75.0% Percentile	95.0% Percentile	99.0% Percentile
1999	86.5%	6.0%	7.0%	65.2%	107.4%	86.4%	90.8%	96.5%	99.9%
2000	85.8%	5.9%	6.9%	66.5%	110.9%	85.8%	89.7%	96.2%	100.4%
2001	79.0%	5.3%	6.7%	62.4%	98.2%	79.0%	82.6%	87.8%	91.7%
2002	79.7%	5.2%	6.5%	63.7%	98.0%	79.7%	83.3%	88.3%	91.9%
2003	78.7%	4.8%	6.1%	65.3%	94.9%	78.7%	82.0%	86.9%	89.6%
2004	74.2%	4.7%	6.4%	60.6%	97.7%	73.9%	77.3%	82.3%	86.4%
2005	74.2%	4.7%	6.4%	61.3%	91.7%	74.0%	77.2%	82.2%	86.8%
2006	70.9%	4.3%	6.0%	59.2%	86.3%	70.8%	73.6%	78.3%	81.7%
2007	69.4%	3.9%	5.6%	58.5%	87.9%	69.3%	72.0%	75.8%	78.9%
2008	72.2%	4.0%	5.6%	59.9%	94.4%	72.1%	74.6%	78.9%	83.0%
Totals	75.6%	1.7%	2.3%	70.3%	83.6%	75.5%	76.7%	78.4%	80.0%

IV.E Stochastic Liability and Capital Calculations

An insurer's obligations to make a payment or payments to a designated party upon some future insured event represent that insurer's largest liability. Whether stochastically or deterministically calculated, a policy liability should be created to recognize the insurer's liability for an insured event that has yet to occur. But uncertainty exists regarding when this event will occur and under what circumstances. Such uncertainty can be addressed through the use of stochastic policy liabilities. We will now explore how a stochastic policy liability can be calculated for a simple 10-year level term product.

It should be pointed out that a policy liability is different from a claim liability, which is calculated for an event that has already occurred, but which has uncertain future payments. An example of a claim liability might involve future payments on a workers' compensation claim that has been reported but not yet fully developed. Claim liabilities are not covered in this case study.

IV.E.1 Background

Unlike deterministically calculated liabilities that rely on a single point estimate, a stochastic policy liability contemplates the volatility of future outcomes, because it is developed from randomly generated scenarios based on certain assumptions; therefore, it allows for an examination of a range of possible liability values. Although the final liability is a single number, the process takes into consideration a distribution of possible outcomes from which liabilities can be set according to the company's risk tolerance. A relatively risk-averse company may set liabilities at the 95th percentile of outcomes from the stochastic output, while a more aggressive company may hold liabilities equal to the median outcome. In either case, stochastic modeling reveals the underlying risk of the product for which the liability has been determined. Any assumption can be modeled, but stochastic modeling is typically limited to those assumptions that exhibit material volatility or uncertainty, and which have a material impact on the calculated liability.

Methods for calculating stochastic liabilities

Several methods can be used to calculate a stochastic liability. The selection will depend on the answers to two key questions:

- **How is the liability in each stochastic scenario defined?**

- **What risk metric will be used to calculate the stochastic liability from the distribution of stochastic outcomes?**

Let us look at each question separately. With respect to the first question, there are two generally accepted approaches: present value of net annual cash flows and greatest present value of accumulated deficiency.

In the first approach – the present value of net annual cash flows – the scenario liability is set equal to the present value of future claims and expenses less the present value of future premium and other income. Given its consistency with textbook exposition of liabilities, we might refer to this approach as the "actuarial first principles approach."

For the second approach, projected future net income is accumulated from the valuation date to each future measurement date. The liability is then set equal to the present value of cumulative future profits up to the point at which cumulative profits are the lowest of any future measurement date. A simple example will clarify this concept.

The 10-year projection of net income shown in Figure IV.E-1 indicates that the greatest accumulated deficiency occurs at the end of year 8 when the cumulated net income is (36). Ignoring interest income, the figure 36 would be used as the liability.

Figure IV.E-1

10-year Projection of Net Income

Table 1

	Projection Year									
	1	2	3	4	5	6	7	8	9	10
Net Income	5	(10)	(5)	6	8	10	(20)	(30)	10	5
Cumulated Net Income	5	(5)	(10)	(4)	4	14	(6)	(36)	(26)	(21)

The approach effectively establishes a liability that is sufficient to keep the company solvent at the worst point in the projection. Because it does not reflect possible future gains beyond the point at which the accumulated deficiency is projected to be the worst, it is slightly more conservative than the first technique, which reflects profits and losses for the entire projection period.

Perhaps the two most commonly used risk metrics are:

- **Value at risk (VaR): an approach in which the liability is set equal to the scenario liability at a chosen percentile.**

- **Conditional tail expectation (CTE): an approach in which the liability is set equal to the average of scenario liabilities above a chosen percentile.**

Both approaches were discussed in considerable detail in Section I.E.

In this case study, we will examine stochastic liabilities under a combination of four techniques summarized in Figure IV.E-2.

Figure IV.E-2

Stochastic Liabilities Under Four Techniques

Table 2

Technique #	How are Scenario Liabilities Defined?	Risk Metric
1	Present Value of Net Annual Cash Flows	VaR
2	Present Value of Net Annual Cash Flows	CTE
3	Greatest Present Value of Accumulated Deficiency	VaR
4	Greatest Present Value of Accumulated Deficiency	CTE

IV.E.2 Detailed Example: Illustration of Stochastic Liabilities

Using the results found in the Excel file "Case Study_Stochastic Reserves.xls" (which can be found on the IAA website www.actuaries.org/stochastic) as a guide, we now turn to a discussion of the concepts used in stochastically generating liability for a 10-year term product. Please consult the tab instructions to use the model referenced above.

Policy characteristics and baseline assumptions

The policy for which we calculated a stochastic policy liability is a 10-year level term product with $1,000 face value written on a 55-year-old male smoker. The policy does not have any embedded options or guarantees, endowment benefits payable at the end of the level term period, nor riders or other additional benefits associated with the base term policy. The level premium is assumed to be paid at the beginning of each year, as are all expenses. Death benefits are assumed to be paid at the end of the year, and liabilities are calculated at the end of policy year 5, the policyholder's attained age 60.

Figure IV.E-3 shows the baseline, deterministic assumptions underlying our analysis.

█ Figure IV.E-3

Baseline Deterministic Assumptions

Interest Rates and Yields	
Valuation Interest Rate	5.0%
Discount Rate (used for pricing)	12.0%
Net Investment Earned Rate	6.0%
Expenses	
Acquisition Expenses	10% of first-year premium
Maintenance Expenses	2.0% of premium
Commissions	15% of first-year premium 5% of second- and third-year premiums 0% thereafter
Demographic Assumptions	
Lapse Rates:	
Policy Year 1 2 3 4 5 6 7 8 9 10	Rate 10% 5% 5% 5% 5% 3% 3% 2% 2% 1%
Mortality:	2001 CSO
Other Assumptions	
Income Tax	35% applied directly to pre-tax net cash flow

For stochastically modeled assumptions (discussed below), we used a stochastic generator that creates scenarios by making adjustments to the baseline assumptions. We calculated the adjustments according to user-defined probability distributions and parameters.

Stochastic assumptions

Assumptions related to lapse rates, mortality, and investment returns on invested assets were modeled stochastically, because they have a material impact on the calculated liability. Stochastic modeling would also be appropriate for variables that exhibit material volatility.

Lapse rates

We used a stochastic generator that calculates additive adjustments to the baseline lapse assumption to generate 1,000 lapse scenarios. The adjustments are generated from a normal distribution with mean 0 and standard deviation 1.5%. For this reason, stochastically generated lapse rates should exhibit a bell-shaped pattern around the baseline assumption, such that approximately 67% of the scenarios are within an additive 1.5% of the baseline assumption.

Mortality

We used a stochastic generator that calculates multiplicative adjustments to the baseline mortality assumption to generate 1,000 mortality scenarios. The adjustments are generated from a normal distribution with mean 1 and standard deviation 0.20. Stochastic mortality scenarios should, therefore, exhibit a bell-shaped pattern around the baseline assumption, such that approximately 67% of the scenarios are between 80% and 120% of the baseline mortality rates.

Pre-tax net investment earned rates

We used a stochastic generator that calculates additive adjustments to the baseline investment earned rates to generate 1,000 investment earned rate scenarios. The adjustments are generated from a normal distribution with mean 0 and standard deviation 1%. Consequently, stochastic interest scenarios are expected to exhibit a bell-shaped pattern around the baseline assumption, such that approximately 67% of the scenarios are between 5% and 7%.

The stochastic generators used in the analysis have been kept relatively simple in order to focus on the key concepts, rather than mathematical mechanics of formula computations. This approach should allow the reader to replicate results without getting bogged down in unnecessarily rigorous calculations. More complex scenario generators are likely to be needed in practice. Sections II.A and II.B contain additional detail on stochastic modeling of certain assumptions.

Overview of calculating stochastic liabilities

Having generated 1,000 scenarios for each of the key risk factors – lapses, mortality, and investment earned rates – we now turn our attention to the generation of stochastic liabilities. The process begins by calculating three initial sets of liabilities, one for each of the three risk factors' 1,000 scenarios discussed above. Because each individual risk reflects only the risk associated with a single assumption, each of these three sets of liabilities is only a stepping-stone and necessary for developing an aggregate set of stochastic assumptions. The assumptions reflect the risk associated with all the stochastically modeled assumptions to be used in the final calculation of aggregate liabilities.

An overview of the procedure is as follows:

1. Run three stochastic projections, one for each of the three assumptions that we are modeling stochastically.

2. Use the results from Step 1 to generate 1,000 aggregate scenarios for lapse, mortality, and yield assumptions.

3. Run a final stochastic projection using the 1,000 aggregate scenarios for use when calculating the final liability.

The results of the model referred to above (Case Study_Stochastic Reserves.xls) for the first step are illustrated on tabs "2.2 – Output" and "2.3 – Sorted Output".

Development of aggregate scenarios

Having run the individual assumption scenarios, we then generated an aggregate set of stochastic scenarios to be used for calculating the final liability. For this step, we had the option of the following two approaches:

- **Run all combinations of the individual risk scenarios.**

- **Combine the individual risk scenarios using variance reduction techniques.**

Even with the relatively limited number of risk factors in this case study, the first option would require us to run 1 billion aggregate scenarios (1,000^3). Because this calculation would typically take years to complete, we strongly preferred the second option.

For this case study, we developed aggregate scenarios using a relatively simple variance reduction approach, which consisted of the following steps:

1. Rank the output (according to liabilities) from each of the three individual risk runs.

2. For each individual risk run, identify the particular scenario that generates results at each decile, i.e., 10th percentile, 20th percentile, ..., 100th percentile. This segmentation yields 10 "representative" scenarios for each of the stochastically modeled assumptions. (The scenarios are considered representative because they are selected at uniform intervals from the distribution of outcomes for each assumption.)

3. Generate 1,000 aggregate scenarios, representing every possible combination of scenarios identified in Step 2.

This technique is certainly not the only acceptable approach for generating the aggregate stochastic scenarios. But it does have certain key advantages. By selecting a small number of scenarios from each stochastically modeled assumption, it greatly reduces the number of possible scenarios from 1 billion to 1,000, and the required run time from years to minutes. Such increased efficiency is carried through in its effectiveness. Because "representative" scenarios are drawn from each stochastically modeled assumption, the selected scenarios should be expected to produce a distribution of results reasonably similar to the full set of 1 billion scenarios. The model includes scenarios that range from "good" outcomes to "bad" outcomes for each of the stochastic assumptions. In this way, we can feel confident that a reasonable sample was taken from the distribution of total possible outcomes. This rationale admittedly does not constitute mathematical proof, but we can test it by increasing the number of aggregate scenarios selected and validating by determining that the distribution of outcomes is relatively similar to the results presented here. For the present case study, 1,000 is deemed an appropriate number of aggregate scenarios for analysis.

Results for stochastic liabilities

The Excel file, Case Study_Stochastic Reserves.xls (which can be found on the IAA website www.actuaries.org/stochastic), presents the results obtained from the 1,000 aggregate scenarios in tab 2.6 – Summary, including those for both approaches discussed (present value of net cash flows and greatest present value of accumulated deficiency) and both risk metrics (VaR and CTE). The level at which liabilities are set will depend upon the company's level of risk aversion and any applicable regulations.

Results for certain percentiles are presented in the tables in Figure IV.E-4 and Figure IV.E-5.

▌ Figure IV.E-4

Risk Metric: Present Value of Net Cash Flows

Table 3 – Summary of Liabilities
Risk Metric: Present Value of Net Cash Flows

Level	Liability (VaR)	Liability (CTE)
99.50%	45.47	45.47
99.00%	44.95	44.95
95.00%	43.06	43.97
90.00%	40.33	43.02
75.00%	35.77	39.46
65.00%	34.54	38.23
50.00%	33.11	36.92

▌ Figure IV.E-5

Risk Metric: Greatest Present Value of Accumulated Deficiency

Level	Liability (VaR)	Liability (CTE)
99.50%	45.47	45.47
99.00%	44.95	44.95
95.00%	43.06	43.97
90.00%	40.33	43.02
75.00%	35.77	39.46
65.00%	34.54	38.23
50.00%	33.11	36.92

In this case study, these two approaches yield the same result, because profits decreased throughout the projection period. This result is typical for a level term product, because mortality rates increase over the projection period (for each individual cell), but premium does not similarly increase to offset the increase in mortality rates.

This case study's result is more generally true. Liabilities developed using either of the two approaches will produce the same result, although the greatest present value of accumulated deficiency approach is considered slightly more conservative, because it does not give credit for positive profits beyond the worst solvency point in the projection; the present value of net annual cash flows approach, however, does.

The graphs in Figures IV.E-6 and IV.E-7 approximate the density function and cumulative distribution function for the liabilities produced by the aggregate scenarios. They are based on a histogram approach rather than a continuous distribution approach. This kind of graphical presentation can be helpful in understanding the volatility of results and the tail risk of the product.

Figure IV.E-6

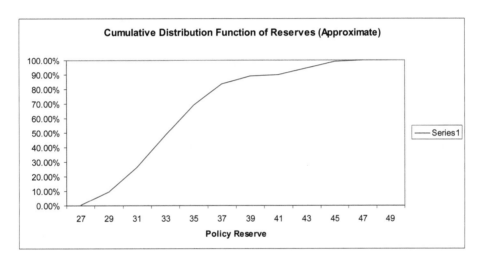

Figure IV.E-7

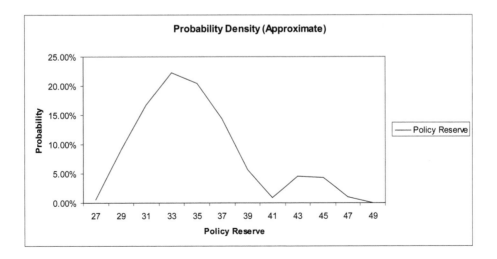

Results: Stochastic risk-based capital

If a company's risk-based capital is viewed as some margin above and beyond the company's liabilities, we can also develop it from the liability model output by simply selecting a higher percentile than that set for the liability. For instance, if stochastic liabilities are set using VaR at the 75th percentile, capital could be set using VaR at the 95th percentile. Such an arrangement would mean that the company's capital is equal to the liability at the 95th percentile, less the liability at the 75th percentile. Selecting the appropriate percentile for determining capital may depend upon a company's level of risk aversion, regulatory considerations, and targeted investment rating, when applicable.

IV.E.3 Assumption Setting: Use of Margins

The level of margin (or provision for adverse deviation), including assumptions used to develop liabilities, is generally a matter of regulatory concern; nonetheless, a few general comments are appropriate here.

Judgment plays a considerable role not only in determining the appropriate parameters to use in the stochastic generators, but also in determining the appropriate level of margin associated with those parameters. The level of margin can be approached from two perspectives: qualitative and quantitative. The qualitative approach suggests that the greater the uncertainty related to the credibility or applicability giving rise to a particular assumption, the greater the margin. The quantitative approach, on the other hand, is based on a rigorous review of historical data. Given this approach, margin can be quantitatively adjusted by either selecting data from particularly volatile historical periods or by setting the standard deviation in the stochastic generator equal to 125% (or some other level) of the historical standard deviation.

There are numerous statistical techniques beyond the scope of this book, which could be used to incorporate additional levels of margin into the model.

IV.E.4 Peer Review and Audit of Results

An actuary who undertakes a review of the stochastic liability calculation would likely look into a number of issues. Among the most important questions to ask are:

- **Is the median liability from the distribution of outcomes consistent with the liability calculated using deterministic assumptions? If not, are there valid reasons for the difference, such as the use of a skewed distribution to generate the stochastic scenarios?**

- **Is the distribution of liabilities smooth? If not, are any bumps or spikes explainable by product features, e.g., embedded guarantee.**

IV.F Economic Capital for a Multi-line Non-life Insurance Company

This case study presents an economic capital (EC) analysis of a multi-line non-life insurance company, focusing on parameterization of the simulation model. The firm DFA Insurance Company (DFAIC) is a regional multi-line non-life insurance company writing personal lines and main street commercial business. Background information and financial statement data for DFAIC were obtained from a call paper request in CAS Forum (2001). But before delving into the main topic, let us first briefly describe the risk matrix and simulation model. (More detailed descriptions of the model and the economic capital framework have been provided in other sections of this book.)

IV.F.1 Risk Metric and Time Horizon

This case study uses the 99% conditional tail expectation (CTE-99, also known as the Tail Value at Risk [$TVAR_{99}$]) of economic value capital as its risk matrix. The CTE-99 is the average of the worst 1% of losses in economic capital over the next year. Economic capital is calculated as the excess of the market value of assets over the market value of liabilities. The fact that insurance company liabilities are not commonly traded will require us to estimate their market value by using a risk-adjusted discount rate, as noted by Butsic (1988).

This case study will use a forecast horizon of one year—a timeframe that is consistent with many insurers' budgeting cycles. This approach assumes that shortfalls in economic capital can be replenished in one year. The use of a one-year horizon decreases the difficulty in modeling reasonable outcomes for economic scenarios, operational changes, and underwriting cycles. One disadvantage of a short horizon, however, is that it doesn't allow sufficient time to incorporate possible strategy changes into the model or for the consideration of the long-term adverse impact of existing strategies. If significant strategy changes are anticipated, it may be more appropriate to use a longer forecast horizon.

IV.F.2 Description of the Model

The simulation model is composed of four modules:

- **Economic scenario**
- **Underwriting**
- **Asset**
- **Accounting and taxation**

The economic scenario generator is used to simultaneously develop inputs for both the asset and the underwriting modules. This modeling approach allows us to properly reflect the correlation among the asset and underwriting returns caused by changes in the underlying economic values, such as interest rates, inflation rates, and other economic variables. The results of the asset and underwriting modules are then combined and fed through the accounting and tax calculations.

Economic scenario module

The economic scenario module generates stochastic scenarios of the economic variables that are used as inputs to the underwriting and assets models. The economic variables generated by this module include short-term interest rates for bank deposits or government notes, bond yields for government and corporate bonds of various maturities, equity appreciation and dividend yields, economic growth rates, and inflation rates. A detailed description of an economic scenario generator is provided in Section IV.B.

Underwriting module

The underwriting module simulates the insurance company operations and calculates the resulting cash flows and accruals relating to issuing policies, claim payments, and company expenses.

For modeling purposes, lines of business with similar characteristics are typically grouped. In general, the extent of grouping depends on the volume of business and similarity of the lines, the purpose of the analysis, and the availability of data. This case study uses the following product groupings:

- **Private passenger auto liability (PPA)**
- **Commercial auto liability (CA)**
- **Homeowners**
- **Workers' compensation (WC)**
- **Commercial multiple peril (CMP)**
- **Property**
- **Other direct**
- **Assumed**
- **Expenses are modeled in these four groups:**
- **Commissions (as a percentage of written premium)**
- **General underwriting expense (as a percentage of earned premium)**
- **Unallocated loss adjustment expenses (ULAE), half as a percentage of paid loss and half as a percentage of earned premium**
- **Allocated loss adjustment expenses (modeled with losses)**

Asset module

The asset module processes the investment activity of the company. Asset market values are updated based on the economic scenario generators. Cash flows from investments (coupons, dividends, and maturities) and net cash flows from insurance operations are invested. Investments are rebalanced to a desired mix by asset type.

Assets are modeled using the following groupings:

- **Tax-free bonds**
- **Taxable bonds**
- **Equities**
- **Cash**
- **Other**

Accounting and taxation module

The accounting and taxation module combines the results of the underwriting and investment modules to produce financial statements and calculate income taxes. In this case study, undiscounted statements were created and used as the basis for comparison with the historical financials and the income tax calculation. Economic value (market value) statements were developed as a way of assessing our desired metric, economic capital.

IV.F.3 Inputs and Parameterization

As a base scenario for this case study, we assume the company will write business at a steady rate for one year following the starting date of the simulation. No planned rate changes or exposure changes are modeled.

The calculation of the parameters for the PPA line is shown in this section and is illustrated in the Excel file "SectionIV_E_NonLifeEC.xls" (which can be found on the IAA website www.actuaries.org/stochastic). The parameters for other lines of business are not discussed or shown in the workbook, but they were calculated in a similar manner. In many cases, the supplied data was not sufficient to calculate the needed parameters. In these cases, we made assumptions or approximations to derive the parameters. The additional assumptions or approximations used are also described in this section.

Premium

The premium calculations are shown in the Premium tab of the Excel file referred to in the previous paragraph.

Direct written premium is modeled by multiplying the prior year written premium by a random error term.

$$\text{WrittenPrem1} = \text{WrittenPrem0} * (1 + \text{error term}) \qquad \text{(IV.F-1)}$$

where error term is randomly drawn from a distribution with a mean of 0.

The error term represents the difference between the expected or budgeted threshold and the threshold actually realized. For premium, the error term would include differences from the expected number of policies issued, differences in the average policy size, and differences in the final charged rates.

We would prefer to calculate the error term based on a history of expected versus actual premiums, but this information is unavailable. Instead, we will develop an approximation by fitting an exponential regression to 10 years of direct earned premium. The error term is selected to be a normal distribution with a mean of 0 and a standard deviation equal to the standard error of the y estimate from the regression.

For PPA liability

$$\text{WrittenPrem1} = 793{,}144 * (1 + N(0, 0.0929)) \qquad \text{(IV. F-2)}$$

We calculate earned premium by multiplying written premium by an earning pattern. We assumed that premium earning and collection occur over two years. The earning pattern is calculated from the ratio of unearned premium to written premium. Collected premium and the collection pattern are calculated in a similar manner.

$$\text{EarningPattern2} = \text{Unearned Premium} / \text{Written Premium} \qquad \text{(IV. F-3)}$$

$$\text{EarningPattern1} = 1 - \text{Earningpattern2} \tag{IV.F-4}$$

$$\text{EarningPattern2} = 211{,}134 \ / \ 593{,}000 = 0.356$$

$$\text{EarningPattern1} = 1.0 - 0.356 = 0.644$$

We selected the reinsurance rate—defined as the ratio of ceded premium to direct premium—at 26% for PPA liability, after observing the historical ratios over the previous 10 years. If more detailed information about historical reinsurance, rates, and retentions had been available, we could have further refined this estimate. Still, this simple approach should produce an adequate estimate.

Expenses

The expense calculations are shown in the Expenses tab of the Excel file referred to at the beginning of this section. Expenses are calculated as follows:

$$\text{Commission Expense} = \text{Written Premium} * \text{Rate} * (1 + \text{error term}) \tag{IV.F-5}$$

$$\text{Other Underwriting Expense} = \text{Earned Premium} * \text{Rate} * (1 + \text{error term}) \tag{IV.F-6}$$

$$\text{ULAE} = (\text{Earned Premium} + \text{Paid Loss}) \ / \ 2 * \text{Rate} * (1 + \text{error term}) \tag{IV.F-7}$$

We calculated the commission rate from the ratio of direct commission to direct written premium. We calculated the other underwriting expense rate from the ratio of the remaining underwriting expenses to earned premium. The unallocated loss adjustment expense rate was selected based on a review of the ratios for the prior 10 years.

ULAE was the only expense category with enough historical data to allow for an estimate of the standard deviation of the error terms. We used the coefficient of variation (the ratio of the standard deviation to the mean) for ULAE to calculate the standard deviations for the commission rate error and the other underwriting expense error.

Losses

Losses are modeled by line of business in four groups:

- **Runoff of starting loss liability**
- **Individual large losses**
- **Aggregate small losses**
- **Catastrophe losses**

Runoff of starting liability

The runoff of the starting liability, also known as liability risk, projects the possible outcomes of future payments made on claims that have already occurred as of the projection date.

Models are often parameterized using company financial statements containing only summarized information about claims which have occurred prior to the start of the modeling period. Individual claim information may not be available regarding the size of individual claims or the historical reinsurance retentions to use to calculate the ceded portion of each claim. For this reason, we modeled the runoff on a net of reinsurance basis separately from the future claims.

If individual claim information is available, then we can model the runoff of the starting liability in the same manner we model future claims. We describe this process later in this case study.

$$\text{Runoff Losses} = \text{Starting Net Loss Liability} * (1 + \text{error term}) \tag{IV.F-8}$$

The error terms for the starting liability and the payout pattern were estimated using the procedures described in the case study in Section IV.D above.

Future claims

Accurate modeling of reinsurance is important for an economic capital analysis. Modeling excess of loss reinsurance requires knowledge of the size of each individual claim size to properly apply the per claim retention and limit. Yet the enormous computing power and run time needed to determine the size of each individual claim size, subject to per-claim retention and limit in an excess of loss (XOL) arrangement, is typically prohibitive. Fortunately, it is only necessary to individually model claims which exceed the XOL reinsurance retention. The remaining smaller claims may be modeled in aggregate with no effect on the accuracy of the reinsurance calculations.

A large claim refers to any claim in excess of a threshold that is less than or equal to the XOL reinsurance retention.

Catastrophe losses are modeled separately for several reasons. They can often have a significant impact on the financial condition of the company. They can affect multiple lines of business. Their distribution has a significantly heavier tail, so it is typically easier to model them separately than it would be to include them in the small-loss distribution. Further, recognition of the catastrophe reinsurance terms, including limits on coverage and reinstatement premiums, requires modeling the individual catastrophe events.

Individual large losses

Large losses are modeled by generating individual claims that exceed the reinsurance retention of 500,000. We need to simulate both the number of claims and the size of each claim.

Because the call paper data did not include any individual large-claim data, we must supplement the company data with industry data, which is assumed to be representative of the company's large-claim experience, as noted by the Texas Department of Insurance (2000). The industry data, however, does not include PPA liability, which requires that CA be used as a proxy.

We used the maximum likelihood method described earlier in this book to fit lognormal and Pareto distributions to the data. But before these adjustments are made, the claims must be trended to the starting date of the simulation, developed to ultimate value, adjusted for any differences in policy limits, and grouped into intervals by claim size. For this case study, we assumed these steps produce the grouped data shown in the Data tab of the Excel file referred to at the beginning of this section.

The lognormal and Pareto parameters were obtained by using Solver to minimize the sum of negative log likelihood for claim size intervals exceeding $500,000. Both distributions have two parameters, a feature that allows us to determine the distribution with the better fit to the data based on which one has a smaller sum of negative log likelihood. If distributions have different numbers of parameters, the Akaike (AIC) and Bayesian (BIC) information criteria can be used to select among alternative distributions.

The large-loss frequency is the number of large claims per million of premium. The historical frequency can be calculated by dividing the ceded losses by earned premium (in millions) and then by the average ceded loss per large claim. This case study uses a Poisson distribution for the claim frequency, with the parameter lambda equal to the large-loss frequency.

Aggregate small losses

Small losses are the remaining non-catastrophic losses on claims with sizes less than $500,000. They are modeled as follows:

Small Losses = Direct Earned Premium * Small Loss Ratio * (1 + error term)   (IV.F-9)

We calculated the small-loss ratio by selecting a net loss ratio based on the historical net data. We then converted the net loss ratio to a percentage of direct premium by grossing up by the ceded premium percentage. Next, we subtracted the retained portion of large losses and catastrophe losses. This calculation results in the portion of losses to be modeled by the small-loss ratio.

The standard deviation of the small-loss ratio error term can be calculated if we assume that the coefficient of variation of small losses is the same as the coefficient of variation of net losses. This assumption admittedly simplifies our analysis. Alternatively, the standard deviation of small losses can be derived by using a bootstrap model as illustrated in Section IV. D, by using industry data sources or by reducing the net standard deviation by the impacts of the standard deviations of the retained portions of large and cat losses. We used a normal distribution to model the small-loss ratio error. Given the parameters of this case study, it is unlikely that a negative small-loss ratio could be simulated. If this were not the case, we would need to either have a different error distribution or make changes to the calculations to ensure that a negative loss ratio is not produced.

A more refined model might separately consider variations in exposure and rate. Both exposure and rate would directly affect premium whereas exposure variability would directly affect losses and rate variability might indirectly affect losses via adverse selection.

The loss payment pattern for each line of business is calculated using a paid loss development triangle. We estimated the ratio of paid to ultimate loss for each development age, and we used the incremental differences between ages as the payment pattern. The same payment pattern is also used for large losses and catastrophe losses. The payment pattern for the starting liabilities is calculated from the accident year payment pattern by applying the remaining pattern as of each accident year age.

A refinement to the parameterization for another analysis would be to derive a specific payment pattern for each type of loss: small, large, and catastrophe. The data required to make these derivations was not available for this case study. We could then also select the payment patterns for each type of loss in a way that they balance in total to the accident year payment pattern.

Catastrophe losses

A realistic analysis with significant catastrophe exposure would typically require inputs from a catastrophe model. For this case study, catastrophe losses were simulated from a frequency distribution and a severity distribution, an approach similar to that taken in the large-loss model. Based on information provided in the call papers, which contained only limited information about the company's catastrophe losses, we assumed catastrophe loss to have an annual frequency of 0.2 with severity that followed a Pareto distribution for a minimum severity of $1 million, and a 1% chance of a loss exceeding $160 million.

Investment model

For this case study, we grouped assets into broad categories: taxable bond, non-taxable bond, stock, and cash, among others. Investment returns are obtained from the economic scenario generator. We assumed the asset mix to remain the same as that for the starting assets from the financial statements.

IV.F.4 Correlation

Different lines of business are often affected by common variables such as inflation, and changes in company operations tend to ripple across the entire company. For these reasons, many insurers' loss ratios are correlated across lines of business.

Some correlation is induced by the use of a common economic scenario for all lines of business. Additional correlation is induced through the error terms for the small-loss ratio and the large-claim frequency.

For an illustration of how the correlation matrix is calculated in this case study, the reader can refer to the Correlation tab of the Excel file referred to at the beginning of Section IV.F.3. The example shows that the correlation across the small-loss ratio errors was determined by calculating the correlation of the net loss ratios among lines of business. We first adjusted the net loss ratios by backing out the impact of changes in the inflation rate. We then calculated loss ratio changes caused by movements in inflation assuming a duration of two for the short-tailed homeowners and property lines and a duration of three for the remaining lines.

We assumed the correlations for large-claim frequency to be the same as the correlations for the small-loss ratios. If individual large-claim data had been available, we could have calculated the frequency correlations directly.

No explicit correlation is modeled between the small-loss ratio error term and the large-claim frequency term. They will remain correlated to the extent that they exhibit the common reliance on economic scenarios and company operations (e.g., pricing changes).

IV.F.5 Validation and Peer Review

Similar to the life and health company case study, we used three forms of review in this case study. We reviewed the calculation of the model input parameters and confirmed with the historical data. We also reviewed input assumptions and compared them to historical data for reasonableness. And finally, we reviewed projected financial result outputs.

Case study correlations calculated based on the data were accepted without further review. In practice, small positive correlations among lines of business would typically be expected; however, the data for this case study produced a mixture of positive and negative correlations, some of which showed strong correlations among seemingly unrelated lines of business. This result is probably due to our use of fictitious data; most likely, such correlations would not have occurred if we had used live data. If live data had produced the unusual correlations, the modeler should investigate whether there are reasons for the unusual results or whether the results are due to random fluctuation. Depending on the result of this investigation the modeler may accept the parameters as calculated or may choose to modify the correlation parameters used for the model projections.

IV.F.6 Communication of Results

A histogram of the change in economic value for the case study is graphed in Figure IV.E-1. The smooth line is the kernel density estimate, which can be calculated using a statistical package such as R. We also could have used a table to present these results.

▌ Figure IV.F-1

Change in Economic Capital

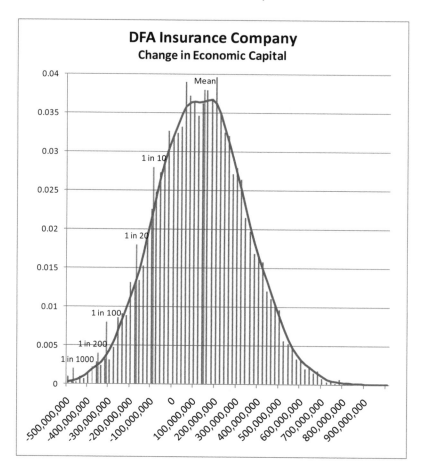

The simulation results are shown in Figure IV.F-2 for several confidence levels. In 1% of the simulation trials – the cut-off point that the case study's economic metric of 99% Tail Value at Risk – DFAIC suffered a loss of more than $319 million. Averaging these events produces a figure of $380 million – the required economic capital for DFAIC for a one-year horizon. This result is good news for DFAIC, which had a starting economic capital of $1.2 billion or approximately $800 million in excess capital. It is important to note that this measurement of excess capital applies only to this particular metric – a one-year horizon, 99% TVAR. In practice, this level of excess capital is seldom observed using this metric. Also, companies typically consider other constraints such as regulator or rating bureau requirements, shareholder requirements, and to protect from multiyear periods of adverse results when selecting their target amount of economic capital.

Figure IV.F-2

Simulation Results for Confidence Levels

	DFA Insurance Company Economic Capital	
Probability Level	**Value at Risk (VAR)**	**Tail Value at Risk (TVAR or CTE)**
.999	-465,257,000	-504,337,000
.995	-362,839,000	-417,605,000
.99	-319,797,000	-380,046,000
.95	-188,048,000	-266,557,000
.90	-114,224,000	-208,086,000

We can use the simulation results, presented on an undiscounted basis at various percentiles, for comparison purposes with historical financial statements that are also on an undiscounted basis.

Differences in valuation, however, prevent us from making a direct comparison between the values in the table and the economic capital values. These differences include loss liabilities and capital, which are calculated at undiscounted values rather than discounted, and bonds valued at amortized value rather than market value. Also, changes in capital include net income plus changes in unrealized capital gains.

Figure IV.F-3

Summary of Model Results

DFA Insurance Company – Summary of Financial Model Results

Undiscounted Basis (000's)						
	Prior	**5th Percentile**	**25th Percentile**	**50th Percentile**	**75th Percentile**	**95th Percentile**
Earned Premium	2,353,625	2,286,157	2,411,291	2,499,749	2,584,702	2,690,509
Incurred Losses	1,778,434	2,269,583	2,034,779	1,910,075	1,782,538	1,598,585
Total UW Expenses	693,794	863,550	816,782	780,941	739,911	686,993
UW Income	-118,604	-535,307	-315,666	-182,987	-66,533	102,767
Investment Income	351,388	299,673	322,140	331,673	350,047	377,482
Total Income	226,648	-206,876	20,389	155,506	264,726	435,125
Invested Assets	4,792,399	4,865,191	5,037,222	5,146,363	5,261,755	5,404,305
Unpaid Claims	2,328,543	2,630,835	2,490,697	2,409,822	2,323,251	2,207,649
Capital	1,604,297	1,432,540	1,677,965	1,818,025	1,949,704	2,127,822

References for IV.F

Butsic, Robert (1988). Determining the proper discount rate for loss reserve discounting: An economic approach. 1988 Casualty Actuarial Society Discussion Paper Program – Evaluating Insurance Company Liabilities, pp. 147-188. Retrieved Sept. 21, 2009, from http://www.casact.org/pubs/dpp/dpp88/88dpp147.pdf.

Casualty Actuarial Society (CAS) Forum (2001). 2001 call for papers- dynamic financial analysis, a case study. Casualty Actuarial Society - Arlington, Virginia , Spring: 1-24. Retrieved Sept. 21, 2009, from http://www.casact.org/pubs/forum/01spforum/01spf001.pdf.

Texas Department of Insurance (2000). The 2000 Texas Liability insurance closed claim annual report. Retrieved Sept. 21, 2009, from http://www.tdi.state.tx.us/reports/pc/documents/taccar2000.pdf.

IV.G Combining Economic Capital Results for Life and Non-life Companies

This case study illustrates how results from separate life and non-life economic capital (EC) models can be combined to calculate total EC for a company that writes business in both sectors. To arrive at a total EC figure, this case study will draw on the results from the case studies in Sections IV.B and IV.F.

We assume throughout this case study that life and non-life lines have been modeled separately, but with appropriate interaction and cooperation between the life and non-life teams. We note that aggregate economic capital (for life and non-life combined) could be calculated using a single economic capital model; in reality, however, using a single model is uncommon and is, therefore, not covered in this case study. In the remainder of this case study we will only address a situation in which life and non-life results are modeled separately and then combined as a final step of the process.

IV.G.1 Background

Management at OmniEG Insurance Company, a large multinational, multi-line insurance company, is concerned about its capital adequacy because of the rising frequency of catastrophes worldwide and a rapidly changing economic environment. OmniEG previously analyzed the health of its life company XYZ Life Insurance Company – a large, multi-line life and health insurance company writing primarily par individual life, variable annuity, and group health business – and its non-life company DFA Insurance Company, a regional non-life multi-line insurance company writing personal lines and main street commercial business. The results of these analyses were presented above in the case studies in Sections IV.B and IV.F, respectively. XYZ Life and DFA are OmniEG's only subsidiaries.

The company could be headquartered anywhere in the world, allowing for a broad, non-specific country discussion of EC analysis in this case study. In practice, however, the risk factors in a fully robust EC model should include country-specific risks.

IV.G.2 Considerations for Companies with Both Life and Non-life Business

When performing stochastic modeling, a company that writes both life and non-life business should consider the following factors:

Covariance effects

A covariance effect occurs when risks are less than perfectly correlated, such as when the total combined risk for two products is less than the sum of the individual risks. For example, the mortality risk posed by traditional whole life insurance is different from, and offsets to some degree, the risk of payout annuities. As mortality falls, whole life results tend to improve, but those for the annuity product tend to deteriorate. The reverse relationship also occurs. Consequently, modeling each line separately would not reveal a covariance effect and could lead to an inappropriate level of EC.

Products may not necessarily be negatively correlated (as in the example above) in order to merit a covariance adjustment; it is only necessary that the products be less than perfectly correlated. The exact nature of the covariance effect, if any, depends on the specific product features. It is reasonable to expect that, in many cases, life and non-life products are less than perfectly correlated. For example, cash flows from an annuity line of business are likely uncorrelated (or perhaps even negatively correlated) with cash flows from a line of business covering property damage in a hurricane-prone area. The examples provided above are not intended to limit the generality of the covariance effect. The covariance effect applies to many, if not most, combinations of life and non-life policies.

Adjusting for covariance is clearly a possibility that needs to be considered in modeling life and non-life products, whether the analysis is performed on an individual segment or aggregate basis.

Cross-line subsidization

Related to covariance, cross-line subsidization can occur when an underperforming product is in some way subsidized by a strongly performing product. For example, if the new money rate available for reinvesting the projected cash flows of high-performing Product B is less than the interest rate charged on the borrowed funds needed to support loss-producing Product A, one possibility might be to subsidize Product A with the positive cash flows projected for Product B. Such a move could improve the company's overall financial results, and might indicate that the company's total economic capital requirement is less than the sum of Product A's requirement and Product B's requirement. This simple example is but one of many circumstances in which capital requirements could be lowered when modeling the company's cash flows in aggregate.

Consistency of scenarios

Life and non-life models should be reviewed to ensure that appropriate assumptions, particularly economic assumptions, are consistent across models. It is unlikely that a model would produce useful results if different assumptions regarding inflation were used in the two separate models with the same currency.

Logistical considerations

Life and non-life teams frequently have different perspectives on the fundamentals of the business. For example, non-life team members may be more focused on a one-year time horizon, given that many non-life products can be cancelled annually by the insurer. Life products, on the other hand, typically require a long-term EC perspective. Life and non-life actuaries may also have quite different educational backgrounds, as is the case in the United States, and they may not thoroughly understand each other's commonly accepted actuarial practices. For these reasons, setting common goals may be a challenge, but can be overcome by agreeing to certain basic questions such as: What is our target level of confidence? What risk metric will be used? What is the relevant time horizon?

Ideally, the life and non-life teams will coordinate their efforts in advance of the EC modeling process. In this case, it would be possible to select a common economic scenario generator. The results could then be simply combined. This case study is intended to address the more complex situation in which two separate and distinct EC models have been developed – one for the life business and one for the non-life business.

IV.G.3 Combining the EC Models

One of two approaches can be used to combine scenarios generated by the separate life and non-life EC models. They include:

- **Generating output for all possible scenarios reflecting all risk factors. It is worth noting that a total of 1 billion scenarios (1,000^3) would be necessary if the model used 1,000 scenarios for each of three risk factors.**

■ **Using scenario reduction techniques to select the scenarios contributing to the tail of the distribution. Scenario reduction techniques are discussed in some detail in Section I of this book.**

Given the large number of risk factors associated with the life and non-life models, we believed the first option to be computationally unfeasible. We therefore used the scenario reduction technique to isolate the scenarios most likely affecting the tail of the distribution.

The first step involved calculating the annual value of non-life operating income (defined as pre-tax profit excluding investment income) for each of the 10 stochastic claims scenarios using 1,000 economic scenarios consistent with the life model. This process generated a total of 10,000 non-life scenarios[75] – 10 loss scenarios for each of the 1,000 economic scenarios. Using the 10,000 scenarios, we calculated an average operating income and the deviation of operating income for each year of the projection. The 10,000 scenarios were also used to adjust the life scenarios.

For the life and annuity business, we used scenario reduction techniques to select the 250,000 worst scenarios across all risk factors and all scenarios. This process involved:

■ Summing the present value of annual deviation in profits (relative to the baseline projection) for each line of business, scenario, and risk.

■ Applying a random process to linearly combine the deviations into 250,000 scenarios.

■ Ranking the scenarios based on the present values of the aggregate deviations from the baseline. The purpose of the ranking was to estimate the combination of scenarios that correspond to the worst 1% of outcomes.

A detailed description of the 250,000 worst scenario process can be found the case study in Section IV.B above.

We combined the 250,000 scenarios of deviations for the life and annuity business with the 10,000 scenarios of deviations for the non-life business as follows:

■ For each of the 250,000 scenarios, a random number from 1 to 10 was chosen, corresponding to one of the 10 non-life loss scenarios. Each of the 250,000 scenarios was paired with a non-life scenario that had the same underlying economic scenario as the life scenario and had the loss scenario corresponding to the random number selected. For example, if the random number chosen was 9 and the interest and equity return scenario was 937 (of the 1,000 economic scenarios), then the deviation of operating income of the non-life scenario (calculated in Step 1 at the beginning of the process), which is based on loss scenario 9 and interest and equity scenario 937, was added to the chosen life scenario.

■ The resulting 250,000 combined life/non-life scenarios were sorted to determine the new worst 2,500 or 1% of the scenarios based on operating income. This subset is the combination of adverse scenarios that give rise to the calculation of the CTE-99.

The 2,500 worst combined scenarios were then run through an aggregate model to calculate the investment income and income taxes.

Our approach implicitly considers some of the cross-line subsidization effects discussed above. More specifically, if results in the life segment are favourable under a particular economic scenario and results of the non-life segment are unfavourable under that same scenario, the offset would be captured by this procedure. It might indicate a possible net reduction in total EC relative to the sum of the EC requirements for the life and non-life components.

---

[75] In practice a larger number of scenarios would typically be used. The total number will depend on the heaviness of the tail for the non-life results and the size of the non-life book compared to the life book.

Because non-life loss scenarios are randomly assigned to a corresponding life scenario, the loss experience on the non-life business is implicitly assumed to be uncorrelated to the life business. This assumption is appropriate if the non-life experience is perfectly uncorrelated to the life experience (i.e., correlation coefficient is zero), as was the case in our present analysis. If the actuary, however, believes there may be non-zero correlation between the life and non-life components, an explicit covariance adjustment might be appropriate.

IV.G.4 Presentation of Results

Under the risk metric used in this case study, OmniEG will need to hold economic capital if the present value of future profits becomes negative after adjusting for the deviation of present value of profits at the 99-CTE level. The amount of EC, if any, is equal to the deficiency. An example will help clarify this point.

The combined baseline present value of future profits is $3,679 million for OmniEG, which consists of $3,428 million of the baseline present value of future profits, net of credit defaults and operational risk, over the 30-year projection horizon for the life business (as shown in the case study in Section IV.B) and $251 million in present value of future profits from the baseline scenario for the non-life business (as shown in the case study in Section IV.F above). Using the 2,500 worst scenarios, the deviation in present value of profits at the 99-CTE level is $2,282 million.

The $2,282 million adjustment to present value of profits, which was calculated as the mean of this distribution, indicates that the present value of future profits is $1,397 million at the 99-CTE level. Because the present value of future profits is positive at the 99-CTE level, no economic capital is required for the combined life and non-life businesses. If the adjusted present value of profits had been negative (that is, if the average deviation exceeded the baseline present value of profits), economic capital would have been required. The table in Figure IV.G-1 also illustrates these results.

Figure IV.G-1

Combined Economic Capital

Combined Economic Capital of OmniEG Insurance Company
Indicated Economic Capital Using CTE-99 Present Value of Future Profits

	PV of Future Profits Baseline	Average Deviation of 2,500 Worst	Adjusted PV of Future Profits
Life & Annuity, net of credit and operational risk (from Case Study B)	3,428	n/a	n/a
Non-Life (from Case Study F)	251	n/a	n/a
Total	3,679	(2,282)	1,397

IV.G.5 Peer Review of Results

While the non-specific country assumptions of this case study prevent the inclusion of a comprehensive review checklist, some general questions are provided for consideration when reviewing EC results. They include:

- Has the model been reviewed by an actuary who is familiar with the fundamentals of the business being modeled?

- Are the aggregate results consistent with the separate life and non-life models? Note that this step may involve cross-checking the means and percentiles of the life, non-life, and aggregate results and possibly examining the shape of the aggregate distribution in light of the pieces. If the aggregate distribution does not look like a hybrid combination of the two pieces, are there valid reasons why?

- Is the total EC consistent with the sum of the parts? For example, if life and non-life results are less than perfectly correlated, is the total EC less than the sum of the life EC and non-life EC? If not, the actuary should seek to understand why risk is being amplified rather than mitigated.

- Has the actuary appropriately modeled the interaction of different lines of business? For example, if non-life loss scenarios are randomly assigned to life scenarios when the results were combined (as in this case study), does the actuary have reason to believe that life and non-life results are not correlated? The key to successfully combining life and non-life results lies in appropriately modeling any interaction between these lines.

- Where appropriate, are assumptions consistent across models? If inconsistencies exist, are there valid reasons for the differences?

V. References, Abbreviations and Author Biographies

References

Society of Actuaries [SOA] Sources

Article from Small Talk Newsletter: A Better Random Number Generator. Davis, Chris.
http://www.soa.org/library/newsletters/small-talk/2006/june/stn-2006-iss26-davis.pdf

A Stochastic Investment Model for Actuarial Use. Wilkie, A.D.
http://www.soa.org/library/monographs/50th-anniversary/investment-section/1999/january/m-as99-2-06.pdf

An Actuarial Layman's Guide to Building Stochastic Interest Rate Generators. Tilley, James A.
http://www.soa.org/library/monographs/50th-anniversary/society-of-actuaries-50th-anniversary/1999/january/m-av99-1-07.pdf

Article from the Financial Reporter: More Efficient Monte Carlo Simulations for Mortality Assumption Testing. Robbins, Douglas L.
http://www.soa.org/library/newsletters/financial-reporter/2003/june/frn-2003-iss53-robbins.pdf

Article from Financial Reporter: Highlights from the 2003 Stochastic Modeling Symposium. Brerendsen, Robert.
http://www.soa.org/library/newsletters/financial-reporter/2003/november/frn-2003-iss55-berendsen.pdf

Article from Health Section News: Medical Aggregate Stop Loss Claim Frequencies (results of the Monte Carlo simulation). Olsho, David and Mark McAllister.
http://www.soa.org/library/newsletters/health-section-news/2000/august/hsn-2000-iss38-OlshoMcAllister.pdf

Article from Product Matters!: A Note Regarding "Risk Neutral" and "Real World" Scenarios- Dispelling a Common Misperception. Hatfield, Gary.
http://www.soa.org/library/newsletters/product-development-news/2009/february/pro-2009-iss73-hatfield.pdf

Article from Risks and Rewards Newsletter: Deflators- The Solution to Stochastic Conundrum?. Wilson, Don.
http://www.soa.org/library/newsletters/risks-and-rewards/2004/july/rrn-2004-iss45-wilson.pdf

Article from Risks and Rewards Newsletter: When Is It Right to Use Arbitrage-Free Scenarios?. Britt, Stephen.
http://www.soa.org/library/newsletters/risks-and-rewards/2000/september/rar-2000-iss35-britt.pdf

Article from Small Talk Newsletter: Using Monte Carlo Simulation to Understand Morality. Guth, Robert W.
http://www.soa.org/library/newsletters/small-talk/2000/december/stn-2000-iss16-guth.pdf

Article from the Financial Reporter: Principles of Capital Market Modeling. Vilms, Andres.
  http://www.soa.org/library/newsletters/financial-reporter/2003/september/frn-2003-iss54-vilms.pdf

Critical Review of Simulation Literature and Applications for Health Actuaries. Anderson, Louise H. Brian C. Martinson, Ian G Duncan and Katherine M. Hall.
  http://www.soa.org/files/pdf/critical-review-stoc-report.pdf

Estimating the Probability of a Rare Event via Elliptical Copulas. Peng, Lian.
  http://www.soa.org/library/journals/north-american-actuarial-journal/2008/april/naaj-2008-vol12-no2-peng.pdf

Estimation of Stochastic Volatility Models by Stimulated Maximum Likelihood Method. Choi, Ji Eun.
  http://www.soa.org/library/proceedings/arch/2005/arch05v39n1_3.pdf

Managing Volatility in a Market-to-Market World: The Stochastic Funding Method. Winklevoss, Howard, and Mark Ruloff, Steve Strake.
  http://www.soa.org/library/monographs/retirement-systems/the-future-of-pension-plan-funding-and-disclosure-monograph/2005/december/m-rs05-1-viii.pdf

Multiple Currency Option Selection using Stochastic Constraints. Au, Kelly T., and Joel R. Barber, David C. Thurston.
  http://www.soa.org/library/research/actuarial-research-clearing-house/1990-99/1996/arch-2/arch96v23.pdf

Article from Product Matters!: Nested Stochastic Pricing - The Time Has Come. Reynolds, Craig and Sai Man (Milliman).
  http://www.soa.org/library/newsletters/product-development-news/2008/june/pro-2008-iss71-man.pdf

Pricing Options Using Lattice Rules. Boyle, Phelim P., and Yongzeng Lai, Ken Seng Tan.
  http://www.soa.org/library/pdftest/journals/north-american-actuarial-journal/2005/july/naaj0503-3.pdf

Quasi- Monte Carlo Methods in Numerical Finance. Boyle, Phelim, and Corwin Joy, Ken Seng Tan.
  http://www.soa.org/library/monographs/50th-anniversary/investment-section/1999/january/m-as99-2-02.pdf

Representative Interest Rate Scenarios. Christiansen, Sarah L. M..
  http://www.soa.org/library/pdftest/journals/north-american-actuarial-journal/1998/july/naaj9807_3.pdf

Stochastic Analysis of Long-Term Multiple-Decrement Contracts. Clark, Matthew, and Chad Runchey.
  http://www.soa.org/library/journals/actuarial-practice-forum/2008/august/apf-2008-08-clark.pdf

Stochastic Management without Tears. Ostaszewski, Krzysztof M.
  http://www.soa.org/library/monographs/finance/asset-liability-integration/2002/january/m-fi02-1-08.pdf

Stochastic Pricing for Embedded Options in Life Insurance and Annuity Products. Hill, Tim, and Dale Visser, Ricky Trachtman.
  http://www.soa.org/files/pdf/research-2009-stochastic-pricing.pdf

Applications of Quasi- Monte Carlo Methods (PowerPoint). Boyle, Phelim, and Ken Seng Tan.
  http://www.soa.org/files/pdf/02-Boston-BoyleTan-144a.pdf

Applied Modeling Concepts (PowerPoint). Grant, Becky, and Ron Harasym, Rebecca Burton.
  http://www.soa.org/files/pdf/03-SanDiego-BurtonGrant-7.pdf

Economic Capital - The Market Perspective (PowerPoint). Mueller, Hubert.
  http://www.soa.org/files/pdf/07-Washington-AbbeyMatson-20.pdf

Effective Stress Testing (PowerPoint). Chaplin, Mark.
  http://www.soa.org/files/pdf/07-Washington-Khalil-38.pdf

Practical Applications of Stochastic Modeling for Disability Insurance (PowerPoint). Gant, Keith E., and Richard Carlson Leavitt, Yidong Liu.
  http://www.soa.org/files/pdf/hspring07-085bk.pdf

Scenario Generation for Economic Capital Models (PowerPoint). Mossmon, Jonathon A., and Andrew Ching Ng.
  http://www.soa.org/files/pdf/2008-qc-mossman-ng-73.pdf

Setting Long-Term Investment Assumptions for Actuarial Models: "Fair Value" in the Marketplace (PowerPoint). Zinkovsky, Vadim, and Ghalid Bagus (Milliman).
> http://www.soa.org/files/pdf/011bk_rev-life06.pdf

Stochastic Modeling in Disability and Long-Term Care (PowerPoint). Pahl, Amy, and Edward B. McEllin.
> http://www.soa.org/files/pdf/037bk_rev-health06.pdf

Stochastic Modeling in Health Benefits (PowerPoint). Guo, Lijia.
> http://www.soa.org/files/pdf/hspring07-095Guo.pdf

Stochastic Modeling for Life Insurance (PowerPoint). Robbins, Douglas L..
> http://www.soa.org/files/pdf/07-Washington-RobbinsWeinsier-119.pdf

Stochastic Modeling in Health Insurance (PowerPoint). Hendrickson, Jonathan Mark (Milliman), and Edward B. McEllin, Armand M. Yambao.
> http://www.soa.org/files/pdf/076_bk_hlth05.pdf

Stochastic Modeling in the Financial Risk Management (PowerPoint). Harasym, Ron.
> http://www.soa.org/files/pdf/03-Washington-Haraysm-68.pdf

Casualty Actuarial Society (CAS) Sources

Stochastic Modeling and Error Correlation in Dynamic Financial Analysis. Tu, Son T.
> http://www.casact.org/pubs/forum/98sforum/98sf207.pdf

A Stochastic Planning Model for the Insurance Corporation of British Columbia. Kreps, Rodney E., and Michael M. Steel.
> http://www.casact.org/pubs/forum/96spforum/96spf153.pdf

A Stochastic Investment model for asset and liability management. Yakoubov, Y., and M. Teeger, D. B. Duval.
> http://www.actuaries.org/AFIR/colloquia/Tokyo/Yaboubov_Teeger_Duval.pdf

A Comparison of Actuarial Financial Scenario Generators. Ahlgrim, Kevin C., and Stephen P. D'Arcy, Richard W. Gorvett.
> http://www.variancejournal.org/issues/02-01/111.pdf

An Introduction to Markov Chain Monte Carlo Methods and their Actuarial Applications. Scollnik, David P. M..
> http://www.casact.org/pubs/proceed/proceed96/96114.pdf

A Comparison of Stochastic Models that Reproduce Claim Ladder Reserve Estimates. Mack, Thomas, and Gary Venter.
> http://www.actuaries.org/ASTIN/Colloquia/Tokyo/Mack_Venter.pdf

Hospital Self-Insurance Funding: A Monte Carlo Approach. Bickerstaff, Dave.
> http://www.casact.org/pubs/forum/89spforum/89sp089.pdf

Markov Chain Monte Carlo Estimation for Regime Switching Vector Autoregressions. Harris, Glen R.
> http://www.casact.org/library/astin/vol29no1/47.pdf

A Formal Approach to Catastrophe Risk Assessment and Management. Clark, Karen M.
> http://www.casact.org/pubs/dpp/dpp85/85dpp062.pdf

Other Sources

Stochastic Modeling of the Dynamics of OASDI. Tuljapurkar, Shripad, and Ronald Ree, Michael Anderson.
   http://mrrc.isr.umich.edu/publications/conference/pdf/cp00_anderson.pdf

Stochastic Processes. Sewell, Martin.
   http://www.stats.org.uk/stochastic-processes/stochastic-processes.pdf

Accelerated Option Pricing in Multiple Scenarios. Dirnstorfer, Stefan, and Andreas J, Grau.
   http://arxiv.org/ftp/arxiv/papers/0807/0807.5120.pdf

Simulating Bermudan Interest Rate Derivatives. Carr, Peter, and Guang Yang.
   http://www.math.nyu.edu/research/carrp/papers/pdf/mkt.pdf

Stochastic Claims Reserving in General Insurance. England, P.D., and R.J. Verrall.
   http://www.actuaries.org.uk/__data/assets/pdf_file/0014/31721/sm0201.pdf

Insurance Modeling and Stochastic Cash Flow Scenario Testing: Effective Sampling Algorithms to Reduce Number of Runs. Chueh, Yvonne C.
   http://www.contingencies.org/novdec03/workshop.pdf

Efficient stochastic modeling for large and consolidated insurance business: Interest rate sampling algorithms. Yvonne, Chueh, C.
   http://findarticles.com/p/articles/mi_qa4030/is_200207/ai_n9093230/

Stochastic Trend Models in Casualty and Life Insurance. Gluck, Spencer M., and Gary G. Venter.
   http://www.ermsymposium.org/2009/pdf/2009-gluck-stochastic.pdf

Stochastic Modeling in the Insurance Industry. Hutchings, David.
   http://www-math.mit.edu/~verahur/18.104/David%20Hutchings%20-%20Final%20Draft.pdf

Stochastic Modeling of Insurance Business. Silvestrov, D., and E. Silvestrova, A. Malyarernko, M. Drozdenko.
   http://www.stat.ucl.ac.be/Samos2002/silvestetal.pdf

Stochastic Claims Reserving Methods in Insurance. Wüthrich, Mario V., and Michael Merz.
   http://www.wiley.com/WileyCDA/WileyTitle/productCd-0470723467.html

Introductory Stochastic Analysis for Finance and Insurance. Lin, X. Sheldon..
   http://www.wiley.com/WileyCDA/WileyTitle/productCd-0471716421.html

Stochastic Control in Insurance. Hanspeter, Schmidli,.
   http://www.springer.com/math/probability/book/978-1-84800-002-5

Modeling External Events: for Insurance and Finance (Stochastic Modeling and Applied Probability). Embrechts, Paul, and Claudia Kluppelberg, Thomas Mikosch.
   http://www.amazon.com/Modelling-Extremal-Events-Stochastic-Probability/dp/3540609318

Stochastic Methods in Finance. Back, Kerry, and Tomasz Bielecki, Christian Hipp, Shige Peng, Walter Schachermayer.
   http://www.amazon.com/gp/product/3540229531

Essentials of Stochastic Finance: Facts, Models, Theory, Vol. 3. Shiryaev, Albert N., and Al'bert Nikolaevich Shiriaev.
   http://search.barnesandnoble.com/booksearch/isbninquiry.asp?r=1&ean=9810236050

Abbreviations

ACAM	Autorité de contrôle des assurances et des mutuelles
AIC	Akaike information criterion
AIDS	Acquired immune deficiency syndrome
AG	Actuarial Guideline
AGG	Aggregate
ALAE	Allocated Loss Adjustment Expense
ALM	Asset Liability Management
ANAV	Adjusted net asset value
APD	Automobile physical damage
APRA	Australian Prudential Regulation Authority
AR	Autoregressive
ARCH	Autoregressive conditional heteroskedasticity
ARIMA	Autoregressive integrated moving average
ASRF	Asymptotic single risk factor
AV	Account Value
BaFin	Bundesanstalt für Finanzdienstleistungsaufsicht
BIC	Bayesian information criterion
BNM	Central Bank of Malaysia (Bank Negara Malaysia)
Bp	Basis point
bps	Basis points
BSCR	Basic SCR
BSM	Black-Scholes-Merton
CA	Commercial Auto Liability
CARVM	Commissioner's annuity reserve method
CAS	Casualty Actuarial Society
CDC	Centers for Disease Control
CDF	Cumulative distribution function [also appears as "cdf" and "c.d.f."]
CDenF	Cumulative density function
CDS	Credit default swaps
CE	Certainty equivalent
CEIOPS	Committee on European Insurance and Occupational Pensions Supervisors
CEV	Constant elasticity of variance
CEVL	Certainty equivalent value of liabilities
CFO	Chief financial officer
CFT	Cash Flow Testing
CHC	Claim handling costs
CIA	Canadian Institute of Actuaries
CIA	Central Intelligence Agency (U.S.)
CIRC	China Insurance Regulatory Commission
CL	Chain ladder
CMP	Commercial Multiple Peril
CMT	Constant maturity treasury
CNHR	Cost of residual non-hedgeable risks
COC	Cost of target capital

CoCM	Cost of capital margin
COS	Cost of solvency
CPI	Consumer Price Index
CSO	Commissioner Standard Ordinary
CTE	Conditional tail expectation
CTE70	Conditional tail expectation at the 70th percentile, e.g.
CTE-99	99% conditional tail expectation
DAC	Deferred acquisition cost
DCAT	Dynamic Capital Adequacy Testing
dfa	Degrees of freedom adjustment factor
DFA	Dynamic financial analysis
DFAIC	DFA Insurance Company
diff.	Differences
DNB	De Nederlandsche Bank (Dutch regulator)
D. of F.	Degrees of freedom
DRM	Dynamic risk models
EAFE	International Equity
EC	Economic capital
ECR	Enhanced Capital Requirement
EEV	European Embedded Value
EQE	EQECAT
ERM	Enterprise risk management
ESG	Economic scenario generator
EU	European Union
EV	Embedded Value
EVT	Extreme value theory
FAS	Financial Accounting Standards
FCOC	Frictional cost of capital
FOPI	Federal Office of Private Insurance (Swiss regulator)
FSA	Financial Services Authority (UK regulator)
FSB	Financial Services Board
FSC	Financial Supervisory Commission (Chinese Taipei, South Korea)
FSS	Financial Supervisory Services (South Korea)
FX	Foreign exchange
GAAP	Generally accepted accounting principles
GARCH	Generalized ARCH (autoregressive conditional heteroskedasticity)
GBM	Geometric Brownian motion
GDP	Gross domestic product
GLB	Guaranteed living benefits
GLM	General [Generalized] linear model [modeling]
GLWB	Guaranteed lifetime withdrawal benefits
GMB	Guaranteed minimum benefit
GMAB	Guaranteed minimum accumulation benefit
GMDB	Guaranteed minimum death benefit
GMIB	Guaranteed minimum income benefit

GMWB	Guaranteed minimum withdrawal benefit
GN9	"Guidance Note on Actuarial Review of Insurance Liabilities in respect of Employees' Compensation and Motor Insurance Businesses"
GPVL	Greatest present value of accumulated loss
Group MCEV	Group Market-Consistent Embedded Value
hetero	Heteroscedasticity
HGB	German local statutory accounting
HHS	U.S. Department of Health and Human Services
HIV	AIDS virus
HJM/BGM	Heath-Jarrow-Morton/Brace-Gatarek-Musiela
IAA	International Actuarial Association
IAJ	Institute of Actuaries of Japan
IASB	International Accounting Standards Board
IBNER	Incurred but not enough reported
IBNR	Incurred but not reported
ICA	Individual Capital Assessment
ICAS	Individual Capital Assessment System
ICG	Inversive congruential generator
IFRS	International Financial Reporting Standards
IFRS 4	First guidance from the IASB on accounting for insurance contracts
i.i.d.	Independent and identically distributed
ILN	Independent lognormal
IMB	Internal Model-based
IRDA	Insurance Regulatory and Development Authority (India)
IRIS	Insurance Regulatory Information System
IRP	Interest rate parity
IRR	Internal rate of return
ISVAP	Italian prudential regulator for insurers
ITM	In-the-money
JPY	Japanese yen
LCG	Linear congruential generator
LDF	Loss development factors
LIBOR	London interbank offered rate
LMM	LIBOR market model
LOB	Line of business
LTC	Long-term care
M&E	Mortality and expense
MAS	Monetary Authority of Singapore
MC	Monte Carlo
MCEV	Market-consistent Embedded Value
MCEVM	Market-consistent Embedded Value model
MCR	Minimum Capital Requirement
MLE	Maximum likelihood estimator
MVM	Market value margin

NAIC	National Association of Insurance Commissioners
NCTC	U.S. National Counterterrorism Center
obs.	Observation
ODP	Over-dispersed Poisson
OIC	The Office of the Insurance Commission, Thailand
OLS	Ordinary least squares
OSFI	Office of the Superintendent of Financial Institutions Canada
pa	Per annum
PCA	Principal component analysis
pdf	Probability density function [also appears as "p.d.f."]
PDR	Premium Deficiency Reserve
PFAD	Provisions for adverse deviations
PPA	Private Passenger Auto Liability
Private PI	Private placement bonds
PRNG	Pseudo random number generator
PV	Present value
PVF	Present value of future
PVFP	Present value of future profits
QIS	Quantitative impact study
QIS4	Fourth published quantitative impact study
QS	Quota share
RBC	Risk-based capital
resid.	Residuals
RFD	Domestic nominal continuous risk-free rate
RFF	Foreign nominal continuous risk-free rate
RMS	Risk Management Solutions
ROA	Return on assets
RSLN	Regime-switching lognormal
RSLN-2	RSLN (regime-switching lognormal) with two regimes
RSM	Required Solvency Margin
S&P	Standard & Poor's
S&P 500	Standard & Poor's 500 index
SARS	Severe acute respiratory syndrome
SB BIG	Bond
SCR	Solvency Capital Requirement
SDE	Stochastic differential equation
SEC	Securities and Exchange Commission
SIC	Sample Insurance Company
SOA	Society of Actuaries
SQP	Sequential quadratic programming
SRG	Shift register generator
SST	Swiss Solvency Test
SUSEP	Superintendência de Seguros Privados

Tail VaR	Tail Value at Risk
TEV	Traditional embedded value
TOPIX	Japanese equity index
TRNG	True random number generator
TSE300	Toronto Stock Exchange
TVar	Tail Value at Risk (also appears as "TVAR")
TVOG	Time value of options and guarantees
UCG	Unrealized capital gains
ULAE	Unallocated loss adjustment expense
UPR	Unearned Premium Reserve
U.S.	United States of America
USD	U.S. dollars
VA	Variable annuity
VACARVM	Variable Annuity Commissioners' Annuity Reserve Valuation Method
VaR	Value at Risk
VAR	Vector autoregressive
VIF	Value of in-force covered business/Value of business in force
VIX	Chicago Board Options Exchange (CBOE) Volatility Index
VWA	Volume weighted average
WC	Workers' compensation
WCE	Worst conditional expectation
WHO	World Health Organization
XOL	Excess of loss
XOR	"Exclusive-or" function

Author Biographies

Primary Life Authors

James G. Stoltzfus is a Principal and Consulting Actuary in Milliman's Philadelphia office and a primary author contributing to Life and Health sections of the book. In addition to overseeing the development of the text, Jim contributed heavily to Section III of the book (related to calibration, validation, auditing and communication of results) and to the morbidity and other health-specific sections of the text.

Jim's professional experience includes extensive work on actuarial appraisals for mergers and acquisitions, product development for life, health, and annuity plans; asset and liability analysis with emphasis on valuation of fixed income securities and derivatives; cash flow testing; statutory and GAAP valuations; embedded value analyses; claim liability analyses; and other life and health insurance consulting.

Jim is a Fellow of the Society of Actuaries and a Member of the American Academy of Actuaries.

Andrew H. Dalton is an Actuary in Milliman's Philadelphia office and a primary author contributing to Life sections of the book. In addition to reviewing and editing life-related sections of the text, Andrew contributed to sections on stochastic vs. non-stochastic modeling, stochastic deflators, and case studies related to Life Economic Capital, Combining Life and Non-Life Economic Capital models, and stochastic reserves and capital.

Andrew's professional experience includes work on actuarial appraisals for mergers and acquisitions, asset and liability analysis, cash flow testing, and economic capital for life and health companies.

Andrew is a Fellow of the Society of Actuaries and a Member of the American Academy of Actuaries. He holds a Masters Degree in Business Administration, concentrating in Finance and Statistics, from the Leonard N. Stern School of Business of New York University.

Contributing Life Authors

Ghalid Bagus is a Principal and Financial Risk Management Consultant in the Chicago office of Milliman. Ghalid contributed to the material on mortality modeling.

Ghalid is a Fellow of the Society of Actuaries, a Fellow of the Institute of Actuaries, a Member of the American Academy of Actuaries and a Chartered Financial Analyst charterholder.

Neil J. Cantle is a Principal and Consulting Actuary in the London office of Milliman. Neil contributed review and oversight on several sections of the text and provided input to the text from a European perspective.

Neil is a Fellow of the Institute of Actuaries.

Ji-Eun Choi is a Financial Risk Management Consultant in the Chicago office of Milliman. Ji-Eun contributed to the material on Monte Carlo simulation and lattice models.

Ji-Eun is holds a Doctor of Philosophy (PhD) in Statistics from the University of Waterloo.

Fang Fang is a quantitative analyst in Milliman's Financial Risk Management practice in Chicago. She is actively involved in the development of Milliman's MG-Hedge® Valuation System. Prior to joining Milliman, she worked for LaSalle Bank's Capital Markets Group, where she developed valuation models for mortgage-servicing applications, employing arbitrage-free interest-rate scenarios. She has played a key role in expanding the interest-rate-scenario-generation techniques in MG-Hedge.

She holds a PhD in Physical Chemistry from Purdue University and a Masters in Financial Engineering from the University of California at Berkeley

Gary S. Finkelstein is the leader of Milliman's Financial Risk Management practice in London. Gary contributed to the material on random number generators.

Gary is a Fellow of the Institute of Actuaries and an Associate of the Society of Actuaries. He holds a Masters of Business Science from the University of Cape Town.

Mark Hadley conducts quantitative research within Milliman's Capital Markets Group in Chicago. He has developed several market-consistent option-pricing techniques with applications to EIA and VA valuation and dynamic hedging strategy design. He has also developed new statistical methods for replicating equity, fixed-income, and hedge-fund-return dynamics with liquid derivative instruments.

He holds a Bachelors of Science from the Wharton School of the University of Pennsylvania and is an associate of the Society of Actuaries and a certified Financial Risk Manager with GARP.

Rikiya Ino is a Principal and Senior Consultant in the Tokyo office of Milliman. He contributed to the material on regime switching models and risk measures.

Rikiya is a Fellow of the Institute of Actuaries of Japan and a Chartered Member of the Securities Analysts Association of Japan. He holds a Masters Degree in Mathematics from the Graduate School of Tohoku University.

Ram Kelkar is the Managing Director for Capital Markets and Trading in the Financial Risk Management practice of Milliman's Chicago office. He contributed to the material on credit risks.

Ram is a Chartered Financial Analyst charterholder and holds a Masters Degree in Business Administration from the Wharton School of the University of Pennsylvania.

Daren M. Lockwood leads the Quantitative Development Group within Milliman's Financial Risk Management practice in Chicago. This group oversees the development of Milliman's MG-Hedge® Valuation System. The scenario-generation methodologies in this system are used to model financial derivatives in insurance liabilities, including equity-linked investment products and embedded-interest-rate derivatives. Applications have included market-consistent option valuation, capital requirements, and VaR measures.

He holds a PhD in Chemical Physics from the University of Texas, and is a certified Financial Risk Manager with GARP.

Wade Matterson is a Senior Consultant and leader of Milliman's Australian Financial Risk Management practice. Wade contributed review and oversight on several sections of the text and provided input to the text from an Australian perspective.

Wade is a Fellow of the Institute of Actuaries of Australia.

Sam Nandi is the leader of the actuarial team within Milliman's Financial Risk Management practice and is located in the Chicago office. Sam contributed material on risk neutral versus real world scenarios.

Sam is a Fellow of the Society of Actuaries and a Member of the American Academy of Actuaries. He holds a Masters Degree in Economics from the University of Wisconsin.

Craig Roberts is a life actuary in the Seattle office of Milliman. Craig contributed material on nested stochastic modeling.

Craig is a Fellow of the Society of Actuaries and a Member of the American Academy of Actuaries.

William M. Sayre is a Principal and Consulting Actuary in the New York office of Milliman. Bill contributed material to the case study regarding the combination of Life and Non-Life Economic Capital models.

Bill is a Fellow of the Society of Actuaries and a Member of the American Academy of Actuaries.

Adam Schenck leads the Research and Development Group within Milliman's Capital Markets Group in Chicago. He has developed market-consistent option-pricing techniques used by leading EIA and VA writers to model their hedge assets, developed optimization techniques used to calibrate liability-side scenario generators to changes in asset prices, and written software to simulate dynamic trading strategies with user-defined time intervals under both simulated and actual historical market conditions. These techniques are critical to addressing both fair valuation requirements and hedge-strategy evaluation.

Adam holds a Masters in Financial Mathematics from the University of Chicago, and is also a certified Financial Risk Manager with the Global Association of Risk Professionals (GARP).

Marc Slutzky is a Principal and Consulting Actuary in the New York office of Milliman. Marc contributed material to case studies regarding Life Economic Capital Models and the combination of Life and Non-Life Economic models.

Marc is a Fellow of the Society of Actuaries, a Member of the American Academy of Actuaries, and Chartered Enterprise Risk Analyst.

Peter H. Sun is a Consulting Actuary with the Financial Risk Management group in the Chicago office of Milliman. Peter contributed material on exchange rates.

Peter is a Fellow of the Society of Actuaries and a Member of the American Academy of Actuaries. Peter holds a Masters Degree in Mathematics from the University of Connecticut.

Lotte Van Delft is a Consulting Actuary in the Amsterdam office of Milliman and was responsible for establishing a financial risk management practice in Amsterdam. Lotte contributed to the case study regarding embedded value.

Lotte is a Fellow of the Actuarieel Genootschap (Dutch Society of Actuaries) and holds a Masters Degree in Actuarial Science from the University of Amsterdam.

Henny Verheugen is a Consulting Actuary in the Amsterdam office of Milliman. Henny contributed to the case study regarding embedded value.

Henny is a Fellow of the Actuarieel Genootschap (Dutch Society of Actuaries).

David Wang is a life actuary in the Seattle office of Milliman. David contributed to the case study regarding pricing and risk management of a variable annuity product and to sections on policyholder dynamic behavior.

David is a Fellow of the Society of Actuaries, a Fellow of the Institute of Actuaries, and a Member of the American Academy of Actuaries. David holds a Masters Degree from the Haas School of Business of the University of California, Berkeley.

Primary Non-Life Authors

Mark R. Shapland is a Consulting Actuary in Milliman's Milwaukee office and a primary author contributing to Non-Life sections of the book. In addition to reviewing and editing all non-life-related sections of the text, Mark contributed heavily to the case study on reserve variability for a non-life insurer.

Mark's area of expertise is non-life insurance, particularly pricing (personal and commercial lines), reserving (including reserve variability and asbestos liabilities), individual risk and association-type dividend plans and premium rates for large accounts, reinsurance, data management, and dynamic risk modeling. Mark has international experience, having worked in Europe for four years, as well as shorter assignments in many other countries. He also has extensive experience in the development of actuarial software tools and is the lead actuary for the Milliman Reserve Variability software development team.

Mark is a Fellow of the Casualty Actuarial Society, an Associate of the Society of Actuaries and a Member of the American Academy of Actuaries.

Stephen A. Finch is an Actuary in Milliman's Denver office and a primary author contributing to Non-Life sections of the book. In addition to reviewing and editing non-life-related sections of the text, Steve contributed to the section on non-life financial models, the Non-Life Economic Capital case study, and the Combining Life and Non-Life Economic Capital Models case study.

Steve's professional experience includes commercial lines reserving and pricing with an emphasis on workers compensation. He has also had extensive experience in the development of computerized actuarial tools, including

Milliman's DFA software, where Steve was the lead actuary on the development team. Steve was also involved in specification development for the Milliman Reserve Variability tool and has developed Excel based tools for reinsurance pricing, retrospective premium calculators, deductible calculators, and financial modeling.

Steve is a Fellow of the Casualty Actuarial Society and a Member of the American Academy of Actuaries. He holds a Masters Degree in Business Administration, with a concentration in Finance, from the University of Colorado.

Contributing Non-Life Authors

Wayne Blackburn is a Principal and Consulting Actuary in the New York office of Milliman. Wayne contributed to the material on casualty models.

Wayne is a Fellow of the Casualty Actuarial Society and a Member of the American Academy of Actuaries.

Joshua Corrigan, Senior Consultant, Milliman Financial Risk Management. Joshua is a Senior Consultant in Milliman's financial risk management practice. Joshua is a qualified actuary with 15 years of experience in financial risk management and wealth management.

He is an active member of the Institute of Actuaries UK and Australia, having contributed to various working parties and committees. He is also a frequent speaker at conferences and has published numerous articles on guarantee product development and risk management. He is a Fellow of the Institute of Actuaries in both the UK and Australia, and has held a CFA designation from the CFA Institute since 2000.

Jeff Courchene is a Principal and Consulting Actuary in the Munich office of Milliman. In addition to reviewing non-life-related sections of the text, Jeff contributed to the material on country / region specific issues.
Jeff is a Fellow of the Casualty Actuarial Society and a Member of the American Academy of Actuaries.

Biresh Giri is a Consulting Actuary in the Dehli office of Milliman. Biresh contributed to the material on country / region specific issues for India.

Biresh is a Fellow of Institute of Actuaries of India.

Akshar Gohil is an Associate Actuary in the New York office of Milliman. Akshar contributed to the material on casualty claim models and country / region specific issues.

Akshar is an Associate of the Casualty Actuarial Society.

Patrick Grannan is a Principal in the Seattle office of Milliman and is the firm's CEO. Pat reviewed the Executive Summary material.

Pat is a Fellow of the Casualty Actuarial Society, a Member of the American Academy of Actuaries and a former president of the Casualty Actuarial Society. He has a Masters degree in Mathematics from the University of Virginia.

Roger Hayne is a Principal and Consulting Actuary in the Pasadena office of Milliman. Roger contributed to the material on stochastic models including methods to estimate parameters including maximum likelihood.

Roger is a Fellow of the Casualty Actuarial Society and a Member of the American Academy of Actuaries. He holds a PhD in Mathematics from the University of California.

Derek Jones is a Principal and Consulting Actuary in the New York office of Milliman. Derek reviewed and edited all non-life-related sections of the text.

Derek is a Fellow of the Casualty Actuarial Society and a Member of the American Academy of Actuaries.

Scott Kurban is a Principal and Consulting Actuary in the Denver office of Milliman. Scott contributed to the material on country / region specific issues.

Scott is a Fellow of the Casualty Actuarial Society and a Member of the American Academy of Actuaries.

Jessica (Weng Kah) Leong is a Consulting Actuary in the New York office of Milliman. Jessica contributed to the material on casualty models and on the country /region specific issues.

Jessica is a Fellow of the Institute of Actuaries in Australia, a Fellow of the Casualty Actuarial Society and a Member of the American Academy of Actuaries.

Claus Metzner is a Consulting Actuary in the Milwaukee office of Milliman. Claus contributed to the material on combining life and non-life models to obtain an aggregate capital need for a multi line company, on the appropriate processes of conducting a peer review of results and on the presentation of results.

Claus is a Fellow of the Casualty Actuarial Society, a Fellow of the Society of Actuaries, a Member of the American Academy of Actuaries, an Aktuar-SAV (Fellow of the Swiss Association of Actuaries) and a Chartered Enterprise Risk Analyst.

Mark Mulvaney is a Principal and Consulting Actuary in the Denver office of Milliman. Mark contributed to the material on copulas.

Mark is a Fellow of the Casualty Actuarial Society and a Member of the American Academy of Actuaries.

Derek Newton is a Principal and Consulting Actuary in the London office of Milliman. Derek contributed to the material on country / region specific issues in the UK and helped edit the rest of Europe.

Derek is a Fellow of the Institute of Actuaries and a Fellow of the Society of Actuaries in Ireland.

Chris Tait is a Principal and Consulting Actuary in the Philadelphia office of Milliman. Chris peer reviewed several of the non-life sections.

Chris is a Fellow of the Casualty Actuarial Society and a Member of the American Academy of Actuaries.

Gary Wells is a Principal and Consulting Actuary in the London office of Milliman. Gary contributed to the material on country / region specific issues in the UK and helped edit the rest of Europe.

Gary is a Fellow of the Institute of Actuaries and a Fellow of the Society of Actuaries in Ireland.

Other Contributors

In addition to those mentioned above, Milliman would like to thank the many individuals who contributed to this text, including reviewers, editors and assistants. Without the contributions of these individuals, this text would not be possible.

Milliman would also like to thank the members of the International Actuarial Association ad-hoc project oversight group, who have provided invaluable support, review, and assistance in the preparation of this text throughout the entire process.

Appendix A
CFO Forum

The CFO Forum principles can be found online (at http://www.cfoforum.nl) and are summarized as follows:

Principle 1: Market-consistent Embedded Value (MCEV) is a measure of the consolidated value of shareholders' interests in the covered business. Group Market-consistent Embedded Value (Group MCEV) is a measure of the consolidated value of shareholders' interests in covered and non-covered business.

Principle 2: The business covered by the MCEVM should be clearly identified and disclosed.

Principle 3: MCEV represents the present value of shareholders' interests in the earnings distributable from assets allocated to the covered business after sufficient allowance for the aggregate risks in the covered business. The allowance for risk should be calibrated to match the market price for risk where reliably observable. MCEV consists of the following components:

- Free capital allocated to the covered business
- Required capital
- Value of in-force covered business (VIF)

The value of future new business is excluded from MCEV.

Principle 4: The free capital is the market value of any assets allocated to, but not required to support, the in-force covered business at the valuation date.

Principle 5: Required capital is the market value of assets, attributed to the covered business over and above that required to back liabilities for covered business, whose distribution to shareholders is restricted.

Principle 6: VIF consists of the following components:

- Present value of future profits, where profits are post-taxation shareholder cash flows from the in-force covered business and the assets backing the associated liabilities (PVFP)
- Time value of financial options and guarantees as defined in Principle 7
- Frictional costs of required capital as defined in Principle 8
- Cost of residual non-hedgeable risks as defined in Principle 9

Principle 7: Allowance must be made in MCEV for the potential impact on future shareholder cash flows of all financial options and guarantees within the in-force covered business. The allowance for the time value of financial options and guarantees must be based on stochastic techniques using methods and assumptions consistent with the underlying embedded value. All projected cash flows should be valued using economic assumptions such that they are valued in line with the price of similar cash flows traded in the capital markets.

Principle 8: An allowance should be made for the frictional costs of required capital for covered business. The allowance is independent of the allowance for non-hedgeable risks.

Principle 9: An allowance should be made for the cost of non-hedgeable risks not already allowed for in the time value of options and guarantees or the PVFP. This allowance should include the impact of non-hedgeable non-financial risks and non-hedgeable financial risks. An appropriate method of determining the allowance for the cost of residual non-hedgeable risks should be applied and sufficient disclosures provided to enable a comparison to a cost of capital methodology.

Principle 10: New business is defined as that arising from the sale of new contracts and in some cases increases to existing contracts during the reporting period. The value of new business includes the value of expected renewals on those new contracts and expected future contractual alterations to those new contracts. MCEV should only reflect in-force business, which excludes future new business. The value of new business should reflect the additional value to shareholders created through the activity of writing new business.

Principle 11: The assessment of appropriate assumptions for future experience should regard past, current, and expected future experience and any other relevant data. The assumptions should be best estimate and entity-specific rather than being based on the assumptions a market participant would use. Changes in future experience should be allowed for in the VIF when sufficient evidence exists. The assumptions should be actively reviewed.

Principle 12: Economic assumptions must be internally consistent and should be determined such that projected cash flows are valued in line with the prices of similar cash flows traded on the capital market. No smoothing of market or account balance values or unrealized gains is permitted.

Principle 13: VIF should be discounted using discount rates consistent with those that would be used to value such cash flows in the capital markets.

Principle 14: The reference rates used should, wherever possible, be the swap yield curve appropriate to the currency of the cash flows.

Principle 15: Stochastic models and the associated parameters should be appropriate for the covered business being valued, internally consistent, and, where appropriate, based on the most recent market data. Volatility assumptions should, wherever possible, be based on those implied from derivative prices rather than the historical observed volatilities of the underlying instruments.

Principle 16: For participating business the method must make assumptions about future bonus rates and the determination of profit allocation between policyholders and shareholders. These assumptions should be made on a basis consistent with the projection assumptions, established company practice, and local market practice.

Principle 17: MCEV results should be disclosed at a consolidated group level using a business classification consistent with the primary statements, with clear description of what business is covered by MCEVM and what is not. Except where they are not considered material, compliance with the MCEV principles is compulsory and should be explicitly disclosed.

Appendix B
Country Practice

B.1 Europe

For the member countries of the European Union (EU), the Solvency I regime is expected to be replaced by the Solvency II regime, beginning in 2012. All member countries have to adopt the new regime. For this reason, this section discusses Europe-specific issues in the context of the anticipated new regime, followed by country-specific issues in the pre-Solvency II regulatory context.

Solvency II

Solvency II is an updated set of insurance regulations for the EU, facilitating the creation of a single market for insurance services in the EU, introducing economic risk-based solvency requirements, and strengthening the role of the group supervisor. Solvency II rules compel insurers to devote significant resources to the identification, measurement, and proactive management of risks.

The framework that, as of 2008, is likely to be adopted by the EU Commission will be based on a three-pillar approach as follows:

- Pillar 1 will represent the quantitative assessment of regulatory capital requirements. The Solvency Capital Requirement (SCR) is a function of market, credit, underwriting, and operational risks. In assessing their SCRs, firms have the choice to use the industry's standard formula or to derive SCRs using their own internal models. In addition to SCR, there will also be a Minimum Capital Requirement (MCR), which will act as a lower trigger for mandatory supervisory action.

- Pillar 2 is the review process. It will address internal controls and risk management practices, supervisory practices, supervisory powers, supervisory peer reviews, investment management and ALM rules, and fit and proper criteria. The review process itself may occasionally lead a supervisory authority to apply capital guidance in the form of a capital add-on.

- Pillar 3 sets the information disclosure requirements. There will be public disclosures on business overview and performance, governance, and the valuation basis employed for solvency. In addition, there will be non-public disclosures on risk and capital management.

What are the key risk modules of the standard SCR formula?

A modular approach has been adopted for the standard SCR formula. In each module, proxies for individual risks are transformed into capital charges, which are combined to generate an estimate of the SCR. The parameters used for the calculation of the SCR are intended to reflect a VaR risk measure calibrated to a confidence level of 99.5% over a one-year time horizon.

- Market risk (QIS4, Section TS.IX) arises from the volatility of market prices of financial instruments. Exposure is measured by the impact of movements in financial instruments and variables. A correlation matrix is defined to aggregate these risks.

- Counterparty default risk (QIS4, Section TS.X) is the risk of possible losses because of unexpected default, or deterioration in the credit standing of the counterparties or debtors in relation to risk mitigating contracts, such as reinsurance arrangements.

- Life underwriting risk (QIS4, Section TS.XI) is split into biometric risks (comprising mortality risk, longevity risk, and disability/morbidity risk), lapse risk, expense risk, revision risk, and catastrophe risk. Except for revision risk the capital charges do not include the potential risk mitigation effect of future profit sharing.

- Health underwriting risk (QIS4, Section TS.XII) is intended to cover underwriting risk for all health and workers' compensation guarantees and is split into three sub-modules: long-term health, which is practiced on a similar technical basis to that of life assurance (which exists only in Germany and Austria), short-term health, and workers' compensation. A correlation matrix is used to combine the various risks. Except for short-term health, the capital charges include an adjustment for the risk-mitigating effect of future profit sharing.

- Non-life underwriting risk (QIS4, Section TS.XIII) is the risk arising from insurance contracts. It includes uncertainty about the amount and timing of the eventual claim settlements in relation to existing liabilities, the volume of business to be written, and the premium rates at which it will be written. This module uses a correlation matrix to combine the two main sources of underwriting risk – premium risk and reserve risk – and then adds a risk charge for catastrophe risk assuming independence.

- Operational risk (QIS4, Section TS.VIII.B) is the risk of losses arising from failed internal processes, people, systems, or external events, including legal risks. Reputation risks and risks arising from strategic decisions are not considered operational risks. This module is designed to address operational risks to the extent that these have not been explicitly covered in other risk modules.

As of QIS4, the method of calculating the MCR is a linear approach constrained by a cap of 50%, and a floor of 20%, of the SCR, and is a function of the net technical provisions or the net written premium (QIS4, Section TS.XV).

How are risk modules aggregated in the standard formula?

For the aggregation of the individual risk modules to an overall SCR, simple linear correlation techniques are applied to all modules via a matrix of correlation coefficients, except for operational risk, in order to calculate the Basic SCR (BSCR). The setting of correlation coefficients is intended to reflect potential dependencies in the tail of the distributions, as well as the stability of any correlation assumptions under stress conditions. Risk charges for operational risk as well as adjustments for risk-absorbing effects of future profit sharing are added to the BCSR to calculate the SCR (QIS4, Section TS.VIII).

What are the criteria for an undertaking to use an internal model?

Regulators can permit, and in some cases require,[76] insurers to calculate SCR using internal models, as long as the models:

- Are validated and approved by the regulator

- Include risk measures and time horizons

- Include a scope of risks at least as prudent as the standard formula

Regulators may seek an independent opinion as to the suitability and accuracy of such models. It is anticipated that most large and specialist insurance operations will use internal models, and it seems likely that their use will be more widespread than this.

The regulations are being developed under the leadership of the Committee of European Insurance and Occupational Pensions Supervisors (CEIOPS). CEIOPS provides three tests that internal models should pass to be accepted by regulators, namely:

- **Internal risk management "use" test:** The board of directors needs to document and communicate its risk strategy, which is an integral part of a business strategy. The risk strategy shall document how the internal model is used to achieve these goals. The objectives should be broken down as they relate to the responsible business unit.

- **Regulatory capital requirement "calibration" test:** Insurers are required to quantify the relationship between their own internal economic capital calibrations and the Solvency II SCR calibration objectives, with the goal of making the degree of prudence explicit.

- **Base methodology "statistical quality" test:** Regulators expect to receive complete, exact, and adequate datasets that demonstrate reasonableness and reliability.

Partial internal models are also permitted under certain well-defined circumstances, for example to ease the transition from the standard formula to "full" internal models. Of necessity, partial internal models must be consistent with the SCR standard formula.

Non-life technical provisions

Solvency II is based on the 2011 release of the International Financial Reporting Standards (IFRS). The anticipated IFRS balance sheet will differ from many local statutory and GAAP accounting practices in a number of ways. Under the anticipated IFRS, the appropriate valuation basis of the technical provisions is the discounted best estimate gross of reinsurance plus a risk margin[77] net of reinsurance, with an asset held to account for the ceded amounts. To date (up to and including QIS4) the following guidance has been made public:

- Best estimate outstanding claims provisions should include claim handling expenses. Best estimate premium provisions should be calculated separately.

- At least two reliable and suitably different standard actuarial methods based on runoff triangles are to be used where practicable.

---

[76] Article 117 of the draft directive states, "Where it is inappropriate to calculate the Solvency Capital Requirement in accordance with the standard formula, as set out in Subsection 2, because the risk profile of the insurance and reinsurance undertakings concerned deviates significantly from the assumptions underlying the Solvency Capital Requirement, the supervisory authorities may, by a decision stating the reasons, require the undertakings concerned to use an internal model to calculate the Solvency Capital Requirement, or the relevant risk modules of thereof."

[77] As of 2008, the Solvency II specifications for technical provisions differ from the latest IFRS specifications (the latter of which includes a service margin in addition to a risk margin). We anticipate eventual convergence between the two.

The risk margin should be derived via the use of an annual cost of capital factor of 6% above the risk-free interest rate. The level of the cost of capital factor is still under discussion, and there is a possibility it will be reduced.

The goal of the risk margin is to set the overall technical provisions (best estimate plus risk margin) at market value, similar to the IFRS (Solvency II, Commission of the European Communities, 2008).

Equalization reserves

Contingency reserves for future earthquakes, windstorms, and other catastrophes are required in various European countries. These reserves generally increase incrementally based on prescribed technical formulas. Contingency reserves can only be released following a catastrophe of required magnitude, and generally under insurance regulatory approval. This reserve is, therefore, more like a segregation of capital than a true loss reserve. These reserves can be significant and pose a strain on the release of capital for modeling purposes. Under IFRS rules, these reserves are treated as part of the capital account, not as a liability.

B.2 Germany

Non-life regulatory reporting

As part of regulatory reporting, non-life insurers have to submit information in a number of standardized forms to the German regulator, Bundesanstalt für Finanzdienstleistungsaufsicht (BaFin).

Form 242 includes details, split between the current financial year and previous years, on:

- The number of reported and IBNR claims
- The composition of the claims provisions into their individual components (reported claims, IBNR, etc.)
- The development of claims provisions and claims payments by accident year

From this, runoff triangles (for paid claims and for the number of unsettled claims) may be derived with a length of up to 12 years.

The returns of individual insurers described above are not available to the public; however, industry-wide aggregated triangle information is made publicly available by BaFin.

Case loss and loss adjustment expense reserves

Case reserves for loss and associated claim expenses are estimated by claims adjusters. Estimates have consistently developed downward because of the dominant effect of the prudence principal (Vorsichtsprinzip) in German local statutory accounting (HGB).

IBNR

For estimating IBNR, there is generally a preference for methodologies free from judgment, including the chain ladder method according to Mack (1993), specifically the Munich Chain Ladder method (Mack and Quarg).

Claim handling costs

Claim handling costs (CHC) are generally split between external (direct) and internal (indirect) costs, the former being attributable to a known claim. HGB accounting prescribes a method of estimating the internal CHC known as the "Formel 48."

B.3   France

Non-life regulatory reporting

Following the merger in 2003 of the French regulator for insurance companies and the French regulator for mutual insurance companies, there is now a unique independent prudential regulator named *Autorité de contrôle des assurances et des mutuelles* (ACAM).

The ACAM reviews the asset/liability management of companies, as well as their solvency position. In 2008, they were following Solvency I rules established by the EU.

Non-life insurers must submit accounting statements to the French regulator on a yearly basis. Aggregated, industry-wide returns are publicly available on the regulator's Web site, but individual returns are not. These statements provide information, such as the balance sheet, profit and loss accounts, and detailed information by line of business, including premiums, exposure, notified claims, average cost per claim, and claim handling cost.

The French local statutory accounting follows the principal of prudence. In 2008, Solvency II was still under discussion; there are no requirements from the French regulator for insurance companies to provide risk margins in their reporting.

As part of its preparatory work regarding its Solvency II QIS4 submission, ACAM published a report in November 2007 explaining methods for obtaining best estimate reserves by line of business.

B.4   Switzerland

Switzerland is not a member of the EU, but as Swiss companies have a strong presence abroad, their interest in EU regulation is pivotal.

Capital adequacy

Swiss legislation is ahead of the EU Solvency II process by several years. The Swiss Parliament implemented the current Insurance Supervisory Act at the beginning of 2006.

The act introduced the Swiss Solvency Test (SST), which has a risk-based capital framework. SST is principles-based as opposed to formula-based. Transparency and market consistency are two basic elements of SST. Compatibility with the foreseeable EU framework is a main objective of SST, with the SST also adopting a three-pillars approach. Both the old and the new solvency regime will be in force for reporting purposes until 2012, when the old system will be fully phased out.

Companies are encouraged to use internal models to determine their solvency requirements, where they are superior to the standard model. Internal models are required where the standard model is not applicable, especially for reinsurers.

There are some differences to Solvency II as it stood in 2008: The confidence level required by SST is 99.0% Tail Value at Risk (TVaR) as opposed to 99.5% Value at Risk in Solvency II. The Minimum Capital Requirement is 60% of the Solvency Capital Requirement, instead of the 20%-50% range in the current draft of Solvency II. In SST, operational risk is not taken into account as part of Pillar I, as it is not considered sufficiently quantifiable.

The insurance and financial scenarios stipulated by the regulator need to be aggregated by the model in order to include historically unobserved risks.

Reserves

The new Insurance Supervisory Act also requires all insurance companies to appoint a Responsible Actuary, who produces an annual report on reserves, development of technical results, and the quality of the assets covering insurance liabilities. The Swiss Actuarial Association has published several guidelines.

Technical liabilities include a discounted best estimate and a Market Value Margin (MVM).[78] The MVM represents "what a rational investor would demand in excess of the best estimate of the liabilities." The MVM is estimated by calculating the Cost of Capital Margin (CoCM). The CoCM is the cost of future regulatory capital needed for the whole runoff of a portfolio. The CoCM is market-based in that, if an insurer were to purchase the portfolio, it has to set up future incremental regulatory capital until the portfolios have runoff completely, so the insurer selling the portfolio has to compensate the buyer via the CoCM. The Swiss regulator, the Federal Office of Private Insurance (FOPI), has issued guidance on how to calculate the CoCM.[79]

B.5   United Kingdom

In the United Kingdom, financial services, including insurance, are currently regulated by the Financial Services Authority (FSA).

Individual Capital Assessment System

In 2005, the FSA introduced the Individual Capital Assessment System (ICAS). The FSA wanted to introduce a regime that would force insurers to review their underlying risks and to manage those risks actively. They took note of developments within the banking world and, thus, designed a three-pillar approach similar to Basel II. The three pillars are essentially:

- **Minimum standards:** e.g., asset and liability valuation rules, formula-driven capital requirements
- **Supervisory review:** e.g., the regulator checking that all firms have in place internal controls and sound risk evaluation and management processes
- **Market discipline:** through frequent and relevant public disclosure

From this thinking emerged the ICAS. The ICAS regime for solvency capital is comprised of four elements:

---

[78]   www.bpv.admin.ch/themen/00506/00552/00727/index.html?lang=en
[79]   www.bpv.admin.ch/themen/00506/00552/00727/index.html?lang=en

- **Minimum Capital Requirement (MCR):** calculated as before, with some revision, which was known as Solvency I.

- **Enhanced Capital Requirement (ECR):** like the MCR, this is formula-driven, but the parameters are intended to ensure that insurers have financial strength at least equal to S&P's BBB rating (i.e., a risk of failure within the next year of no more than 0.5%).

- **Individual Capital Assessment (ICA):** this is calculated by the insurers based entirely on their own assessment of the business risks they are bearing. The FSA has issued several papers providing guidance on how to go about performing an ICA (based on what the FSA has seen as market best practice), and the FSA requires all ICA submissions to be accompanied by an explanatory report as well as a set of key numbers in the form of a prepared template; however, there is no prescribed approach for insurers in undertaking their ICAs.

- **Individual Capital Guidance (ICG):** this is effectively the FSA's view of an insurer's capital requirements, formed after detailed review of the ICA submission. It is possible they will consider the ICA to be inadequate and, in such circumstances, would set a higher Individual Capital Guidance figure.

Individual Capital Assessments

Under ICAS, insurers must consider their insurance risk, market risk, credit risk, liquidity risk, group risk, and operational risk.

The first major challenge for all insurers is to identify their risks and the potential consequences. To that end the FSA encourages all insurers to draw up and maintain a risk register. The next challenge is to evaluate these risks.

The evaluation of insurance risk, which comprises both underwriting risk and liability risk, readily lends itself to stochastic approaches. It is in the estimation of the liability risk that UK actuaries are now widely using stochastic liability techniques.

In introducing the ICAS regime, the FSA has largely left the evaluation and reporting of reserves unchanged, at "prudent best estimates." To the extent that there is uncertainty in the reserve estimates, or indeed any lack of prudence, it expects this to be captured in the insurance risk component of an ICA.

It should be noted that the development of the ICAS regime started slightly before the development by the European Union of Solvency II; however, the Solvency II framework has many similarities to ICAS.

Although the UK regulatory principle has been "freedom with disclosure," it should be noted that ICA submissions by insurers to the FSA and the consequential Individual Capital Guidance letters from the FSA back to insurers are not made public.

Professional guidance

UK actuaries are expected to adhere to professional guidance as issued by their professional bodies, the Faculty and Institute of Actuaries (until June 2006) and the Board for Actuarial Standards (since June 2006).

Guidance Note GN12 is the professional guidance note regarding formal actuarial reports on non-life insurance business. In the version of GN12 introduced in June 2006 there is a clause stating:

"The report should normally indicate the nature, degree and sources of uncertainty surrounding the results and sensitivities to key assumptions. Uncertainty should normally be quantified where practicable, but otherwise should normally be reported using an appropriate descriptive summary."

In the above clause, "should normally" indicates that members must comply with a particular requirement, unless the circumstances are such that non-compliance is consistent with the standards of behaviour the public might reasonably expect of a member.

In a recent review of liability reports submitted by syndicates, the Council of Lloyd's noted that roughly 80% included a quantification of reserve uncertainty. Of those, roughly half based the quantification primarily upon a bootstrap approach, although many also supplemented the stochastic approach by other methods, such as stress/scenario tests.

B.6 Italy

The ISVAP is the Italian prudential regulator for insurers. As of 2008, the ISVAP was following Solvency I rules.

Non-life regulatory reporting

As part of regulatory reporting, non-life insurers have to submit accounting statements to the Italian regulator on an annual basis. These returns are not available to the public, but instead are aggregated and then made publicly available. For motor third-party liability, the report is very detailed and includes data by accident year such as premium, reported claims, average cost per claim, claim handling cost, etc.

Prior to the implantation of Solvency II there is no requirement from the Italian regulator for insurance companies to provide measures of uncertainty in their technical provisions. In recent years, interest in stochastic liability has increased. As part of its preparatory work for Solvency II, the ISVAP published a report in October 2006 regarding stochastic claims liability models.[80]

B.7 The Netherlands

Non-life regulatory reporting

As part of regulatory reporting, non-life insurers have to submit a number of standardized forms to the Dutch regulator, DNB, once a year. As of financial year 2007, a new reporting framework ("Wet op het financieel toezicht") has been implemented. The most important alterations are the new risk section and the liability adequacy test for non-life insurers. In the risk section, the insurers give information about the organization, strategy, governance, and, most of all, the risk management and risk profile of the company.

Forms that are publicly available include the actuarial report which describes, for each class of business, the composition of the class, the liability testing methodology, and the last financial-year changes in assumptions and methodologies. A statement from the actuary (similar to an opinion) is only obligatory for discounted reserves and some specific provisions. For this reason, most non-life insurers are not obligated to obtain an actuarial statement.

---

[80] www.isvap.it/isvap/imprese_jsp/PagePubblicazioniList.jsp?nomeSezione=PUBBLICAZIONI_ E_STATISTICHE&ObjId=98422

The form "Schade- en afloopstatistiek" includes the following information for each class of business, for the last 10 loss years:

■ Triangles for paid claims gross of reinsurance

■ Runoff results gross of reinsurance, including IBNR and IBNER

■ Runoff results of reinsurance reserves

As of 2007, non-life insurers must perform a liability adequacy test for both premium and claim reserves. In this test an adequate risk margin should be taken into account. In most cases, a qualitative test is allowed, although the definition of a qualitative liability adequacy test is not described specifically by the regulator. For a quantitative test, no specific methods or assumptions are prescribed, except for the discounting rates to be used. Insurers are also free to use their own methods to determine the adequate risk margin. The regulator invites the market to develop a best practice; however, there must be an explicit distinction between the best estimate and the risk margin. Commonly used methods include the bootstrap, GLM, and the Mack methods.

B.8 Romania

Non-life regulatory reporting

There are currently no statutory drivers for stochastic modeling in Romania. Regulators are still developing their prudential supervision and actuarial capabilities; however, many players in the insurance industry are subsidiaries of multinational groups and may, therefore, wish to use their group's internal model for Solvency II purposes.

B.9 Australia

Non-life regulatory reporting: Liability

The Australian Prudential Regulation Authority (APRA) is the prudential regulator of non-life insurers in Australia. APRA uses risk-based capital requirements and policy statements where companies are required to develop their own policies, procedures, and risk management practices, similar to the Financial Services Authority in the UK.

All companies are required to have an approved actuary who reports to the board and to APRA. One reporting requirement is to estimate the central estimate of insurance liabilities as well as the risk margin.

Risk margins relate to the inherent uncertainty in the central estimate values for insurance liabilities. Risk margins are evaluated for each class individually, and then in total with an allowance for diversification. APRA requires that the minimum value of total insurance liabilities (central estimate plus risk margin) must be the greater of:

■ A 75th percentile level of sufficiency

■ The central estimate + ½ standard deviation above the mean

In a 2006 non-life insurance survey (Gibbs and Hu, 2007), 76% of surveyed actuaries responded that they were involved in deriving risk margins, of which 85% of them said they use stochastic quantitative analysis in determining risk margins. The next most popular methodology was the use of research papers. There are two well-known research papers – Bateup and Reed (2001), and Collings and White (2001) – that provide benchmark multiples for a

75th-percentile range around reserves for different classes of business, as well as benchmarks for diversification benefits.

In determining diversification methodologies, respondents favored the use of general reasoning, the analysis of one's own data, and the use of benchmarks in research papers.

Non-life regulatory reporting: Capital adequacy

In July 2002, APRA implemented Prudential Standard GPS 110 – Capital Adequacy for Non-life Insurers, which requires insurers to select one of two methods to determine their Minimum Capital Requirement. Insurers can either develop an APRA approved in-house model – known as the Internal Model-based (IMB) Method – or use a formulaic method (Prescribed Method).

The use of the IMB Method requires APRA's approval. APRA's requirements are, broadly:

■ The model must ascertain an amount of capital sufficient to reduce the insurer's probability of default over a one-year time horizon to 0.5% or below.

■ The model must include all major risk types: catastrophe, underwriting, liability, market, credit, and operational risk, as well as risk dependencies and correlations.

■ The model should show the relationships among the insurer's risk appetite, capital requirements, expected shareholder returns, and external credit ratings. There should be explicit risk tolerances, risk limits, and delegations across the organization.

■ The board and senior management must be actively involved and the model must be integrated into the day-to-day risk management process of the insurer.

■ The model should be independently reviewed by consulting actuaries on a yearly basis.

B.10 New Zealand

In 2007 the Reserve Bank of New Zealand announced that it would become the prudential regulator for insurers, in what was previously a self-regulated industry. As of 2008, legislation on the insurance prudential regulatory framework was expected to be brought into force in 2010.

New Zealand Society of Actuaries currently has in effect Prudential Standard No. 4, which applies to all reports on the technical liabilities of non-life insurers. This stipulates the creation of a prudential margin that allows for:

■ The actuary's confidence in the valuation approach and assumptions

■ The quality and depth of the historical data available

■ Statistical fluctuations affecting the ultimate claim costs

■ The actual development and outcomes of past provisions for the insurer

B.11 Asia

Australian actuaries working in the Asian region have had some influence on regulators. Singapore and Malaysia have both adopted the requirement to hold reserves at the 75th percentile or higher, as in Australia. The bootstrap and Mack methods are commonly used for this purpose.

Singapore

Singaporean insurance companies are regulated by the Monetary Authority of Singapore (MAS). In 2005, the MAS implemented a risk-based capital solvency regime. The new minimum capital requirements are determined by applying charges to liability, market, credit, and mismatching risk and concentration risks.

In conjunction with this new framework, the MAS issued a series of insurance regulations. Insurance companies are required to appoint a qualified actuary to estimate the claims and premium liabilities and determine a prudential margin set at the 75th percentile. The Singapore Actuarial Society provides guidance on how to determine the prudential margin, suggesting two Australian papers by Bateup and Reed (2001) and Collings and White (2001). where benchmarks could be obtained. They also suggest the use of stochastic modeling, such as stochastic chain ladder methods, generalized linear models (GLM), and credibility models.

Malaysia

In 2007 the insurance regulator in Malaysia, the Central Bank of Malaysia (Bank Negara Malaysia or BNM) introduced a risk-based capital solvency regime that is to be enforced in 2009. In 2008, companies were required to submit risk-based capital solvency calculations quarterly. Currently this follows a formula-based approach, with capital charges for the credit, market, insurance, and operational risks of an insurer.

The BNM also requires companies to appoint a qualified actuary to estimate claim and premium liabilities. Like Singapore and Australia, the actuary is required to determine an explicit prudential margin for insurance liabilities at the 75th percentile.

Hong Kong

The Office of the Commissioner of Insurance issued "Guidance Note on Actuarial Review of Insurance Liabilities in respect of Employees' Compensation and Motor Insurance Businesses" (GN9), which requires a non-life insurer to appoint a qualified actuary to conduct an actuarial review of its employees' compensation and motor insurance liabilities, if the reserves are significant in size.

Under GN9, a risk margin is not a statutory requirement, but it should be included if considered appropriate by the actuary; however, it does not describe how the risk margin is to be quantified. Many actuaries in Hong Kong, typically consulting actuaries also doing work in Singapore, voluntarily calculate the 75th percentile as a means of quantifying the risk margin.

China

In China, the use of deterministic actuarial methods applied by an appointed actuary was brought into legislation with the release of "Measures on Administration of Reserves for Non-life Insurance Business of Insurance Companies (Tentative)" by the China Insurance Regulatory Commission (CIRC) in 2005; however, these reserves were only used to determine the solvency of companies beginning in 2007.

Currently the statutory solvency requirement ("SCR") of non-life companies in China is the higher of two prescriptive formulas, one being a function of the last 12 months' net written premium, and the other, a function of the last three years of net paid claims.

Chinese Taipei

The Financial Supervisory Commission (FSC) is the regulator for the banking, securities, and insurance sectors in Chinese Taipei. Under the Insurance Act, a non-life insurer is required to appoint a qualified actuary to conduct an annual actuarial reserve review. Risk margins are not a statutory requirement.

Non-life insurers are required to hold special risk reserves in addition to the best estimates of policy liabilities as provisions for unexpected catastrophes and potential deterioration of loss experience. The calculation methods of the special reserves are formulaic and prescribed in the regulations.

The FSC implemented a risk-based capital regime in 2003, and in 2007 amended the original formulaic calculation to include operational risk.

Japan

The Japanese insurance industry is regulated by the Financial Services Agency. In 2006, they introduced the requirements for deterministic actuarial methodology to estimate IBNR. Before this, prescribed formulas were used. Currently, appointed actuaries are required to review and confirm the appropriateness and adequacy of the IBNR and the premium liabilities and then issue an opinion letter to the board.

There is also a requirement for contingency reserves for various future catastrophes. These reserves generally increase incrementally, based on prescribed technical formulas utilizing net premium income, paid loss, and other parameters. One exception is that for fire (property) lines in which a risk curve must be estimated using a model for floods, typhoons, and earthquakes, and where the reserve increases based on the risk curves and prescribed return periods. These reserves can be released when loss ratios for these lines are greater than the thresholds prescribed by the regulator.

Claim expenses including unallocated loss adjustment expenses are not required or established in Japan.

Thailand

In Thailand, the common deterministic actuarial methodologies are just now gaining acceptance into insurance regulations. Under regulations current as of 2008, a non-life insurer is required to hold an IBNR reserve, which is not less than 2.5% of the net premiums written in the past 12 months, in addition to the total case reserves of reported and outstanding losses. The Office of the Insurance Commission, Thailand (OIC) introduced a new regulation requiring insurance companies to file actuarial reserve reports with the OIC at the end of the 2008 financial year, although enforcement of the solvency requirements using the actuarial reserves will come at a later date. This new regulation requires insurance companies to appoint actuaries to calculate actuarial reserves using common actuarial methods.

The current capital requirement in Thailand is 10% of net written premiums. However, as of 2008 the regulators were developing a risk-based capital approach similar to those used in Singapore and Malaysia.

South Korea

The Korean insurance industry is regulated by the Financial Supervisory Service (FSS) and Financial Services Commission (FSC). Under regulations current as of 2008, there was no requirement for stochastic analysis of actuarial reserves. Korean companies are required to hold an IBNR reserve based on a statistical approach (deterministic) chosen by the appointed actuary of a company. Also, a company is required to hire an independent actuary to review and confirm the appropriateness and adequacy of the IBNR and the premium liabilities and report the independent actuary's opinion to the FSS.

A company is required to establish equalization reserves (contingency reserves, catastrophe reserves) of up to 50% of in-force premium incrementally by a prescribed formula every year, and these reserves can be released when loss ratios for these lines are greater than the thresholds as prescribed by the regulator.

Minimum required capital is established by a prescribed formula which is a maximum of 17.8% of in-force premiums or a three- year average of historical claims.

India

The Insurance Regulatory and Development Authority (IRDA), the Indian regulator, is slowly trying to bring in regulations that would require companies to use advanced actuarial techniques; however, as of 2008 there was no regulation that makes stochastic modeling mandatory for insurers.

IRDA requires all insurers to have an Appointed Actuary, who makes the best estimate of technical liabilities. No range or risk margin is required. IRDA has issued guidance on this calculation.

The IRDA circular for "(Valuation of) Assets, Liabilities and (calculation of) Solvency Margin of insurers" prescribes the formula for calculation of Required Solvency Margin (RSM) for non-life insurers in India. The capital requirement calculation is not risk-based. The RSM is, instead, a function of the net or gross written premium during the evaluation period, or a function of claims incurred during the evaluation period, whichever is higher.

B.12 The Americas

Canada

In Canada, the federal and provincial governments are both involved in the regulation of the insurance industry. The Office of the Superintendent of Financial Institutions Canada (OSFI) regulates federally registered insurance companies as well as Canadian branches of foreign insurers. Provincial regulators supervise the provincially incorporated insurers. Over three-quarters of the insurers doing business in Canada are federally regulated.

In January 2008, a joint committee of the OSFI, Autorité des Marchés Financiers (the solvency regulator in the province of Québec) and Assuris, produced a "Framework for a New Standard Approach to Setting Capital Requirements" that would introduce regulatory changes requiring a solvency buffer in order for a company to withstand adverse economic conditions 39 times out of 40, or with a significance level of 97.5%.

January 1, 2011, is the expected date for all Canadian public companies, including all insurance companies, to move to the IASB accounting standards.

Reserves

The Canadian Insurance Companies Act requires insurers to appoint an actuary to value the insurer's technical liabilities. The claim liabilities and premium liability reflect the time value of money and include provisions for adverse deviations (PFAD). The explicit PFAD consists of three elements:

- Claims Development PFAD

- Reinsurance Recovery PFAD

- Investment Return Rate PFAD

Claims PFAD reflects the risks underlying the insurer's claims practices, the underlying data, and the nature of the lines of business. Reinsurance Recovery PFAD reflects risks relating to the insurer's ceded claim ratio and potential problems with reinsurers. Investment Return Rate PFAD reflects risks relating to the insurer's investment portfolio yield, claims payout patterns, and the investment climate in general. To calculate the PFAD, the regulator prescribes a range of percentages applied to the discounted best estimate of reserves. The actuary uses professional judgment to select a percentage from within this range.

Dynamic capital adequacy testing

The Canadian Insurance Companies Act requires that the appointed actuary conduct an evaluation of an insurer's financial condition via Dynamic Capital Adequacy Testing (DCAT), which involves forecasting its financial position under a variety of adverse scenarios.

With these scenarios, DCAT's purpose is to identify:

- Plausible threats to an entity's satisfactory financial condition

- Action that lessens the likelihood of those threats

- Action that would mitigate a threat if it materialized

An entity's financial condition is considered satisfactory if, during the forecast period:

- It is able to meet its future obligations under the base scenario and plausible adverse scenarios

- It meets the minimum regulatory capital requirement under the base scenario

The forecast period for a typical property and casualty insurer would be three fiscal years, and adverse scenarios are usually defined as 1-in-100-year event. The regulator prescribes areas in which the scenarios must test (for instance, catastrophes and yield curve shifts), but the scenarios themselves are left to the judgment of the actuary.

United States of America

Non-life regulatory reporting

In the United States of America (U.S.), the National Association of Insurance Commissioners (NAIC) promulgates the risk-based capital (RBC) formulas and the Insurance Regulatory Information System (IRIS) tests ratios. Companies are rated and monitored based on the results of these tests. A document providing an overview of the current RBC models that apply to life companies, non-life companies, and health companies can be found on the NAIC Web site.

Although stochastic liability is not required, non-life companies in the United States are beginning to more frequently use stochastic models, such as the bootstrap model, to evaluate reserve ranges, tail factor at risk, and for enterprise risk management, encouraged by the rating agencies.

Reserves

It is expected that the current insurance accounting system of U.S. GAAP will eventually be replaced by IFRS, possibly in 2013. Major changes to current liability practices would be (1) the recognition of the time value of money through the discounting of loss reserves, and (2) establishment of an explicit risk margin.

Unearned Premium Reserve (UPR) in the United States is required, but no formula is mandated. The daily pro rata method is widely used. Additionally, companies are required to estimate a Premium Deficiency Reserve (PDR) and a loss incurred but not reported (IBNR) reserve, but no formulas are mandated. Non-life insurance companies in the United States are required to have a qualified actuary[81] provide opinions on the adequacy of their total reserves (case + IBNR), both net and gross of reinsurance. As of 2008, the opining actuary can either produce a single actuarial central estimate, a range, or a range and a central estimate. The American Academy of Actuaries only specifies that the range must be a "range of reasonable reserve estimates." The actuary needs to include this result and the company's carried reserve in the Actuarial Opinion Summary, which is not publicly available like the actuarial opinion itself. Many actuaries estimate a range, and some are beginning to use stochastic methods to determine these ranges.

Latin America

Non-life regulatory reporting

The general regulatory framework for most countries in Latin America (Central and South America) follows Solvency I guidelines as defined by the European Union. In several countries, minimum capital requirements are determined and prescribed by the lines of business the company is engaged in.

Some countries, however, are moving to update their solvency requirements. Mexico, for instance, has been moving to establish solvency requirements closer to the concept of risk-based capital, requiring a dynamic solvency test equivalent to the cash flow testing used in the United States.

Brazil passed a new regulation on capital requirements in late 2006,[82] followed by a change in December 2007,[83] which provides incentives for insurers to develop internal risk models, starting with underwriting risk. This initiative is setting a trend towards the use of stochastic models in calculating economic capital.

Countries such as Mexico, Brazil, and Chile have announced their commitment to adopt IFRS. Others are studying the preliminary pronouncements of the European Union with regards to Solvency II in anticipation of adopting some

---

[81] The American Academy of Actuaries annually publishes a practice note on Statements of Actuarial Opinion on Property and Casualty Loss Reserves, including qualification standards of the appointed actuary.

[82] CNSP Resolution No. 158 defined two sets of tables to calculate the capital required for insurers. The first table shows a very demanding capital requirement while the second set implies a less demanding capital requirement, but can only be used by companies that develop internal underwriting risk models.

[83] The 158 Resolution tables were changed by SUSEP Circular 355. The market pressure was such that SUSEP released a less demanding set of tables to calculate capital requirements.

of its new requirements locally. Recently the Mexico National Commission of Insurance released a timeline proposal to the industry in order to implement its Solvency II version.

Discussions with regards to the adoption of stochastic models is beginning to take place in countries such as Brazil, Mexico, and Chile, where the conceptual approach is moving towards supervision based on risk; however, for the rest of the region, this discussion is limited by the lack of actuarial experience that would be able to manage and regulate these processes and the lack of quality historical data.

Unearned premium reserves

Most countries in Latin America use the familiar daily pro rata method for calculating unearned premium reserves. Exceptions do exist: for example, in Colombia the rule of eighths is currently used.[84] Colombian insurers are also required to establish the unearned premium reserve on 80% of the premiums retained during the year (for most lines of business). The remaining 20% of premium is assumed to cover prepaid commissions and administration expenses. In Mexico the unearned premium reserves includes the premium deficiency reserve. In other countries, premium deficiency reserves are calculated separately according to prescribed formula.

IBNR

Technical notes are generally required to be filed documenting the methodology used to calculate IBNR. The most common method used in the region is the incurred loss development method. The requirements for IBNR methodology are relatively recent in Latin America. Brazil and Mexico, for example, first introduced IBNR requirements approximately 10 years ago. In some jurisdictions, companies must submit a chosen methodology and follow it. In others, the insurance regulator prescribes a methodology that companies must abide by. For example, in Colombia (Decreto) and Peru (Resolución S.B.S. N°) the 2008 prescribed methodologies do not use loss development triangles.

Judicial claims

Judicial claims (claims with attorney) in Brazil are categorized with either a probable/possible/remote chance of eventual payment to the claimant. Attorneys have demonstrated an inconsistent approach to this categorization. Insurance companies also differ in how much reserve they book for each category. One particular challenge is that these claims are often maintained outside the company claim system, and a claim history can be difficult to track. These same kinds of reserves also exist in Mexico, which are mandatory by the Commissioner whenever a dispute or a suit arises. A robust actuarial review of these judicial claims and their liability processes may be necessary when developing a stochastic model in Latin America.

Catastrophe reserves

Contingency reserves for future earthquakes, hurricanes, and other catastrophes are required in various Latin America countries. These reserves generally increase incrementally based on prescribed technical formulas utilizing probable maximum loss, net sum insured or premiums, and other parameters. These reserves can only be released following a catastrophe of required magnitude, and generally under insurance regulatory approval.

---

[84] The rule of eighths is based on the assumption that annual policies are written evenly over each quarter and risk is spread evenly over the annual policy term. For example, the unearned premium reserve at the end of the year is calculated as one-eighth of first quarter written premium, three-eighths of second quarter written premium, five-eighths of third quarter written premium, and seven-eighths of fourth quarter written premium.

The catastrophe reserves are a contingency reserve for future events that may or may not occur. This reserve is, therefore, more like a segregation of capital than a true loss reserve. These reserves can be significant, and pose a strain on the release of capital for modeling purposes. Under IFRS rules, these reserves are treated as part of the capital account, not as a liability.

ULAE

Although future expenses directly attributable to individual claims (Allocated Loss Adjustment Expense or ALAE) are generally accounted for in the liability process, reserves for claim expenses not directly assignable to individual claims (Unallocated Loss Adjustment Expense or ULAE) are not required or established in Latin America.

Data considerations

In certain jurisdictions, the lack of quality historical data will be a limiting factor as to how fast the industry will be able to adopt stochastic modeling in both its internal management practices as well as its supervision requirements. Although the capture and maintenance of quality data has significantly improved in recent years, several companies today still do not maintain historical loss payments or claim reserves, as new payments or reserve changes simply overwrite previous entries within claim systems.

Currency risk

Several countries in Latin America allow insurance coverage to be issued in either their local currency or in U.S. dollars. Historically, the U.S. dollar has been the stronger currency and this is used by consumers as a hedge against local inflation.

Asset/liability matching

The lack of proper investment instruments corresponding to the nature of the liabilities assumed creates serious issues and reinvestment risk for companies in almost all countries in the region. The issue of asset and liability matching is not only related to duration issues, but also currency, as mentioned above.

Inflation

Although inflation rates in the 1980s and 1990s were extremely volatile in most Latin America jurisdictions, the region has exhibited a stabilization of moderate rates in more recent years. As economic climates can quickly change, projected inflation should still be carefully considered for any stochastic modeling.

Reinsurance

Reinsurance requirements vary from country to country, where Mexico and Chile have the strongest reinsurance regulatory environment. It is worth noting that the reinsurance market in Brazil has historically been monopolized by the state-owned IRB Brasil Re. As approved in December 2007 (see CNSP Resolution No. 168 for details), this reinsurance sector is currently in the process of opening to international markets.

B.13 South Africa

The Financial Services Board(FSB) oversees the South African non-banking financial services industry, including the insurance industry.

Capital adequacy

As of 2008, the minimum capital requirement was set at a percentage of the net premium
written during the 12 months preceding the date of valuation. In January 2007, the FSB published an "Issues Paper" proposing a new financial condition reporting solvency margin test, expected to be implemented in 2010. The solvency margin test requires a 99.5% sufficiency level over a one-year horizon.

Under the new rules, non-life insurers will be able to use one of three models to determine their capital adequacy requirements. These are:

- A prescribed model (formulaic method)

- A certified model (medium-term solution for insurers making a transition to an internal model)

    - This model allows for the consideration of the insurer's individual risk profile to determine inputs to the prescribed model

- An internal model, which is subject to approval by FSB. Insurers would need to use stochastic models to determine the adequacy of their capital. Risk factors that should be addressed in the model include:

    - Investment risks

    - Insurance risks, including premium projection risk, outstanding claims risk, concentration risks, and reinsurance risk

    - Credit risk

    - Operational risk

    - New business risk

    - Parameter and model risks

    - Correlation among risks

Based on a survey by PricewaterhouseCoopers, 12 of the 13 major non-life insurers indicated that they plan on using an internal model to measure capital adequacy.

References for Appendix B

Agencia Nacional de Saude Suplementar (ANS, Brazil). For more information, see the Web site at http://www.ans.gov.br/portalv4/site/home/default.asp.

American Academy of Actuaries. For more information, see the Web site at http://www.actuary.org.

American Academy of Actuaries, Committee on Property and Liability Financial Reporting (December 31, 2007). Statements of actuarial opinion on property and casualty loss reserves. Retrieved Sept. 23, 2009, from http://www.actuary.org/pdf/practnotes/pc_loss07.pdf.

Asociacion Aseguradores de Chile A.G. (AACH). For more information, see the Web site at http://aach.cl/home.asp.

Asociacion Mexicana de Instituciones de Seguros A.C. (AMIS). For more information, see the Web site at http://www.amis.com.mx/yotedigocomo/splash/.

Australian Prudential Authority. For more information, see the Web site at http://www.apra.gov.au.

Autorité de contrôle des assurances et des mutuelles (ACAM). For more information, see the Web site at http://www.acam-france.fr/info/00.

Autorité de contrôle des assurances et des mutuelles (ACAM). Aggregated, industry-wide returns. Retrieved Sept. 22, 2009, from http://www.acam-france.fr/stats/statistiques/xls/NI_DA05_20061206.xls.

Autorité de contrôle des assurances et des mutuelles (ACAM). "As part of its preparatory work regarding its Solvency II QIS4 submission, ACAM published a report in November 2007" ... www.acam-france.fr/fichiers/Rapport_Assurance_ Dommages_090108_uk_492.pdf in English.

Banco de Mexico. For more information, see the Web site at http://www.banxico.gob.mx/.

Bank Negara Malaysia, Central Bank of Malaysia. For more information, see the Web site at http://www.bnm.gov.my/.

Bank Negara Malaysia (March 2007). Guidelines on the role of the appointed actuary for Takaful operators.

Bank Negara Malaysia (April 2007). Revised risk-weighted capital adequacy framework. Implementation from January 2008.

Bank Negara Malaysia (April 2007). Risk-based capital framework for insurers. Implementation from January 2009.

Bateup, Robyn & Reed, Ian for the Institute of Actuaries of Australia (Nov. 20, 2001). Research and data analysis relevant to the development of standards and guidelines on liability valuation for non-life insurance.

CNSP Resolution No. 168 (re: Brazil).

Bundesanstalt für Finanzdienstleistungsaufsicht (BaFin). For more information, see the Web site at http://www.bafin.de/.

Canadian Institute of Actuaries (January 2008). *Standards of practice*. Retrieved Sept. 23, 2009, from http://www.actuaries.ca/SOP_Doc/Complete/SOP_e_Complete.pdf.

China Insurance Regulatory Commission. For more information, see the Web site at http://www.circ.gov.cn/portal45/default2727.htm.

China Insurance Regulatory Commission (2006). Measures on administration of reserves for non-life insurance business of insurance companies (tentative) 2006-11-14. Retrieved Sept. 23, 2009, from http://www.circ.gov.cn/Portal45/InfoModule_6831/38816.htm.

Collings, S. & White, G. (2001). APRA risk margin analysis. The Institute of Actuaries of Australia's XIIIth General Insurance Seminar.

Commission of the European Communities (2008). Amended proposal for a directive of the European Parliament and of the Council on the taking up and pursuit of the business of insurance and reinsurance (Solvency II). Retrieved Sept. 22, 2009, from http://ec.europa.eu/internal_market/insurance/docs/solvency/proposal_en.pdf.

Committee on European Insurance and Occupational Pensions Supervisors (CEIOPS). For more information, see the Web site at http://www.ceiops.org.

Committee on European Insurance and Occupational Pensions Supervisors (2008). *QIS4 technical specifications*. Retrieved Sept. 22, 2009, from http://www.ceiops.eu/media/docman/Technical%20Specifications%20QIS4.doc.

Decreto 839/91 for methodology details (re: Colombia).

Fasecolda (Colombia). For more information, see the Web site at http://www.fasecolda.com/fasecolda/.

Federal Office of Private Insurance (March 28, 2006). The Swiss experience with market consistent technical provisions - the cost of capital approach.

Financial Services Agency (Japan). For more information, see the Web site at http://www.fsa.go.jp/en/index.html.

Financial Supervisory Commission (Taiwan, R.O.C.). For more information, see the Web site at http://www.fsc.gov.tw/Layout/main_ch/index.aspx?frame=1.

Foreign Non-Life Insurance Association of Japan www.fnlia.gr.jp/index(E).html.

FSB (2007). Issues paper by FSB concerning FCR –proposed solvency assessment for short-term insurers" ftp://ftp.fsb.co.za/public/insurance/IssPpcomment09012007.pdf.

General Insurance Association of Japan (GIAJ). For more information, see the Web site at http://www.sonpo.or.jp/en/.

Gibbs, J. and Hu, S. on behalf of the Non-life insurance Practice Committee of the Institute of Actuaries of Australia (2007). Australian reserving practices. An analysis of the 2006 non-life insurance claims reserving and risk margins survey.

http://www.apra.gov.au/General/General-Insurance-Prudential-Standards-and-Guidance-Notes.cfm.

Institute of Actuaries of Japan. For more information, see the Web site at http://www.actuaries.jp/english/menu_e.html.

IRB Brasil Re. For more information, see the Web site at http://www2.irb-brasilre.com.br/site/.

Insurance Regulatory and Development Authority (India). For more information, see the Web site at http://www.irdaindia.org/.

Insurance Regulatory and Development Authority (India) (May 6, 2005). Guidelines on estimation of IBNR claims provision under general insurance business. Retrieved Sept. 23, 2009, from http://www.irdaindia.org/cirnonlife/cirnonlife06may05.pdf.

Isapres de Chile. For more information, see the Web site at http://www.isapre.cl/principal.php.

ISVAP. Non-life regulatory reporting requirements. Retrieved Sept. 22, 2009, from http://www.isvap.it/isvap_cms/docs/F17044/allcirc0568.xls.

Mack, Thomas (1993). Distribution-free calculation of the standard error of chain ladder reserve estimates. *ASTIN Bulletin* 23.

Mack, T., & Quarg, G. Munich Chain Ladder Blätter. DGVFM XXVI (4), 597-630.

Monetary Authority of Singapore. For more information, see the Web site at http://www.mas.gov.sg/.

Monetary Authority of Singapore (2004). Insurance act (chapter 142) insurance (valuation and capital) regulations 2004. Retrieved Sept. 23, 2009, from http://www.mas.gov.sg/resource/legislation_guidelines/insurance/sub_legislation/Insurance%20(Valuation%20and%20Capital)%20Regs%202004.pdf.

Monetary Authority of Singapore (2009). List of regulations. Retrieved Sept. 23, 2009, from http://www.mas.gov.sg/legislation_guidelines/insurance/sub_legislation/Subsidiary_Legislation_Administered_by_MAS_ID.html.

National Association of Insurance Commissioners (NAIC). For more information, see the Web site at http://www.naic.org/index.htm.

National Association of Insurance Commissioners (July 15, 2009). Risk-based capital: General overview. Retrieved Sept. 23, 2009, from http://www.naic.org/documents/committees_e_capad_RBCoverview.pdf.

New Zealand Society of Actuaries. Professional standard no.4 – general insurance business.

Office of the Commissioner of Insurance (Hong Kong). For more information, see the Web site at http://www.oci.gov.hk/.

Office of the Commissioner of Insurance (Hong Kong) Guidance note on actuarial review of insurance liabilities in respect of employees' compensation and motor insurance businesses.

Office of the Insurance Commission, Thailand. For more information, see the Web site at http://www.oic.or.th/th/home/index.php.

Office of the Superintendent of Finance Institutions Canada. For more information, see the Web site at http://www.osfi-bsif.gc.ca/.

PricewaterhouseCoopers. Emerging trends and strategic issues in South African insurance.

Resolución S.B.S. N° 1048-99 for methodology details (re: Peru).

Schoeman, H. (November 2004). Short-term insurers could need additional capital in the wake of FCR. *Cover*. Retrieved Sept. 23, 2009, from http://www.guardrisk.co.za/pages/116?PHPSESSID=7a6a69480fc0c1eb4e4cc24dd0b0b72d.

Singapore Actuarial Society (SAS). For more information, see the Web site at http://www.actuaries.org.sg/.

Singapore Actuarial Society (Nov. 18, 2004). SAS GN G01: Guidance note for actuaries investigating policy liabilities relating to general insurance business. Retrieved Sept. 23, 2009, from http://www.actuaries.org.sg/files/library/guidance_notes/SAS%20GN%20G01.pdf?download.

South Africa (2009). Marsh captives. Retrieved Sept. 23, 2009, from http://global.marsh.com/risk/captives/captives SouthAfrica.php?pv=1.

Superintendência de Seguros Privados (SUSEP, Brazil). For more information, see the Web site at http://www.susep.gov.br/principal.asp.

Superintendencia Financiera de Colombia. For more information, see the Web site at http://www.superfinanciera.gov.co/.

Superintendencia Nacional de Salud (Supersalud, Colombia). For more information, see the Web site at http://www.supersalud.gov.co/.

Superintendencia Valores y Seguros (SVS, Chile). For more information, see the Web site at http://www.svs.cl/sitio/index.php.

Swiss Actuarial Association. Guidelines on the actuarial report for non-life insurance guidelines for loss reserves in non-life insurance. For more information, see the Web site at http://www.actuaries.ch.

Swiss Financial Market Supervisory Authority (FINMA). For more information, see the Web site at http://www.finma.ch/e/Pages/default.aspx.

Swiss Parliament. www.bpv.admin.ch/dokumentation/00437/01248/01290/index.html?lang=en.

The key documents on SST issued by the Swiss Federal Office of Private Insurance are: www.bpv.admin.ch/themen/00506/00552/index.html?lang=en, 1.   White Paper on the Swiss Solvency Test, 2. Technical Document on the Swiss Solvency Test, 3. SST Fieldtests 2005, 2006 & 2007, 4. SST 2008.

U.S. Securities and Exchange Commission (SEC). For more information, see the Web site at http://www.sec.gov/.

Viver Seguro (Brazil). For more information, see the Web site at http://www.fenaseg.org.br/.

Vorsichtsprinzip. § 252 HGB Allgemeine Bewertungsgrundsätze. For more information, see the Wikipedia entry at http://de.wikipedia.org/wiki/Vorsichtsprinzip.

Additional Resources

Europe

The following are Web links to the governmental regulatory bodies and associations of insurance companies, respectively, for the larger European countries.

Austria

http://www.fma.gv.at
http://www.vvo.at/

Belgium

http://www.cbfa.be

Bulgaria

http://www.fsc.bg

Cyprus

http://www.mof.gov.cy

Czech Republic

http://www.cnb.cz

Denmark

http://www.finanstilsynet.dk

Estonia

http://www.fi.ee

Finland

http://www.vakuutusvalvonta.fi

France

http://www.acam-france.fr

Germany

http://www.bafin.de
http://www.gdv.de/index.html

Greece

http://www.pisc.gr

Hungary

http://www.pszaf.hu

Iceland

http://www.fme.is

Ireland

http://www.financialregulator.ie
http://www.pensionsboard.ie

Italy

http://www.isvap.it
http://www.covip.it
http://www.ania.it

Latvia

http://www.fktk.lv

Liechtenstein

http://www.fma-li.li

Lithuania

http://www.dpk.lt

Luxembourg

http://www.cssf.lu
http://www.commassu.lu

Malta

http://www.mfsa.com.mt

Netherlands

http://www.dnb.nl

Norway

http://www.kredittilsynet.no

Poland

http://www.knf.gov.pl

Portugal

http://www.isp.pt

Romania

http://www.csa-isc.ro
http://www.csspp.ro

Slovakia

http://www.nbs.sk

Slovenia

http://www.a-zn.si

Spain

http://www.meh.es

Sweden

http://www.fi.se

Switzerland

http://www.bpv.admin.ch

United Kingdom

http://www.fsa.gov.uk
http://www.thepensionsregulator.gov.uk
http://www.abi.org.uk

Appendix C

Illustrative Market-Consistent Assumptions for Section III

Market-consistent Assumptions as of 12/31/07

| Time | Swap Curve | Implied Volatilities | | | | | |
		S&P 500	Russell 20	NASDAQ	SBBIG	EAFE	Money Mkt
1	4.07%	21.87%	26.60%	35.94%	3.80%	21.87%	1.00%
2	3.81%	22.27%	27.09%	36.59%	3.80%	22.27%	1.00%
3	3.91%	22.86%	27.81%	37.57%	3.80%	22.86%	1.00%
4	4.04%	23.49%	28.57%	38.60%	3.80%	23.49%	1.00%
5	4.18%	24.15%	29.38%	39.69%	3.80%	24.15%	1.00%
6	4.31%	22.74%	27.66%	37.37%	3.80%	22.46%	1.00%
7	4.42%	21.33%	25.95%	35.05%	3.80%	20.77%	1.00%
8	4.54%	19.92%	24.23%	32.74%	3.80%	19.08%	1.00%
9	4.59%	18.51%	22.52%	30.42%	3.80%	17.39%	1.00%
10	4.67%	17.10%	20.80%	28.10%	3.80%	15.70%	1.00%
11	4.73%	17.10%	20.80%	28.10%	3.80%	15.70%	1.00%
12	4.78%	17.10%	20.80%	28.10%	3.80%	15.70%	1.00%
13	4.82%	17.10%	20.80%	28.10%	3.80%	15.70%	1.00%
14	4.86%	17.10%	20.80%	28.10%	3.80%	15.70%	1.00%
15	4.89%	17.10%	20.80%	28.10%	3.80%	15.70%	1.00%
16	4.91%	17.10%	20.80%	28.10%	3.80%	15.70%	1.00%
17	4.93%	17.10%	20.80%	28.10%	3.80%	15.70%	1.00%
18	4.95%	17.10%	20.80%	28.10%	3.80%	15.70%	1.00%
19	4.96%	17.10%	20.80%	28.10%	3.80%	15.70%	1.00%
20	4.98%	17.10%	20.80%	28.10%	3.80%	15.70%	1.00%
21	4.98%	17.10%	20.80%	28.10%	3.80%	15.70%	1.00%
22	4.99%	17.10%	20.80%	28.10%	3.80%	15.70%	1.00%
23	4.99%	17.10%	20.80%	28.10%	3.80%	15.70%	1.00%
24	5.00%	17.10%	20.80%	28.10%	3.80%	15.70%	1.00%
25	5.00%	17.10%	20.80%	28.10%	3.80%	15.70%	1.00%
26	5.01%	17.10%	20.80%	28.10%	3.80%	15.70%	1.00%
27	5.01%	17.10%	20.80%	28.10%	3.80%	15.70%	1.00%
28	5.02%	17.10%	20.80%	28.10%	3.80%	15.70%	1.00%
29	5.02%	17.10%	20.80%	28.10%	3.80%	15.70%	1.00%
30	5.03%	17.10%	20.80%	28.10%	3.80%	15.70%	1.00%

The implied volatilities for the S&P 500 are based on the average of quotes from multiple dealers. The implied volatilities for the Russell 2000 and NASDAQ are based on the S&P implied volatility and the ratios from the long-term volatility assumptions. The implied volatilities for the EAFE will be assumed to be equal to that of the S&P 500.

Appendix D
Bootstrap Model

The Bootstrap Model

The term "bootstrapping" originates in German literature from legends about Baron von Münchhausen, who was known for the often unbelievable tales he recounted of his adventures. In one, he supposedly saves himself from drowning in a swamp or quicksand by pulling himself up by his own hair. Later versions of similar tales told how he lifted himself out of the sea by pulling up on his bootstraps, thus forming the basis for the term bootstrapping.

The term has taken on broad application in many fields of study, including physics, biology and medical research, computer science, and statistics. Though the concept has ultimately grown to mean different things in each of the above applications, the approach generally starts with a simple set of information on which more complex systems are built bit by bit. Like the Baron, who needed nothing more than what he already had to pull himself out of the sea, the technique often uses no more data than what is immediately available to estimate or project more complex information about that data.

Much of the credit for expanding the concept of the bootstrap estimate into the realm of statistics goes to Bradley Efron, chairman of the Department of Statistics at Stanford University. In his work, "bootstrap" refers to the re-sampling of existing data that gives rise to a new sample from which others are created. Efron suggests this promulgation can be achieved by duplicating the original sample as many times as computing resources allow, and then by treating this expanded sample as a virtual population. Further samples can then be drawn with replacements from the population to verify the estimators.

Several writers in actuarial literature have applied this concept to the process of loss liability. The most commonly cited examples are from England and Verrall (1999 and 2002), Pinheiro et al. (2001), and Kirschner et al. (2008). In its simplest form, they suggest using a basic chain ladder technique to square a triangle of paid losses, randomly, stochastically repeating this procedure a large number of times by which to evaluate the distribution of the outcomes.

D.1.a A Simple Paid Loss Chain Ladder Simulation

For a review of the algorithm's steps, we will examine one of the most basic forms of the technique: a simulation of possible future outcomes based on the paid loss triangle and the basic chain ladder approach. Using random sampling from a triangle of residuals, the model simulates a large number of "sample" triangles, uses the chain ladder model to estimate the future payment triangles (lower right), and then calculates a distribution from the many random estimates of future payments.

The following steps outline the functions performed by the model (although in the reality, they would be somewhat more complex):

13. Use a triangle of cumulative paid losses as input. Calculate the volume weighted averages of age-to-age development factors.

14. Calculate a new triangle of "fitted values," i.e., use the age-to-age factors to "undevelop" each value in the latest diagonal to form a new triangle of values predicted by the model assumptions.

15. Working from the incremental versions of the original value and fitted value triangles, calculate a triangle of residuals – what are known as "unscaled Pearson residuals" in the model.

16. Standardize the residuals so they are independent and identically distributed (i.i.d.).

17. Adjust the standardized residuals for degrees of freedom, resulting in "scaled Pearson residuals."

18. Create a new incremental sample triangle by randomly selecting with replacement from among the triangle of scaled Pearson residuals.

19. Develop and square that sample triangle, adding tail factors and estimating ultimate losses.

20. Add process variance to the future incremental values from Step 7 (which will change the estimated ultimate).

21. Calculate the total future payments (estimated unpaid amounts) for each year and in total for this iteration of the model.

22. Repeat the random selection, new triangle creation, and resulting unpaid calculations in Steps 6 through 9, X times.[85]

23. The result from the X simulations is an estimate of a distribution of possible outcomes. From these outcomes, we can calculate the mean, standard deviation, percentiles, etc.

D.1.b A Walk-through of the Basic Calculation, Based on Paid Loss Data

Step 1. Build a basic development model.	Cumulative paid loss data					
		12	24	36	48	60
	2003	352	783	1,045	1,183	1,295
Use the standard chain ladder method and the all-period volume weighted average (VWA) to calculate age-to-age factors.	2004	255	572	710	750	
	2005	279	638	767		
	2006	311	717			
	2007	308				
		12-24	24-36	36-48	48-60	60+
	VWAs	2.264	1.265	1.101	1.095	1.000

---

[85] As noted earlier, the value for X should be a large number of iterations, usually 10,000 to 50,000. Because the companion Excel files are designed for educational use only, they are limited to only 100 iterations.

Step 2.	**Triangle fitted backwards from latest diagonal**				
Create a "fitted" triangle.		12	24	36	48	60
	2003	375	849	1,074	1,183	1,295
Start with the most recent	2004	238	538	681	750	
cumulative diagonal and "un-	2005	268	606	767		
develop" values using the	2006	317	717			
appropriate VWAs.	2007	308				

Step 2.
Create a "fitted" triangle.

Start with the most recent cumulative diagonal and "un-develop" values using the appropriate VWAs.

Triangle fitted backwards from latest diagonal

	12	24	36	48	60
2003	375	849	1,074	1,183	1,295
2004	238	538	681	750	
2005	268	606	767		
2006	317	717			
2007	308				

Step 3.
Calculate Pearson residuals.

Working from the incremental forms of both triangles, subtract the fitted from the actual amount for each cell. Divide each result by the square root of the absolute value of the fitted amount. This results in "unscaled" Pearson residuals.

$$r_{UP} = \frac{C - \hat{m}}{\sqrt{abs(\hat{m})}}$$

C = actual incremental amount

$\hat{m}$ = fitted incremental for matching location in each triangle

Unscaled Pearson residuals

	12	24	36	48	60
2003	-1.18	-1.97	2.45	2.78	
2004	1.12	0.96	-0.40	-3.50	
2005	0.69	1.12	-2.51		
2006	-0.32	0.28			
2007					

Step 4.
Standardize the residuals.

Multiply each "unscaled" residual by the hat matrix adjustment factor.[86]

$$f_{ij} = \frac{1}{\sqrt{1 - h_{ij}}}$$

h_{ij} = the diagonal of the hat matrix H

H = $X(X^T W X)^{-1} X^T W$

X = the design matrix from the GLM model

W = the weight matrix from the GLM model.

Hat matrix adjustment factors

	12	24	36	48	60
2003	1.4922	1.6088	1.4725	1.6849	1.0000
2004	1.3675	1.4675	1.3033	1.3415	
2005	1.4172	1.5350	1.3485		
2006	1.5606	1.7546			
2007	1.0000				

Standardized Pearson residuals

	12	24	36	48	60
2003	-1.76	-3.17	3.60	4.69	
2004	1.54	1.40	-0.53	-4.69	
2005	0.98	1.72	-3.39		
2006	-0.50	0.50			
2007					

---

[86] See Pinheiro et al. (2001) for more details. The hat matrix adjustment factors are beyond the scope of the companion Excel files, but you can enter them manually.

Step 5.
Adjust the residuals for degrees of freedom.

Multiply each standardized residual by the degrees of freedom (D. of F.) adjustment factor (*dfa* below).

$$dfa = \sqrt{\frac{N}{(N-p)}}$$

N = number of non-zero residuals (less outliers)

p = number of parameters in the model (typically the number of columns in the residual triangle + the number of rows in the residual triangle + the number of additional hetero groups − 1)

Scaled Pearson residuals (adjusted for degrees of freedom)

	12	24	36	48	60
2003	-2.60	-4.66	5.30	6.91	
2004	2.26	2.07	-0.78	-6.91	
2005	1.44	2.53	-4.99		
2006	-0.74	0.74			
2007					

Additional statistics calculated

Pearson chi-squared statistic	=	sum of squares of standardized Pearson residuals
	=	90.65
Degrees of freedom	=	# of non-zero residuals in the model *minus* # of parameters (# columns + # rows − 1)
	=	13 − 7 = 6
Scale parameter	=	chi-squared statistic ÷ degrees of freedom
	=	15.11
D. of F. adjustment factor	=	square root of [N ÷ (N − p)]
	=	1.472

Simulation steps:

Step 6.
Randomly create a new triangle of "sample" data.

6a. Build a new triangle by randomly selecting (with replacement) from among the non-zero scaled Pearson residuals in Step 5.

6b. Create a triangle of sample data based on the randomly selected residuals.[87] For each cell:

$$C' = r_{SP}\sqrt{abs(\hat{m})} + \hat{m}$$

Randomly selected residuals

	12	24	36	48	60
2003	2.26	-0.74	-4.99	-0.74	2.26
2004	-4.66	-4.66	2.26	-6.91	
2005	-0.78	6.91	-0.74		
2006	2.07	2.26			
2007	6.91				

Sample incremental triangle calculated based on the random residuals

	12	24	36	48	60
2003	419	458	150	101	136
2004	166	220	170	12	
2005	255	465	152		
2006	353	446			
2007	429				

---

[87] Note that negative incremental values are entirely possible.

Step 7.
Complete the new randomly generated triangle.

Calculate new VWAs and use them to complete the bottom right of the triangle.[88]

Sample cumulative triangle

	12	24	36	48	60
2003	419	877	1,027	1,128	1,264
2004	166	385	555	567	
2005	255	720	872		
2006	353	799			
2007	429				

	12-24	24-36	36-48	48-60	60+
VWAs	2.332	1.238	1.071	1.120	1.000

Completed cumulative triangle with future payments

	12	24	36	48	60
2003	419	877	1,027	1,128	1,264
2004	166	385	555	567	635
2005	255	720	872	934	1,047
2006	353	799	989	1,060	1,187
2007	429	1,001	1,239	1,327	1,487

Step 8.
Introduce process variance.

Calculate the incremental payments in the future payment stream from the cumulative completed triangle.

To add *process variance* in the simulation, replace every future incremental paid amount with a randomly selected point from a gamma distribution[89] where:

Mean = the incremental paid loss amount

Variance = Mean x Scale Parameter (see Step 5)

Completed incremental triangle

	12	24	36	48	60
2003	419	458	150	101	136
2004	166	220	170	12	68
2005	255	465	152	62	113
2006	353	446	190	71	128
2007	429	571	238	88	160

Randomly generated future incremental payments based on above

	12	24	36	48	60
2003					
2004					64
2005				47	79
2006			194	76	143
2007		505	256	69	198

Step 9.
Calculate total unpaid amounts.

Sum the future incremental values to estimate the total unpaid loss by period and in total (in this example, 1,632).

This provides *one* estimated possible outcome.

Total estimated future incremental payments

	12	24	36	48	60	Total
2003						
2004					64	64
2005				47	79	125
2006			194	76	143	414
2007		505	256	69	198	1,028
						1,632

---

[88] The distribution of the sampled VWA age-to-age factors is a measure of the parameter risk.

[89] As a technical note, the gamma distribution is used as an approximation to the over-dispersed Poisson. The use of volume weighted average age-to-age factors is derived from the GLM assumption of an over-dispersed Poisson distribution, but the gamma is a close approximation and runs much faster in simulation software.

Step 10.	Total simulated results (for 10,000 iterations)		
Repeat and summarize.	Mean Unpaid	Standard Error	Coefficient of Variation
	2003	0	0	0.0%
Repeat Steps 6 through 9 the	2004	72	44	61.2%
specified number of times	2005	161	68	42.5%
(e.g., 10,000 or more),	2006	382	115	30.0%
capturing the resulting cash	2007	767	233	30.4%
flows and the unpaid amounts		1,382	311	22.5%

Step 10.
Repeat and summarize.

Repeat Steps 6 through 9 the specified number of times (e.g., 10,000 or more), capturing the resulting cash flows and the unpaid amounts by period and in total for each iteration. The resulting distribution of unpaid amounts from all the iterations can be used to calculate means, percentiles, etc.

Total simulated results (for 10,000 iterations)

	Mean Unpaid	Standard Error	Coefficient of Variation
2003	0	0	0.0%
2004	72	44	61.2%
2005	161	68	42.5%
2006	382	115	30.0%
2007	767	233	30.4%
	1,382	311	22.5%

References for Appendix D

England, Peter D. and Richard J.Verrall. Analytic and bootstrap estimates of prediction errors in claims reserving. *Insurance: Mathematics and Economics* 25 (1999): 281-293.

England, Peter D. and Richard J.Verrall. Stochastic claims reserving in general insurance. *British Actuarial Journal* 8 (2002): 443-544.

Kirschner, Gerald S., Colin Kerley, and Belinda Isaacs. Two approaches to calculating correlated reserve indications across multiple lines of business. *Variance* Vol. 2-1 (2008): 15-38.

Milliman's P&C Insurance Software Team. Using the Milliman Reserve Variability Model: An overview of the Milliman bootstrap modeling system. *Version 1.4*, 2009.

Pinheiro, Paulo J. R., João Manuel Andrade e Silva and Maria de Lourdes Centeno. Bootstrap methodology in claim reserving. *ASTIN Colloquium*, 2001.

Appendix E
Correlation

Correlation

Correlation is a way of measuring the strength and direction of relationships among two or more sets of numbers. In this sense, it is a way to measure the tendency of two variables to move in the same or opposite direction.[90]

The *correlation coefficient* between two variables is indicated (and calculated) using a range of values from -100% to 100%. *Positive correlation* refers to a phenomenon in which two variables tend to move in the same direction, i.e., when the X variable is high, the Y variable tends to be high; if X is low, Y tends to be low. The closer the measured correlation is to 100%, the stronger the tendency is to move in the same direction.

It follows then that *negative correlation* occurs when two variables tend to move in opposite directions, i.e., as the X variable increases, the Y variable tends to decrease, and vice versa. The closer the measured correlation is to -100%, the stronger the tendency is to move in the opposite direction.

A correlation of zero indicates that no relationship is anticipated between the two variables. As such, values or movements of one variable would not be expected to impact the value or movements of a second variable. Under these conditions, the two variables are said to be *independent*.

E.1.a The Correlation Matrix

The development of a stochastic model relies on an understanding of the relationships among the various segments under analysis, which can be gained from the use of a symmetric matrix of the various correlation coefficients between each pair of segments. This is known as a *correlation matrix*.[91] Each segment is along the first column and across the top row. The correlation coefficient describing the expected relationship between any two segments is shown at the intersection of the two.

---

[90] Movement in this context is relative and does not necessarily imply that the average values of the observations are moving (i.e., the averages may or may not be increasing or decreasing). More simply stated, we are describing the movements between one observation and the next and whether the corresponding movements from one observation to the next for another variable are similar or not. Finally, these movements are also relative in size and shape as, for example, one variable could be very small and stable and the other could be very large and volatile.

[91] The top right and bottom left triangles of the matrix are mirror images. In addition, the center diagonal, where each segment intersects with itself, is always filled with the number 1 because any variable is always perfectly correlated with itself.

Figure E-1

Sample Correlation Matrix

	1	2	3	4	5
1	1.00	0.25	0.11	0.34	0.42
2	0.25	1.00	0.15	0.15	0.27
3	0.11	0.15	1.00	-0.19	0.02
4	0.34	0.15	-0.19	1.00	-0.36
5	0.42	0.27	0.02	-0.36	1.00

For example, the sample coefficients in Figure E-1 indicate that Segments 1 and 5 are expected to have the strongest positive correlation, while 4 and 5 are expected to have the strongest negative correlation.

An additional output is a matrix of the p-values that correspond to each correlation coefficient in the correlation matrix. For each correlation coefficient, the p-value is a measure of the significance of the correlation coefficient. A low value (less than 5.0%) indicates the coefficient is significant (i.e., likely to be correct or nearly correct), and a high value (greater than 5.0%) indicates the coefficient is not significantly different from zero.

Figure E-2

P-values for Sample Correlation Matrix

	1	2	3	4	5
1	0.00	0.03	0.81	0.04	0.02
2	0.03	0.00	0.45	0.63	0.07
3	0.81	0.45	0.00	0.29	0.92
4	0.04	0.63	0.29	0.00	0.06
5	0.02	0.07	0.92	0.06	0.00

The table in Figure E-2 indicates that Segments 1 and 5 exhibit the strongest p-value, while 3 and 5 are not likely to exhibit correlation significantly different from zero.

E.1.b Measuring Correlation

There are several ways to measure correlation. In the case study discussed in Section IV.D, we used a non-parametric Spearman's Rank Order calculation to assess the correlation between each pair of segments in the model. As its name indicates, the Spearman's Rank Order formula calculates the correlation of the ranks of the residuals rather than the correlation of the actual residuals. In the calculation, the residuals to be correlated are converted to a rank order, and the differences between the ranks of each observation of the two variables, D, are calculated. The correlation coefficient (ρ) is then calculated as:

$$\rho = 1 - \frac{6\sum D^2}{N(N^2 - 1)}$$

(E-1)

Two examples should prove useful at this point. Consider the residuals for the two segments shown in Figure E-3.

■ Figure E-3

Sample Residuals for Two Segments

Segment A

	12	24	36	48	60
2001	-1.90	-3.07	3.85	4.38	0.00
2002	1.77	1.51	-0.65	-5.50	
2003	1.10	1.74	-3.95		
2004	-0.48	0.43			
2005	0.00				

Segment B

	12	24	36	48	60
2001	-1.23	2.57	-0.98	-1.64	0.00
2002	-1.14	3.19	-4.74	1.56	
2003	0.16	-4.28	6.94		
2004	2.78	-2.74			
2005	0.00				

The ranks and differences (diff.) of these residuals (resid.) can be calculated for each observation (obs.) as shown in Figure AE-4.

■ Figure E-4

Calculation of Residual Ranks

Segment A			Segment B			Ranks	
Obs.	Resid.	Rank	Obs.	Resid.	Rank	Diff.	Diff.^{2}
1	-1.90	4	1	-1.23	5	-1	1
2	1.77	11	2	-1.14	6	5	25
3	1.10	8	3	0.16	8	0	0
4	-0.48	6	4	2.78	11	-5	25
5	-3.07	3	5	2.57	10	-7	49
6	1.51	9	6	3.19	12	-3	9
7	1.74	10	7	-4.28	2	8	64
8	0.43	7	8	-2.74	3	4	16
9	3.85	12	9	-0.98	7	5	25
10	-0.65	5	10	-4.74	1	4	16
11	-3.95	2	11	6.94	13	-11	121
12	4.38	13	12	-1.64	4	9	81
13	-5.50	1	13	1.56	9	-8	64
							496

The Spearman Rank Order correlation coefficient is calculated as:

$$\rho = 1 - \frac{6\sum D^2}{N(N^2-1)} = 1 - \frac{6 \times 496}{13 \times (13^2-1)} = -0.363$$

According to the calculation, the two segments represented above have a negative correlation.

As a second example, consider the residuals shown in Figure E-5.

■ Figure E-5

Sample Residuals for Two Segments

Segment C

	12	24	36	48	60
2001	-1.90	-3.07	3.85	4.38	0.00
2002	1.77	1.51	-0.65	-5.50	
2003	1.10	1.74	-3.95		
2004	-0.48	0.43			
2005	0.00				

Segment D

	12	24	36	48	60
2001	-1.64	-2.74	3.19	6.94	0.00
2002	2.78	1.56	-1.23	-4.74	
2003	0.16	2.57	-4.28		
2004	-1.14	-0.98			
2005	0.00				

The ranks and differences for these residuals are calculated as shown in Figure E-6.

■ Figure E-6

Calculation of Residual Ranks

	Segment C			Segment D			Ranks	
Obs.	Resid.	Rank	Obs.	Resid.	Rank	Diff.	Diff. ^{2}
1	-1.90	4	1	-1.64	4	0	0
2	1.77	11	2	2.78	11	0	0
3	1.10	8	3	0.16	8	0	0
4	-0.48	6	4	-1.14	6	0	0
5	-3.07	3	5	-2.74	3	0	0
6	1.51	9	6	1.56	9	0	0
7	1.74	10	7	2.57	10	0	0
8	0.43	7	8	-0.98	7	0	0
9	3.85	12	9	3.19	12	0	0
10	-0.65	5	10	-1.23	5	0	0
11	-3.95	2	11	-4.28	2	0	0
12	4.38	13	12	6.94	13	0	0
13	-5.50	1	13	-4.74	1	0	0
							0

The Spearman Rank Order correlation coefficient is calculated as:

$$\rho = 1 - \frac{6\sum D^2}{N(N^2 - 1)} = 1 - \frac{6 \times 0}{13 \times (13^2 - 1)} = 1.000$$

And indicates the second pair of the businesses is perfectly positively correlated.

E.1.c Modeling Correlation

A deeper analysis of previous examples reveals that the residuals for Segment C and Segment D are identical to the residuals for Segment A and Segment B, respectively, and it illustrates the concept of "inducing" correlation. Even though the values are the same, they are not in the same order. But the relative orders can be compared to each other, thereby providing a measure of how likely one variable is to move in the same direction as the other variable. It also provides a method to determine their correlation. From here, the correlation between two simulated variables can be induced to a desired level by re-sorting one variable relative to the other.

In order to induce correlation among different segments in the bootstrap model, the correlation matrix first needs to be calculated using the Spearman Rank Order correlation as illustrated above for each pair of segments. The model then simulates the distributions for each segment separately. Using the estimated correlation matrix or another correlation assumption, we can calculate the correlated aggregate distribution by re-sorting the simulations for each segment based on the ranks of the total unpaid for all accident years combined.[92]

Another example will help illustrate this process. As noted above, the first step is to run the bootstrap model separately for each segment. The sample output for three segments is shown below (based on 250 iterations). In the example, results have been included by accident year as well as by future calendar year, which sum to the same total. Other parts of the simulation output (e.g., loss ratios) could also have been included as part of the correlation process.

Step 1: Simulate individual segment distributions

Segment A

	Total Unpaid							Total Cash Flow						
	Accident Year							Calendar Year						
Iteration	1	2	3	4	5	...	Total	1	2	3	4	5	...	Total
1	4	18	219	366	818	...	14,513	3,669	3,268	2,160	2,393	1,469	...	14,513
2	1	75	413	667	1,100	...	16,200	4,280	4,173	2,271	1,887	1,363	...	16,200
3	11	-6	861	773	1,379	...	16,826	4,769	4,120	2,400	1,670	1,347	...	16,826
4	0	126	335	1,299	543	...	17,504	5,233	3,707	3,237	1,505	1,486	...	17,504
:	:							:						
250	38	122	470	575	1,191	...	20,210	4,370	3,767	2,807	2,145	1,450	...	20,210
AVG	19	118	512	782	1,015	...	19,256	5,330	4,260	3,227	2,180	1,613	...	19,256

Segment B

	Total Unpaid							Total Cash Flow						
	Accident Year							Calendar Year						
Iteration	1	2	3	4	5	...	Total	1	2	3	4	5	...	Total
1	420	35	446	592	1,212	...	45,151	11,058	12,762	8,898	5,921	3,024	...	45,151
2	233	802	302	1,484	1,621	...	23,077	10,107	6,151	2,458	2,107	941	...	23,077
3	330	177	737	344	2,548	...	37,989	10,990	12,038	7,029	3,847	2,144	...	37,989
4	738	68	589	540	803	...	18,430	5,291	4,377	4,267	1,776	1,833	...	18,430
:	:							:						
250	0	15	440	1,113	2,453	...	30,816	12,148	8,186	7,066	2,008	1,178	...	30,816
AVG	207	500	658	954	2,213	...	31,930	10,072	8,363	5,681	3,395	2,114	...	31,930

---

[92] Note that the re-sorting is based on total values and the coefficients are based on residuals. Correlating the residuals reflects a far more complex algorithm, but our research has indicated that these different approaches are reasonably consistent. Thus, re-sorting is an easier, although quite robust, algorithm.

Segment C

| | Total Unpaid | | | | | | | Total Cash Flow | | | | | | |
| | Accident Year | | | | | | | Calendar Year | | | | | | |
Iteration	1	2	3	4	5	...	Total	1	2	3	4	5	...	Total
1	0	0	3	3	184	...	4,045	1,445	941	815	239	288	...	4,045
2	0	0	8	2	15	...	3,022	1,432	925	305	235	29	...	3,022
3	8	0	0	39	82	...	3,233	1,181	817	561	324	175	...	3,233
4	0	0	5	40	86	...	3,972	1,475	1,017	748	342	327	...	3,972
:	:							:						
250	0	0	0	121	156	...	2,599	1,113	767	365	142	22	...	2,599
AVG	3	3	5	45	74	...	3,495	1,228	985	584	335	201	...	3,495

Step 2: Rank the simulation results

The simulation results now need to be sorted according to the values of the total unpaid for all years combined. Sorting in ascending order gives us the rank of each simulation.

Segment A

| | Total Unpaid | | | | | | | Total Cash Flow | | | | | | |
| | Accident Year | | | | | | | Calendar Year | | | | | | |
Rank	1	2	3	4	5	...	Total	1	2	3	4	5	...	Total
1	27	84	545	425	581	...	12,123	3,787	3,056	1,868	1,312	1,118	...	12,123
2	27	73	250	750	491	...	12,792	3,800	3,166	2,267	936	1,081	...	12,792
3	1	-209	23	377	692	...	12,883	3,240	3,266	2,337	1,841	1,009	...	12,883
4	-25	200	470	488	812	...	13,240	4,100	2,611	2,392	1,440	969	...	13,240
:	:							:						
250	2	307	653	1,366	1,015	...	30,200	4,522	3,472	2,506	1,874	1,519	...	30,200
AVG	19	118	512	782	1,015	...	19,256	5,330	4,260	3,227	2,180	1,613	...	19,256

Segment B

| | Total Unpaid | | | | | | | Total Cash Flow | | | | | | |
| | Accident Year | | | | | | | Calendar Year | | | | | | |
Rank	1	2	3	4	5	...	Total	1	2	3	4	5	...	Total
1	136	216	263	584	697	...	15,042	5,271	4,843	2,268	1,697	334	...	15,042
2	30	434	222	142	1,822	...	15,658	6,157	4,088	2,122	1,274	1,623	...	15,658
3	463	101	597	104	1,031	...	17,012	6,930	6,794	1,244	954	283	...	17,012
4	182	148	618	835	1,411	...	17,236	6,957	5,052	2,522	1,942	265	...	17,236
:	:							:						
250	382	1,167	1,333	2,264	3,256	...	64,376	14,018	16,007	12,046	9,279	3,238	...	64,376
AVG	207	500	658	954	2,213	...	31,930	10,072	8,363	5,681	3,395	2,114	...	31,930

Segment C

| | Total Unpaid | | | | | | | Total Cash Flow | | | | | | |
| | Accident Year | | | | | | | Calendar Year | | | | | | |
Rank	1	2	3	4	5	...	Total	1	2	3	4	5	...	Total
1	0	27	18	200	59	...	2,285	789	747	349	211	95	...	2,285
2	92	5	1	27	15	...	2,367	807	496	652	143	116	...	2,367
3	0	0	0	4	2	...	2,451	673	818	374	160	351	...	2,451
4	1	0	0	5	90	...	2,524	1,068	658	145	343	213	...	2,524
:	:							:						
250	0	0	0	215	211	...	5,351	1,318	1,159	1,009	629	442	...	5,351
AVG	3	3	5	45	74	...	3,495	1,228	985	584	335	201	...	3,495

Step 3: Generate correlation matrix

The next step – calculating the rank orders – will give us the desired correlation between each segment pair. The following method uses a multivariate normal distribution with the desired correlation matrix and then simulates random values from that distribution. Using the simulated values, the ranks of the simulated values will give us the desired rank orders for the desired correlation.[93]

Iteration	Multivariate Normal A	B	C	Ranks A	B	C
1	-2.652	-0.978	0.030	1	41	128
2	-0.070	0.445	1.136	118	168	218
3	0.030	0.643	-0.536	128	185	74
4	0.915	1.491	0.274	205	233	152
:	:			:		
250	-0.885	1.080	0.412	47	215	165

Step 4: Re-sort the simulation results based on correlation ranks

The individual simulation results for each segment now need to be re-sorted based on the rank orders from Step 3. Once completed, the correlation coefficients for each pair should match the desired correlations specified in the correlation matrix from Step 3.

Segment A

Rank	Total Unpaid — Accident Year 1	2	3	4	5	...	Total	Total Cash Flow — Calendar Year 1	2	3	4	5	...	Total
1	27	84	545	425	581	...	12,123	3,787	3,056	1,868	1,312	1,118	...	12,123
118	0	293	525	805	661	...	18,819	5,095	3,899	2,812	1,826	1,648	...	18,819
128	1	439	388	1,038	1,215	...	19,079	4,838	3,637	3,255	1,995	2,609	...	19,079
205	10	386	362	1,110	1,080	...	21,851	4,398	4,341	4,008	2,644	2,665	...	21,851
:	:							:						
47	1	78	516	697	740	...	16,779	5,551	4,405	2,638	1,708	1,129	...	16,779
AVG	19	118	512	782	1,015	...	19,256	5,330	4,260	3,227	2,180	1,613	...	19,256

Segment B

Rank	Total Unpaid — Accident Year 1	2	3	4	5	...	Total	Total Cash Flow — Calendar Year 1	2	3	4	5	...	Total
41	37	240	135	462	1,170	...	23,945	6,994	6,500	5,222	2,546	1,982	...	23,945
168	134	705	212	1,604	3,135	...	33,764	9,755	9,307	5,790	3,849	1,819	...	33,764
185	329	18	149	1,163	1,579	...	37,006	12,598	9,414	7,085	3,852	2,311	...	37,006
233	181	227	962	897	1,505	...	46,286	14,619	11,230	7,839	4,036	4,029	...	46,286
:	:							:						
215	55	997	763	2,100	2,944	...	41,587	13,804	8,545	8,269	4,718	2,923	...	41,587
AVG	207	500	658	954	2,213	...	31,930	10,072	8,363	5,681	3,395	2,114	...	31,930

---

[93] Simulating the rank orders is beyond the scope of the companion Excel files, but the ranks can be included in a separate file that can then be used to induce correlation for aggregate results.

Segment C

Rank	Total Unpaid Accident Year 1	2	3	4	5	...	Total	Total Cash Flow Calendar Year 1	2	3	4	5	...	Total
128	0	0	0	3	70	...	3,480	1,456	788	672	167	65	...	3,480
218	0	12	0	55	159	...	4,036	1,565	1,461	314	274	195	...	4,036
74	0	0	2	24	29	...	3,163	1,373	824	388	410	157	...	3,163
152	0	0	0	99	112	...	3,595	1,027	1,061	560	377	452	...	3,595
⋮	⋮							⋮						
165	0	0	0	8	17	...	3,644	1,205	853	786	237	357	...	3,644
AVG	3	3	5	45	74	...	3,495	1,228	985	584	335	201	...	3,495

Step 5: Sum the correlated values

To arrive at aggregate results for all iterations, the values need to be summed across the segments.

Total All Segments Combined

Iteration	Total Unpaid Accident Year 1	2	3	4	5	...	Total	Total Cash Flow Calendar Year 1	2	3	4	5	...	Total
1	64	324	680	890	1,822	...	39,548	12,237	10,344	7,762	4,026	3,165	...	39,548
2	134	1,010	737	2,464	3,956	...	56,619	16,415	14,667	8,916	5,950	3,661	...	56,619
3	330	457	540	2,225	2,824	...	59,249	18,809	13,875	10,728	6,256	5,078	...	59,249
4	191	612	1,324	2,106	2,698	...	71,731	20,044	16,632	12,406	7,057	7,146	...	71,731
⋮	⋮							⋮						
250	56	1,075	1,279	2,805	3,701	...	62,010	20,560	13,803	11,693	6,662	4,408	...	62,010
AVG	230	621	1,175	1,781	3,301	...	54,681	16,629	13,609	9,493	5,910	3,928	...	54,681

Step 6: Summarize

The aggregate results for all simulations can now be used to describe the distribution of unpaid claims from all the results, including means and percentiles, among other values. Summaries developed for each individual segment can also be created for the aggregate results (e.g., cash flows, loss ratios, or graphs).

Appendix F

Maximum Likelihood Estimation

To complete our discussion of Maximum Likelihood Estimation (MLE), we refer readers to Klugman et al.[94] for an excellent discussion of MLEs, as well as a specific statement of conditions under which these results hold. These conditions and results are sufficiently important to require a restatement of the primary theorem here. We have provided an Excel file (which can be found at www.actuaries.org/stochastic) "Appendix F – Maximum Likelihood Estimation Examples.xls" that can be used to replicate some of the examples used in this appendix.

Theorem 1

Assume that the probability function $f(x|\theta)$ satisfies the following for θ in an interval containing the true value, replacing integrals by sums for discrete variables:

i. $ln(f(x|\theta))$ is three times differentiable with respect to θ.

ii. $\int \frac{\partial}{\partial \theta} f(x|\theta) dx = 0$. **This allows the derivative to be taken outside the integral, so we are just differentiating the constant 1.**

iii. $\int \frac{\partial^2}{\partial \theta^2} f(x|\theta) dx = 0$. **This is the same concept for the second derivative.**

iv. $-\infty < \int f(x|\theta) \frac{\partial^2}{\partial \theta^2} \ln(f(x|\theta)) dx < 0$. **This establishes that the indicated integral exists, and that the location where the derivative is zero is a maximum.**

v.   **There exists a function $H(x)$ such that** $\int H(x) f(x|\theta) dx < \infty$ **with** $\left| \frac{\partial^3}{\partial \theta^3} \ln(f(x|\theta)) \right| < H(x)$. **This function ensures the population is not too strange with regard to extreme values.**

Then the following results hold:

---

[94]   Klugman, et al., ibid, p. 62.

a. As $n \rightarrow \infty$, the probability that the likelihood equation ($L'(\theta)=0$) has a solution goes to 1.

b. As $n \rightarrow \infty$, the distribution of the MLE $\hat{\theta}_n$ converges to a normal distribution with mean θ and variance such that $I(\theta)\text{Var}(\hat{\theta}_n) \rightarrow 1$ where

$$I(\theta) = -nE\left[\frac{\partial^2}{\partial\theta^2}\ln\left(f\left(x|\theta\right)\right)\right] = -n\int f\left(x|\theta\right)\frac{\partial^2}{\partial\theta^2}\ln\left(f\left(x|\theta\right)\right)dx$$

$$= nE\left[\left(\frac{\partial}{\partial\theta}\ln\left(f\left(x|\theta\right)\right)\right)^2\right] = n\int f\left(x|\theta\right)\left(\frac{\partial}{\partial\theta}\ln\left(f\left(x|\theta\right)\right)\right)^2 dx$$

For any value z, the last statement can be interpreted as the relationship in (F.1).

$$\lim_{n\to\infty}\Pr\left(\frac{\hat{\theta}_n - \theta}{\left(I(\theta)\right)^{-\frac{1}{2}}} < z\right) = \Phi(z) \tag{F.1}$$

In the case that the parameter θ is a vector, then the limiting model is a multivariate normal with the relationship in (b) replaced by

$$\mathbf{I}(\theta)_{i,j} = -nE\left[\frac{\partial^2}{\partial\theta_i\partial\theta_j}\ln\left(f\left(x|\theta\right)\right)\right] = -n\int f\left(x|\theta\right)\frac{\partial^2}{\partial\theta_i\partial\theta_j}\ln\left(f\left(x|\theta\right)\right)dx$$

$$= nE\left[\frac{\partial}{\partial\theta_i}\ln\left(f\left(x|\theta\right)\right)\frac{\partial}{\partial\theta_j}\ln\left(f\left(x|\theta\right)\right)\right] = n\int\frac{\partial}{\partial\theta_i}\ln\left(f\left(x|\theta\right)\right)\frac{\partial}{\partial\theta_j}\ln\left(f\left(x|\theta\right)\right)f\left(x|\theta\right)dx$$

We emphasize here that the asymptotic properties hold *if the sample is drawn from the assumed stochastic model*. Thus, model uncertainty is still very much a concern.

F.1 MLE example – normal model

We begin with the same example we used in discussing matching of moments. Using formulas (I.C-9) and (I.C-20), we obtain the likelihood function in formula (F.2).

$$L\left(x_1, x_2, \ldots, x_n \,\middle|\, \mu, \sigma^2\right) = \prod_{i=1}^{n}\frac{1}{\sqrt{2\pi\sigma^2}}e^{-\frac{(x_i - \mu)^2}{2\sigma^2}} \tag{F.2}$$

The goal now is to find values of the parameters μ and σ^2 that will produce the maximum value for L, defined as the product of a number of elements. In this problem and in many others involving MLEs, it is often very convenient to look not at the likelihood function itself, but at the negative of its natural logarithm. Since the logarithm is a monotonically increasing function, the parameter value that minimizes the negative-log-likelihood function automatically maximizes the likelihood function. So instead of focusing on maximizing L, we will minimize the function in equation (F.3).

$$\ell\left(x_1, x_2, \ldots, x_n \,\middle|\, \mu, \sigma^2\right) = -\ln\left(L\left(x_1, x_2, \ldots, x_n \,\middle|\, \mu, \sigma^2\right)\right)$$

$$= -\ln\left(\prod_{i=1}^{n} \frac{1}{\sqrt{2\pi\sigma^2}} e^{-\frac{(x_i - \mu)^2}{2\sigma^2}}\right) \tag{F.3}$$

$$= \frac{n}{2}\ln\left(2\pi\sigma^2\right) + \sum_{i=1}^{n} \frac{(x_i - \mu)^2}{2\sigma^2}$$

We have a number of options going forward. Many software packages, including Microsoft Excel and the freely available statistical package R, have built-in, general-purpose, optimizing functions that can be used to numerically estimate maxima or minima of functions. Either of these options can be used to numerically solve for the parameters that minimize the negative-log-likelihood function. Indeed, in many complex situations, such a numerical solution may be the only one available.

In the case of the normal model the function is sufficiently tractable to allow for an analytic solution. Because we know from calculus that minima of a continuously differentiable function occur at zeros of the function's derivative, we can differentiate the negative-log-likelihood function and find the derivatives' zeros. Equation (F.4) gives the derivative with respect to the parameter μ, while equation (F.5) gives the derivative with respect to the parameter σ^2.

$$\frac{\partial \ell\left(x_1, x_2, \ldots, x_n \,\middle|\, \mu, \sigma^2\right)}{\partial \mu} = \frac{\partial}{\partial \mu}\left(\frac{n}{2}\ln\left(2\pi\sigma^2\right) + \sum_{i=1}^{n} \frac{(x_i - \mu)^2}{2\sigma^2}\right)$$

$$= -\sum_{i=1}^{n} \frac{2(x_i - \mu)}{2\sigma^2} \tag{F.4}$$

$$= -\frac{1}{\sigma^2}\left(\sum_{i=1}^{n} x_i - n\mu\right)$$

$$\frac{\partial \ell\left(x_1, x_2, \ldots, x_n \,\middle|\, \mu, \sigma^2\right)}{\partial \sigma^2} = \frac{\partial}{\partial \sigma^2}\left(\frac{n}{2}\ln\left(2\pi\sigma^2\right) + \sum_{i=1}^{n} \frac{(x_i - \mu)^2}{2\sigma^2}\right)$$

$$= \frac{n}{2\sigma^2} - \sum_{i=1}^{n} \frac{(x_i - \mu)^2}{2\left(\sigma^2\right)^2} \tag{F.5}$$

$$= \frac{1}{2\sigma^2}\left(n - \frac{1}{\sigma^2}\sum_{i=1}^{n}(x_i - \mu)^2\right)$$

Equation (F.4) shows that the partial derivative with respect to μ is zero when equation (F.6) holds.

$$\hat{\mu} = \frac{1}{n}\sum_{i=1}^{n} x_i \tag{F.6}$$

By finding the zero of equation (F.5) and substituting the relationship in equation (F.6), we obtain the estimate for parameter σ^2 shown in equation (F.7).

$$\hat{\sigma}^2 = \frac{1}{n}\sum_{i=1}^{n}\left(x_i - \frac{1}{n}\sum_{i=1}^{n}x_i\right)^2 \tag{F.7}$$

These results are precisely the same estimates that were derived from the matching-of-moments method, and show in this case the estimate is biased for σ^2 in equation (F.7). For this reason, a slightly revised but unbiased estimator as provided in equation (F.8) is usually used.

$$\hat{\sigma}^2 = \frac{1}{n-1}\sum_{i=1}^{n}\left(x_i - \frac{1}{n}\sum_{i=1}^{n}x_i\right)^2 \tag{F.8}$$

It can easily be seen that the ratio of these two estimators approaches 1 as n becomes large, so that both tend to the same ultimate value, that of σ^2. This result highlights the fact that while the MLE is asymptotically unbiased, it may not be unbiased. Many software packages, including Microsoft Excel, have separate functions for the estimates in (F.7) and (F.8), but care should be exercised when using them. In Excel, the "default" functions (VAR and STDEV) use the formulation in (F.8), while others (VARP and STDEVP) use the formulation in (F.7).

Until this point, our investigation has focused on developing models that quantify process uncertainty. We will now turn our attention to the issue of parameter uncertainty, which can be calculated based on one important feature of MLEs as they relate to a particular theorem. This theorem allows us to estimate the precision and interdependence of the estimators, given the observed sample.

Quantification of parameter uncertainty begins with a consideration of what is called the Fisher information matrix, or simply, the information matrix, which for our purposes is defined as the expected value of the Hessian with respect to the parameters of the negative-log-likelihood function, as written in equation (F.9).

$$I(\theta) = E_x\left(\text{Hessian}_\theta\left(-\ln\left(\ell\left(x_1, x_2, \ldots, x_n \mid \theta\right)\right)\right)\right) \tag{F.9}$$

The Hessian of a function is the matrix of second partial derivatives of that function. The element in the ith row and j^{th} column is the second partial derivative of the function, first with respect to the ith variable and then with respect to the jth variable. In the case of the normal distribution, above, we have the second partials shown in equations (F.10) through (F.12).

$$\frac{\partial^2 \ell\left(x_1, x_2, \ldots, x_n \mid \mu, \sigma^2\right)}{\partial \mu^2} = \frac{\partial}{\partial \mu}\left(-\frac{1}{\sigma^2}\left(\left(\sum_{i=1}^{n}x_i\right) - n\mu\right)\right)$$
$$= \frac{n}{\sigma^2} \tag{F.10}$$

$$\frac{\partial^2 \ell\left(x_1, x_2, \ldots, x_n \mid \mu, \sigma^2\right)}{\partial \mu \partial \sigma^2} = \frac{\partial^2 \ell\left(x_1, x_2, \ldots, x_n \mid \mu, \sigma^2\right)}{\partial \sigma^2 \partial \mu} = \frac{\partial}{\partial \sigma^2}\left(-\frac{1}{\sigma^2}\left(\left(\sum_{i=1}^{n}x_i\right) - n\mu\right)\right)$$
$$= \frac{1}{\left(\sigma^2\right)^2}\left(\left(\sum_{i=1}^{n}x_i\right) - n\mu\right) \tag{F.11}$$

$$\frac{\partial^2 \ell\left(x_1,x_2,\ldots,x_n\middle|\mu,\sigma^2\right)}{\partial\left(\sigma^2\right)^2} = \frac{\partial}{\partial\sigma^2}\left(\frac{1}{2\sigma^2}\left(n-\frac{1}{\sigma^2}\sum_{i=1}^n\left(x_i-\mu\right)^2\right)\right)$$

$$= -\frac{1}{2\left(\sigma^2\right)^2}\left(n-\frac{1}{\sigma^2}\sum_{i=1}^n\left(x_i-\mu\right)^2\right) + \frac{1}{2\sigma^2}\left(\frac{1}{\left(\sigma^2\right)^2}\sum_{i=1}^n\left(x_i-\mu\right)^2\right) \qquad \text{(F.12)}$$

$$= -\frac{1}{2\left(\sigma^2\right)^2}\left(n-\frac{2}{\sigma^2}\sum_{i=1}^n\left(x_i-\mu\right)^2\right)$$

To obtain the information matrix we need to take expected values of these amounts shown in equations (F.13) through (F.15).

$$\mathrm{E}_x\left(\frac{\partial^2 \ell\left(x_1,x_2,\ldots,x_n\middle|\mu,\sigma^2\right)}{\partial\mu^2}\right) = \mathrm{E}_x\left(\frac{n}{\sigma^2}\right)$$

$$= \frac{n}{\sigma^2} \qquad \text{(F.13)}$$

$$\mathrm{E}_x\left(\frac{\partial^2 \ell\left(x_1,x_2,\ldots,x_n\middle|\mu,\sigma^2\right)}{\partial\mu\partial\sigma^2}\right) = \mathrm{E}_x\left(\frac{\partial^2 \ell\left(x_1,x_2,\ldots,x_n\middle|\mu,\sigma^2\right)}{\partial\sigma^2\partial\mu}\right) = \mathrm{E}_x\left(\frac{1}{\left(\sigma^2\right)^2}\left(\left(\sum_{i=1}^n x_i\right)-n\mu\right)\right)$$

$$= \frac{1}{\left(\sigma^2\right)^2}\left(\left(\sum_{i=1}^n \mathrm{E}_x\left(x_i\right)\right)-n\mu\right) \qquad \text{(F.14)}$$

$$= \frac{1}{\left(\sigma^2\right)^2}\left(\left(\sum_{i=1}^n \mu\right)-n\mu\right) = 0$$

$$\mathrm{E}_x\left(\frac{\partial^2 \ell\left(x_1,x_2,\ldots,x_n\middle|\mu,\sigma^2\right)}{\partial\left(\sigma^2\right)^2}\right) = \mathrm{E}_x\left(-\frac{1}{2\left(\sigma^2\right)^2}\left(n-\frac{2}{\sigma^2}\sum_{i=1}^n\left(x_i-\mu\right)^2\right)\right)$$

$$= -\frac{1}{2\left(\sigma^2\right)^2}\left(n-\frac{2}{\sigma^2}\sum_{i=1}^n \mathrm{E}_x\left(\left(x_i-\mu\right)^2\right)\right)$$

$$= -\frac{1}{2\left(\sigma^2\right)^2}\left(n-\frac{2}{\sigma^2}\sum_{i=1}^n \sigma^2\right) \qquad \text{(F.15)}$$

$$= -\frac{1}{2\left(\sigma^2\right)^2}\left(n-2n\right) = \frac{n}{2\left(\sigma^2\right)^2}$$

Thus, equation (F.16) gives the information matrix for an independent sample of size n, all drawn from the same normal model.

$$I(\mu,\sigma^2)=\begin{pmatrix} \dfrac{n}{\sigma^2} & 0 \\ 0 & \dfrac{n}{2(\sigma^2)^2} \end{pmatrix}$$

(F.16)

One of the powerful properties of the MLE related to sampling is asymptotic normality, which holds that, as the sample size becomes large, the MLE tends to have a (multivariate) normal model. Just as a standard normal model has two parameters that happen to equal its mean and variance, a multivariate normal model can be thought of as having two parameters: a vector of means, and a variance-covariance matrix indicating the relationships among the parameters. In the case of the MLE, the inverse of the information matrix approximates the variance-covariance matrix of the limiting multivariate normal model. The variance-covariance matrix for a normal random vector of length m is a positive definite m x m matrix, whose i^{th} row and j^{th} column element is the covariance of the ith variable with the jth variable.

The fact that the inverse of a diagonal matrix is the matrix of the inverses of the diagonal elements, as we may recall, will now allow us to arrive at the variance-covariance matrix of the parameter estimates as shown in equation (F.17).

$$I^{-1}(\mu,\sigma^2)=\begin{pmatrix} \dfrac{n}{\sigma^2} & 0 \\ 0 & \dfrac{n}{2(\sigma^2)^2} \end{pmatrix}^{-1}$$
$$=\begin{pmatrix} \dfrac{\sigma^2}{n} & 0 \\ 0 & \dfrac{2(\sigma^2)^2}{n} \end{pmatrix}$$

(F.17)

Because the MLEs are typically asymptotically unbiased, the MLE value is used in equation (F.17) as an approximation of the true variance-covariance matrix. And because the diagonal of the variance-covariance matrix contains the variance of the random variables, there will be smaller variances (less uncertainty) in the case of MLE for normal model, as the sample size gets large. This example also shows that since the off-diagonal elements are all zero for the normal model, the MLE parameter estimates are not correlated. This convenient characteristic does not hold in general however.

In our example of matching-of-moments, we observed that our estimate of the mean of 9.4 has an approximate variance of about 6.5, while our estimate of the variance of 45.4 has an approximate variance of 588.6. For a normal model, there is approximately a 95% chance that a random draw will be within two standard deviations of the mean. Based on these results, we conclude that the true value of the mean is within ±5.1 (= 2 x (45.4/7)^0.5) of 9.4, and the true value of the variance is within ±48.5 (= 2 x (2 * 45.4^2/7)^0.5) of this value.

In the case of the normal model, there are other approaches that lead to direct, rather than asymptotic, estimates. Such approaches will provide more precise estimates, particularly in the case of smaller samples. However, the MLE approach is quite general and does not depend on the particular functional relationships inherent in the models as do the direct approaches.

F.2   MLE example – lognormal model

In the case of the normal model, we found that the MLE corresponded to the estimates derived from the matching-of-moments method. This is due to the nature of the normal model itself but does not hold in general, as we will see when we apply the MLE approach to the lognormal model. In this case, the likelihood function can be expressed by equation (F.18) and the negative-log-likelihood function by equation (F.19).

$$L\left(x_1, x_2, \ldots, x_n \mid \mu, \sigma^2\right) = \prod_{i=1}^{n} \frac{1}{x_i \sqrt{2\pi\sigma^2}} e^{-\frac{\left(\ln(x_i) - \mu\right)^2}{2\sigma^2}} \tag{F.18}$$

$$\ell\left(x_1, x_2, \ldots, x_n \mid \mu, \sigma^2\right) = \sum_{i=1}^{n} \ln(x_i) + \frac{n}{2}\ln\left(2\pi\sigma^2\right) + \sum_{i=1}^{n} \frac{\left(\ln(x_i) - \mu\right)^2}{2\sigma^2} \tag{F.19}$$

With the exception of the first term that does not involve any of the parameters, (F.19) has the same form as (F.3), with $\ln(x_i)$ substituted for x_i. Thus, the MLEs for the parameters are given by equations (F.20) and (F.21).

$$\hat{\mu} = \frac{1}{n} \sum_{i=1}^{n} \ln(x_i) \tag{F.20}$$

$$\hat{\sigma}^2 = \frac{1}{n} \sum_{i=1}^{n} \left(\ln(x_i) - \frac{1}{n} \sum_{i=1}^{n} \ln(x_i) \right)^2 \tag{F.21}$$

Similar to the normal model, the form in (F.21) is biased; the unbiased estimate in equation (F.22) is often used.

$$\hat{\sigma}^2 = \frac{1}{n-1} \sum_{i=1}^{n} \left(\ln(x_i) - \frac{1}{n} \sum_{i=1}^{n} \ln(x_i) \right)^2 \tag{F.22}$$

In our sample example in the matching-of-moments discussion, (F.20) and (F.22) then give parameter estimates of 0.37 and 2.043 compared to the matching-of-moments estimates of 0.41 and 2.038. Unlike the matching-of-moments method, which provides no further information about the accuracy of the estimates, estimates of the uncertainty inherent in the MLEs can also be obtained by using the Hessian of the negative-log-likelihood function, which can be derived from equations (F.23) through (F.25).

$$\frac{\partial^2 \ell\left(x_1, x_2, \ldots, x_n \mid \mu, \sigma^2\right)}{\partial \mu^2} = \frac{\partial}{\partial \mu} \left(-\frac{1}{\sigma^2} \left(\sum_{i=1}^{n} \ln(x_i) - n\mu \right) \right)$$
$$= \frac{n}{\sigma^2} \tag{F.23}$$

$$\frac{\partial^2 \ell\left(x_1, x_2, \ldots, x_n \mid \mu, \sigma^2\right)}{\partial \mu \partial \sigma^2} = \frac{\partial^2 \ell\left(x_1, x_2, \ldots, x_n \mid \mu, \sigma^2\right)}{\partial \sigma^2 \partial \mu} = \frac{\partial}{\partial \sigma^2} \left(-\frac{1}{\sigma^2} \left(\sum_{i=1}^{n} \ln(x_i) - n\mu \right) \right)$$
$$= \frac{1}{\left(\sigma^2\right)^2} \left(\sum_{i=1}^{n} \ln(x_i) - n\mu \right) \tag{F.24}$$

$$\frac{\partial^2 \ell\left(x_1, x_2, \ldots, x_n \mid \mu, \sigma^2\right)}{\partial\left(\sigma^2\right)^2} = \frac{\partial}{\partial\sigma^2}\left(\frac{1}{2\sigma^2}\left(n - \frac{1}{\sigma^2}\sum_{i=1}^{n}\left(\ln\left(x_i\right) - \mu\right)^2\right)\right)$$

$$= -\frac{1}{2\left(\sigma^2\right)^2}\left(n - \frac{2}{\sigma^2}\sum_{i=1}^{n}\left(\ln\left(x_i\right) - \mu\right)^2\right)$$

(F.25)

These equations follow directly from equations (F.10) through (F.12) by recognizing the relationship between the likelihood functions for the lognormal and normal models. Our parameterization for the lognormal means that μ is the expected value of $ln(x_i)$ and σ^2 is the variance of $ln(x_i)$ and thus, the information matrix for this parameterization of the lognormal is simply (F.16) with the estimated variance-covariance matrix given in (F.17).

In this case, there is an approximate 95% chance that the true value of the μ parameter is within ±0.462 of the 2.043 estimate, and that the true value of the σ^2 parameter is within ±0.40 of the estimate of 0.37. The resulting variance-covariance matrix is shown in (F.26).

$$\begin{pmatrix} 0.0534 & 0 \\ 0 & 0.0400 \end{pmatrix}$$

(F.26)

An assumption can be made that the losses of interest follow the lognormal model and then use the MLEs of those parameters to model the distribution of claims, but this overlooks the fact that the MLEs are estimates and subject to uncertainty. If we move one step at a time and first assume the estimate for the σ^2 parameter is correct, we could simulate our best estimate of the distribution of claims using a two-step process repeated several times as in Algorithm 1.

Algorithm 1

1. **Randomly select a value for the μ parameter using a normal model with mean 2.043 and variance 0.0534.**

2. **Generate a distribution of claims from a lognormal with that amount for the μ parameter and 0.37 for the σ^2 parameter.**

3. **Repeat steps 1 and 2 several times.**

Each iteration gives the view of one potential "universe" for the observed sample. Incorporating both process and parameter uncertainty, multiple iterations will provide a sense of how uncertain the sizes of claims are; however, in this particular situation we do not have to resort to simulation, because of a very convenient property of the normal and lognormal models: Theorem 2 provides a closed-form solution.

Theorem 2

Suppose the random variable X has a lognormal model with parameters m and σ^2. Assume further that σ^2 is known, but that m has a normal model with mean μ and variance τ^2. Then the random variable X has a lognormal model with parameters μ and $\sigma^2 + \tau^2$.

Thus, repeating our simulation will ultimately result in a lognormal model with the same μ parameter as our original, but with a higher coefficient of variation, directly related to the second parameter. There are a number of other models that conveniently replicate in this fashion. Further discussion of them is beyond the scope of this work.

Theorem 2 only addresses one of the parameters of the lognormal. But our conveniently-made assumption that the σ^2 parameter is correct is, in fact, a sufficient basis for applying Theorem 2. And because the two parameter estimates for the lognormal model are independent, a slight modification Algorithm 1 to reflect that both these parameters are unknown can be employed in this situation. Algorithm 2 is one such modification.

Algorithm 2

    1.   **Randomly select a value for the μ parameter using a normal model with mean 2.043 and variance 0.0534 and randomly select a value for the σ^2 parameter using a normal model with mean 0.374 and variance 0.040.**

    2.   **Generate a distribution of claims from a lognormal with those amounts for the μ and σ^2 parameters.**

    3.   **Repeat steps 1 and 2 several times.**

This algorithm will give us a sense of the potential range of claims indicated by the fitted model to include the impact of parameter uncertainty. This approach can be taken because the two parameters are independent. If they were not independent, their correlations would need to be reflected in the simulation.

F.3   MLE estimates – censored and truncated data

Frequently, claims data available from an insurer is incomplete with respect to the entire potential distribution of claims. Sometimes the data are truncated. For example, the data may contain population elements for which information such as claims below a deductible or child mortality data at an insurer with an adult-customer base may not be available. Other times the data are censored. This can occur when there is information about the occurrence of certain claims, but not their actual size, as would be the case on policies that limit payment on individual claims. Assuming policy limits are gross with respect to deductible, equation (F.27) shows the available information y in terms of the actual distribution of the claim size x and the deductible (truncation point) D and maximum-loss limitation (censoring point) M.

$$y = \begin{cases} \text{unavailable if } x \leq D \\ x - D \text{ if } D < x \leq M \\ M - D \text{ if } L < x \end{cases} \tag{F.27}$$

Unlike usual continuous random variables which have a probability that any single value occurs is 0, this random variable has a non-zero probability at claim size $M - D$. The density function for y is given in equation (F.28).

$$f_Y\left(y\middle|\theta\right)=\begin{cases}\dfrac{f_X\left(y+D\middle|\theta\right)}{1-F_X\left(D\middle|\theta\right)} & \text{if } 0\leq y<L-D \\[3mm] \dfrac{1-F_X\left(L\middle|\theta\right)}{1-F_X\left(D\middle|\theta\right)} & \text{if } y=L-D \\[3mm] 0 \text{ otherwise}\end{cases} \tag{F.28}$$

The first term in the expression reflects the truncation from below of the deductible and the second term reflects the concentration of claims at $M-D$ resulting from censoring imposed by the per-claim limit. For a sample of claims, the likelihood function can then be written as in equation (F.29).

$$L\left(y_1,y_2,\ldots,y_n\middle|\theta,\alpha\right)=\prod_{i=1}^{n}f_Y\left(y_i\middle|\theta,\alpha\right) \tag{F.29}$$

The negative-log-likelihood can then be written as shown in equation (F.30).

$$\ell\left(y_1,y_2,\ldots,y_n\middle|\theta,\alpha\right)=\sum_{i=1}^{n}-\ln\left(f_Y\left(y_i\middle|\theta,\alpha\right)\right) \tag{F.30}$$

In turn, the items in the sum in (F-30) take the form shown in equation (F.31).

$$-\ln\left(f_Y\left(y\middle|\theta,\alpha\right)\right)=\begin{cases}\ln\left(1-F_X\left(D\middle|\theta,\alpha\right)\right)-\ln\left(f_X\left(y+D\middle|\theta,\alpha\right)\right) & \text{if } 0\leq y<L-D \\[2mm] \ln\left(1-F_X\left(D\middle|\theta,\alpha\right)\right)-\ln\left(1-F_X\left(L\middle|\theta,\alpha\right)\right) & \text{if } y=L-D \\[2mm] \text{undefined otherwise}\end{cases} \tag{F.31}$$

As an example of this approach, suppose that data is available for 10 claims under policies which each have a coverage limit of $1,000, a deductible of $100 and claim payments to policyholders (limited and net of deductible) of $307, $376, $900, $900, $346, $900, $900, $900, $567, and $17. Suppose further that you are willing to assume the claims follow a two-parameter Pareto model with pdf given by (I.C-15) and, therefore, cumulative density function (cdf) given by equation (F.32).

$$F_X\left(x\middle|\theta,\alpha\right)=1-\left(\dfrac{\theta}{x+\theta}\right)^{\alpha} \tag{F.32}$$

An Excel spreadsheet can be used to calculate the likelihood for each of these observations, five of which are at policy limits, using equation (F.28). In this case, the application of Excel's Solver yields parameter estimates of 860.8195 for θ and 1.0635 for α, and the model has a rather heavy tail and a mean, though its variance is infinite. Estimates of the variance-covariance matrix of the parameters can also be obtained by using the functional form of the Pareto model and the relationship in equation (F.31) to derive the representation of the negative-log likelihood shown in equation (F.33).

$$-\ln\left(f_Y\left(y|\theta,\alpha\right)\right)=\begin{cases}\ln\left(\left(\dfrac{\theta}{D+\theta}\right)^\alpha\right)-\ln\left(\dfrac{\alpha\theta^\alpha}{(y+D+\theta)^{\alpha+1}}\right)\text{ if }0\le y<L-D\\[3mm]\ln\left(\left(\dfrac{\theta}{D+\theta}\right)^\alpha\right)-\ln\left(\left(\dfrac{\theta}{L+\theta}\right)^\alpha\right)\text{ if }y=L-D\\[3mm]\text{undefined otherwise}\end{cases}$$

(F.33)

$$=\begin{cases}(\alpha+1)\ln(y+D+\theta)-\alpha\ln(D+\theta)-\ln(\alpha)\text{ if }0\le y<L-D\\[2mm]\alpha\left(\ln(L+\theta)-\ln(D+\theta)\right)\text{ if }y=L-D\\[2mm]\text{undefined otherwise}\end{cases}$$

Using this equation, we arrived at the second partial derivatives shown in equations (F.34) through (F.36).

$$\frac{\partial^2}{\partial\theta^2}\left(-\ln\left(f_Y\left(y|\theta,\alpha\right)\right)\right)=\begin{cases}\dfrac{\alpha}{(D+\theta)^2}-\dfrac{\alpha+1}{(y+D+\theta)^2}\text{ if }0\le y<L-D\\[3mm]\dfrac{\alpha}{(D+\theta)^2}-\dfrac{\alpha}{(L+\theta)^2}\text{ if }y=L-D\\[3mm]\text{undefined otherwise}\end{cases}$$

(F.34)

$$\frac{\partial^2}{\partial\theta\partial\alpha}\left(-\ln\left(f_Y\left(y|\theta,\alpha\right)\right)\right)=\begin{cases}\dfrac{1}{y+D+\theta}-\dfrac{1}{D+\theta}\text{ if }0\le y\le L-D\\[3mm]\text{undefined otherwise}\end{cases}$$

(F.35)

$$\frac{\partial^2}{\partial\alpha^2}\left(-\ln\left(f_Y\left(y|\theta,\alpha\right)\right)\right)=\begin{cases}\dfrac{1}{\alpha^2}\text{ if }0\le y<L-D\\[2mm]0\text{ if }y=L-D\\[2mm]\text{undefined otherwise}\end{cases}$$

(F.36)

Taking their expected values to get the information matrix, we obtain equations (F.37) through (F.39).

$$E_Y\left(\frac{\partial^2}{\partial\theta^2}\left(-\sum_{i=1}^n\ln\left(f_Y\left(y|\theta,\alpha\right)\right)\right)\right)=\frac{n\alpha}{(D+\theta)^2}\left(1-\frac{1}{(\alpha+2)}\left(\alpha+1+\left(\frac{D+\theta}{L+\theta}\right)^{\alpha+2}\right)\right)$$

(F.37)

$$E_Y\left(\frac{\partial^2}{\partial\theta\partial\alpha}\left(-\sum_{i=1}^n\ln\left(f_Y\left(y|\theta,\alpha\right)\right)\right)\right)=\frac{n}{D+\theta}\left(\frac{1}{\alpha+1}\left(\alpha+\left(\frac{D+\theta}{L+\theta}\right)^{\alpha+1}\right)-1\right)$$

(F.38)

$$E_Y\left(\frac{\partial^2}{\partial\alpha^2}\left(-\sum_{i=1}^n\ln\left(f_Y\left(y|\theta,\alpha\right)\right)\right)\right)=\frac{n}{\alpha^2}$$

(F.39)

In contrast to the case for the normal and lognormal, the expected value of the mixed partial is not generally zero, a result that indicates the two parameters are generally correlated. The variance-covariance matrix is then just the inverse of the sum of these partials evaluated at the MLE and at each of the sample observations. This produces the matrix shown as (F.40) for our sample data.

$$\begin{pmatrix} 598{,}853.5 & 254.297 \\ 254.297 & 0.221 \end{pmatrix}$$

(F.40)

And in contrast to the normal and lognormal examples, the off-diagonal elements of this variance-covariance matrix are non-zero. In this case, the correlation coefficient is 0.70, indicating a relationship between the uncertainty in the two parameter estimates. In the normal and lognormal cases, we were able to make separate statements about the confidence intervals of the two parameters. Although we can still calculate the standard deviation of the two parameters as 773.86 and 0.47 for θ and α respectively, this information alone does not indicate how close the estimates are to the true values of the parameters. In order to quantify the parameter uncertainty, we would need to resort to the asymptotic normality of the MLE and consider the two-dimensional normal model with mean vector from the MLE estimates of the parameter and variance-covariance matrix given by (F.40).

F.4   MLE example – grouped data

The example in the preceding section considered truncated and censored data on individual claims. But there are frequently situations in which individual claim data may not readily be available, and the modeler is forced to use summary data for claims by size interval. While this grouping reduces the amount of information available, MLEs can still be calculated.

Let us suppose that we are again looking at insurance claims that are both censored at a net limit M and truncated below by a deductible D, and that n_i represents the number of claims observed in one of m intervals, between c_{i-1} and c_i with $c_0 = 0$. If the total number of claims at the limit $M - D$ are unknown, then $c_m = \infty$. But if the number of claims at the limit $M - D$ is known, then $c_{m-1} = M - D$, and $c_m = \infty$. Under this framework, (F.41) gives the likelihood of observing the given sample parameters for a model, while (F.42) gives the corresponding negative-log likelihood.

$$L\left(n_1, n_2, \ldots, n_m \mid \theta\right) = \prod_{i=1}^{m} \frac{\left(F_X\left(c_i + D \mid \theta\right) - F_X\left(c_{i-1} + D \mid \theta\right)\right)^{n_i}}{1 - F_X\left(D \mid \theta\right)}$$

(F.41)

$$\ell\left(n_1, n_2, \ldots, n_m \mid \theta\right) = m\ln\left(1 - F_X\left(D \mid \theta\right)\right) - \sum_{i=1}^{m} n_i \ln\left(F_X\left(c_i + D \mid \theta\right) - F_X\left(c_{i-1} + D \mid \theta\right)\right)$$

(F.42)

Similar to the previous examples, estimates of the parameters can be derived by minimizing the negative-log-likelihood function in (F.42) for a given sample. The information matrix can also be approximated by taking the second partials of this same negative-log likelihood and evaluating those partials at the MLE value.

In order to derive the information matrix, we need to consider derivatives of the negative-log-likelihood function. Second derivatives of the natural logarithm of a function g in general can be calculated using the formula in equation (F.43).

$$\frac{\partial^2}{\partial \theta_i \partial \theta_j} \ln\left(g\left(x \mid \theta\right)\right) = \frac{\frac{\partial^2}{\partial \theta_i \partial \theta_j} g\left(x \mid \theta\right)}{g\left(x \mid \theta\right)} - \frac{\left(\frac{\partial}{\partial \theta_i} g\left(x \mid \theta\right)\right)\left(\frac{\partial}{\partial \theta_j} g\left(x \mid \theta\right)\right)}{g^2\left(x \mid \theta\right)}$$

(F.43)

With this formula and the various partial derivatives of the function g, derivatives needed to estimate the information matrix can be evaluated.

Consider now the number of claims by size in the table in Figure 1 from a book of policies with no deductible and limits of 1,000,000.[95]

General Liability Claims

Payment ($)	Number
0 - 2,500	58
2,500 - 7,500	61
7,500 - 12,500	37
12,500 - 17,500	36
17,500 - 22,500	22
22,500 - 32,500	30
32,500 - 47,500	19
47,500 - 67,500	15
67,500 - 87,500	11
87,500 - 125,000	18
125,000 - 175,000	7
175,000 - 225,000	7
225,000 - 325,000	6
325,000 - 475,000	2
475,000 - 675,000	2
675,000 - 1,000,000	2
1,000,000+	3

Assume further these claims arose from a two-parameter Pareto model, which in this case is the negative-log-likelihood function shown in equation (F.44).

$$\ell\left(n_1, n_2, \ldots, n_m \mid \theta, \alpha\right) = -\sum_{i=1}^{m} n_i \ln\left(\left(\frac{\theta}{c_{i-1}+\theta}\right)^{\alpha} - \left(\frac{\theta}{c_i+\theta}\right)^{\alpha}\right) \tag{F.44}$$

To obtain the second derivatives of this function, we can use the relationship in equation (F.43) along with the derivatives shown in equations (F.45) through (F.49).

$$\frac{\partial}{\partial \theta}\left(\left(\frac{\theta}{c_i+\theta}\right)^{\alpha}\right) = \frac{\alpha c_i}{\theta^2}\left(\frac{\theta}{c_i+\theta}\right)^{\alpha+1} \tag{F.45}$$

$$\frac{\partial}{\partial \alpha}\left(\left(\frac{\theta}{c_i+\theta}\right)^{\alpha}\right) = \ln\left(\frac{\theta}{c_i+\theta}\right)\left(\frac{\theta}{c_i+\theta}\right)^{\alpha} \tag{F.46}$$

---

[95] Klugman, et al., ibid., p. 166.

$$\frac{\partial^2}{\partial\theta^2}\left(\left(\frac{\theta}{c_i+\theta}\right)^\alpha\right)=\frac{\alpha c_{i-1}}{\theta^3}\left(\frac{\theta}{c_i+\theta}\right)^{\alpha+1}\left(\frac{(\alpha+1)c_i}{c_i+\theta}-2\right)$$ (F.47)

$$\frac{\partial^2}{\partial\theta\partial\alpha}\left(\left(\frac{\theta}{c_i+\theta}\right)^\alpha\right)=\frac{c_i}{\theta^2}\left(\frac{\theta}{c_i+\theta}\right)^{\alpha+1}\left(1+\alpha\ln\left(\frac{\theta}{c_i+\theta}\right)\right)$$ (F.48)

$$\frac{\partial^2}{\partial\alpha^2}\left(\left(\frac{\theta}{c_i+\theta}\right)^\alpha\right)=\ln\left(\frac{\theta}{c_i+\theta}\right)^2\left(\frac{\theta}{c_i+\theta}\right)^\alpha$$ (F.49)

Although the calculations may be somewhat messy, we can calculate the MLEs of \$14,679.18 for θ and 1.0758 for α, and also derive an estimate of the variance-covariance matrix for the parameter estimates, shown in (F.50).

$$\begin{pmatrix} 8,805,310 & 336.373 \\ 336.373 & 0.0163 \end{pmatrix}$$ (F.50)

This equation implies standard errors of \$2,967.37 for θ and 0.1278 for α, which are much smaller relative to the parameter estimates in our prior example. This variance-covariance matrix also implies a correlation coefficient between the two parameters of about 0.89.

If the goal is then to price an excess layer, this information can first be used to estimate the expected cost in the layer, taking into account both process and parameter uncertainty. However, simply pricing to the expected value ignores the risk assumed by an insurer for which the insurer should be compensated. Considerable discussion has taken place on precisely this issue: How to incorporate risk in pricing of excess layers. One approach suggests using a risk load proportional to the variance of losses in a layer[96], while another suggests the standard deviation.[97]
If the challenge is to price the layer from \$500,000 to \$1,000,000 as is the case in this example, the modeler would need to evaluate its expected value and variance of losses. Because the focus is on losses in a layer rather than losses in excess of a deductible, the variable of interest with lower limit m and upper limit u is given in (F.51).

$$f_Y(y|\theta)=\begin{cases} 0 & \text{if } y<l \\[2mm] \dfrac{f_X(y|\theta)}{1-F_X(l|\theta)} & \text{if } l\le y<u \\[4mm] \dfrac{1-F_X(u|\theta)}{1-F_X(l|\theta)} & \text{if } y=u \\[4mm] 0 & \text{if } u<y \end{cases}$$ (F.51)

The moments are then given in (F.52).

[96] Miccolis, R.S. "On the Theory of Increased Limits and Excess of Loss Pricing." *Proceedings of the Casualty Actuarial Society* LXIV (1977): 27-59.
[97] Kreps, R. "Reinsurer Risk Loads from Marginal Surplus Requirements." *Proceedings of the Casualty Actuarial Society* LXXVII (1990): 196-203.

$$E\left(Y^k\middle|\theta\right)=\frac{\int\limits_l^u x^k\, f_x\left(x\middle|\theta\right)dx+u^k\left(1-F_x\left(l\middle|\theta\right)\right)}{1-F_x\left(l\middle|\theta\right)} \tag{F.52}$$

Equations (I.C-19) and (F-32) can be used in valuing this integral for the Pareto model. However, in cases in which $\alpha < 2$, many software packages will return errors when calculating the second moment using the pdf for the beta model. The corresponding integrals can be calculated using the anti-derivatives given in (F.53) and (F.54).

$$\int x\, f_x\left(x\middle|\theta,\alpha\right)dx=-\left(\frac{\theta}{x+\theta}\right)^{\alpha}\frac{\theta+\alpha x}{\left(\alpha-1\right)} \tag{F.53}$$

$$\int x^2\, f_x\left(x\middle|\theta,\alpha\right)dx=-\left(\frac{\theta}{x+\theta}\right)^{\alpha}\frac{x^2\alpha\left(\alpha-1\right)+2\theta\alpha x+2\theta^2}{\left(\alpha-1\right)\left(\alpha-2\right)} \tag{F.54}$$

Using the only parameters derived from the MLE would indicate an expected value in that layer of about $841,000 with a standard deviation of about $184,000. However, these amounts are uncertain, with the expected loss in the layer having a standard deviation of about $14,000 and the standard deviation for losses in the layer itself having a standard deviation of about $3,000. In short, even though parameter uncertainty is present in this example, it does not appear to be a significant issue.

F.5 MLE example – loss-forecast models

Generally focusing on the size of claims, the examples thus far have involved estimating parameters for a reasonably simple statistical model. This rather narrow approach was taken to clearly demonstrate the mechanics and the power of MLEs. At this point, it would be useful to summarize the framework we have developed to estimate parameters using MLEs. This framework can be outlined in steps as follows:

1.   State a problem in terms of an underlying statistical model, including:

     a.   The probability model(s) involved.

     b.   Interrelationships among the items modeled.

2.   **Make one or more observations that are believed to match the model.**

3.   **Calculate the likelihood of making those observations, given any potential values of the model parameter(s).**

4.   **Select the parameter(s) that maximize the likelihood (or minimize the negative-log likelihood).**

5.   **Assess how well the model fits the data by estimating the information matrix for the parameters and then for their variance-covariance matrix.**

For an example of a more complex use of MLEs,, we turn to a model for non-life insurance loss-emergence patterns, which is presented in greater detail by Hayne[98] and explored here in summary form.

---

[98]   Hayne, R.M. "A Stochastic Framework for Incremental Average Reserve Methods" Casualty Actuarial Society Forum, Fall, 2008.

Non-life actuaries often use the historical emergence of losses as a guide in estimating future amounts on existing claims or policies. Typically, the data underlying such analyses look at the historical emergence of losses on fixed cohorts of progressively less mature claims. These cohorts frequently identify claims by the nature of the risk-bearer's exposure to loss, hence, the term "exposure period." This term can be applied to claims occurring in a particular month (accident month), quarter (accident quarter), year (accident year) or to claims from policies written in a particular year (policy year). Although these are the most common, in general, there is no reasonable restriction on exposure periods.

Each exposure period allows us to study how losses emerge over time by examining snapshots of losses at evenly spaced intervals throughout the exposure period. This approach implies two units of time: The length of the exposure period and the elapsed amount of time between each observation of losses as they relate to a fixed exposure period. In practice, the two time spans under review need not be equal. For example, reviewing accident-year data with quarterly snapshots would be a reasonably common arrangement. For the sake of simplicity however, the following discussion will assume that the exposure periods and the intervals between observations are both one year.

The observed losses at each stage are usually either paid amounts or incurred amounts. This data forms a triangle with a row for each exposure period and entries along the row showing the losses at various stages of maturity. For example, accident-year paid-amount data at annual valuations refers to an array of numbers, with each row representing losses on claims that occurred in different calendar years and each column showing the payments recorded at the end of each calendar year. In this example, the data would be arranged so that the first column represents payments by the end of the accident year, the second payments during the next year, and so forth. This arrangement means that the most recent accident year will have the fewest number of possible observations, with the penultimate year having one more, and so forth for older years, giving rise to a triangular array of data.

With this explanation as background, we will denote the incremental amount (either paid or incurred) as $C_{i,j}$ for the ith exposure year during its jth year of age. For convenience, we will assume accident-year data with annual valuations, though this model can be more broadly applicable to other exposure periods. This triangle arrangement is shown visually in (F.55).

$$
\begin{array}{llllll}
C_{1,1} & C_{1,2} & \cdots & C_{1,n-1} & C_{1,n} \\
C_{2,1} & C_{2,2} & \cdots & C_{2,n-1} \\
\vdots & \vdots & \ddots \\
C_{n-1,1} & C_{n-1,2} \\
C_{n,1}
\end{array}
\qquad\qquad (F.55)
$$

The paid amounts could be either cumulative, representing inception-to-date payments, or incremental, representing payments made during the year. Cumulative incurred amounts are the total of cumulative paid amounts, plus provisions for estimated future payments on known claims placed by claims adjusters, often called case reserves; therefore, incremental incurred amounts are the difference between successive cumulative incurred amounts. They represent the total of the payments during the time period, plus the change in aggregate-case-reserve values during the period.

The goal of a non-life loss forecast is to fill in the lower part of this array, which is typically done by using the upper portion as a guide. While there are a seemingly infinite number of models of varying complexity available for this task, the model used in this example is a reasonably simple, yet quite robust approach, and illustrates the significant flexibility and power of MLE estimates.

Our focus is on the expected incremental average cost-per-unit of exposure $A_{i,j}$. In this case, unit of exposure is either claim count, policy count, or some other measure of expected relative loss size that will vary over accident years. We will assume the expected average cost will vary from one accident year to the next by a constant annual cost trend. Using vehicle claims as our basis, the expected incremental cost per vehicle insured may be considered. Or, if a reasonably accurate forecast of claims counts is available, the incremental amount per forecast-ultimate-claims count could be considered. This assumption is formally stated in equation (F.56).

$$E\left(A_{i,j}\middle|\theta_1,\theta_2,\ldots,\theta_n,\tau\right)=\theta_j\tau^i \tag{F.56}$$

This equation helps clarify our assumption that the averages in each column are expected to fluctuate around a constant, except for a uniform annual trend of τ.

If the observations are assumed to be independent with finite variances, then the central-limit theorem tells us that as the number of observations becomes large, the averages tend to have a normal model. For this reason we will assume for this model that each of the $A_{i,j}$ amounts – which can be viewed as averages of a number of observations – have a normal model with expected values given in (F.56). With this step, we have nearly specified a stochastic model for this problem. At this point, we turn to a normal model, which is completely determined by its mean and variance. If we can make an assumption about the variance of each average, we can then bring the power of MLEs to bear on estimating the parameters.

Many non-life stochastic models assume the variance of amounts in a cell is related to the payment amounts in that cell. Based on this premise, it can be assumed that the variance of the average amounts in each cell is proportional to a power of the expected value of those payments, with both the power and constant of proportionality kept uniform over all values. This assumption is stated in equation (F.57).

$$\operatorname{Var}\left(A_{i,j}\middle|\theta_1,\theta_2,\ldots,\theta_n,\tau,\kappa,p\right)=e^{\kappa}\left(\theta_j\tau^i\right)^{2p} \tag{F.57}$$

This formulation uses the power $2p$ and κ as an exponent to ensure the variance is positive, even if the expected average amount is negative, which is allowed in this particular model. These assumptions can then be summarized in the formal stochastic statement in (F.58).

$$A_{i,j}\sim N\left(\theta_j\tau^i,e^{\kappa}\left(\theta_j\tau^i\right)^{2p}\right) \tag{F.58}$$

Given the observed averages and any value for the parameters, the negative-log likelihood of the observed averages can be calculated, as shown in (F.59).

$$\ell\left(A_{1,1},A_{1,2},\ldots,A_{n,1}\middle|\theta_1,\theta_2,\ldots,\theta_n,\tau,\kappa,p\right)=\sum_{i=1}^{n}\sum_{j=1}^{n-i+1}\frac{\kappa+\ln\left(2\pi\left(\theta_j\tau^i\right)^{2p}\right)}{2}+\frac{\left(A_{ij}-\theta_j\tau^i\right)^2}{2e^{\kappa}\left(\theta_j\tau^i\right)^{2p}} \tag{F.59}$$

As with other examples provided above, the estimation of the parameters reduces to minimizing the negative-log-likelihood function. This process can be done in Microsoft Excel using the Solver feature, or in any number of software packages, including the freely available R. Calculations, which include R code, as well as the approximate variance-covariance matrix can be found in Hayne.[99]

---

[99] Hayne, R.M., ibid.

The normal model provides a number of convenient properties that are of particular interest in estimating total future amounts of non-life claims and their distributions. One such property is that the sum of independent normal variables is, itself, normal, with mean and variance equal to the sum of the means and variances of the component variables respectively. Thus, given the assumptions in (F.58) and that the various cells are independent, we can conclude that future amounts in the aggregate will have an approximate normal model, as parameterized in (F.60).

$$R \sim N\left(\sum_{i=2}^{n} \sum_{j=n-i+2}^{n} \hat{\theta}_j \hat{\tau}^i , \sum_{i=2}^{n} \sum_{j=n-i+2}^{n} e^{\hat{\kappa}} \left(\hat{\theta}_j \hat{\tau}^i \right)^{2\hat{p}} \right)$$ (F.60)

This estimate of future amounts only provides for process uncertainty, but there are other sources of uncertainty, such as the fact that the parameters were estimated from uncertain data. Measuring this uncertainty will once again make use of the asymptotic normality of MLEs. As discussed above, the MLEs converge to a normal model with an expected value equal to the parameters of the model, and a variance-covariance matrix equal to the inverse of the Fisher information matrix. Given the likelihood in (F.59), we can determine the Fisher information matrix, evaluated at the MLEs, and then invert that matrix to estimate the variance-covariance matrix of the parameters.

Using estimates of both the expected value of the parameters and an approximation for their entire distribution from the observed losses, the model of parameters can be overlaid with the model of future indications in (F.60) to obtain a model for forecasting loss. It should be pointed out that because of the complex ways the parameters enter into the forecast in (F.60), it may not be possible to derive a closed-form representation for this posterior distribution. However, we can investigate the shape of distribution by using a simulation as described in Algorithm 3.

Algorithm 3

1. Randomly select a parameter vector $(\theta_1, \theta_2, \ldots, \theta_n, \tau, \kappa, p)$ from a multivariate normal model with mean vector $(\hat{\theta}_1, \hat{\theta}_2, \ldots, \hat{\theta}_n, \hat{\tau}, \hat{\kappa}, \hat{p})$ and variance-covariance matrix $\mathbf{I}^{-1}(\hat{\theta}_1, \hat{\theta}_2, \ldots, \hat{\theta}_n, \hat{\tau}, \hat{\kappa}, \hat{p})$.

2. Randomly select future payments for the ith exposure year and j^{th} development year from a normal model with mean $\hat{\theta}_j \hat{\tau}^i$ and variance $e^{\hat{\kappa}} \left(\hat{\theta}_j \hat{\tau}^i \right)^{2\hat{p}}$ for each value i = 2, 3, ..., n and j = n – i +2, ... n.

3. Repeat steps 1 and 2 several times.

Each iteration of Algorithm 3 provides an observation of future amounts that incorporates, at least approximately, both process uncertainty and parameter uncertainty. This approach is an improvement over always selecting the MLE vector (step 1), a method which only accounts for process uncertainty in the distribution of future amounts.

There is a practical issue in implementing this algorithm, however. Most common software packages, such as Excel or R, contain built-in functions for generating univariate normal random numbers. But Excel does not have a feature to generate multivariate random variables; however, the software package R accomplishes this calculation with its function rvnorm.

Simulating a multivariate normal random variable is a relatively simple matter. To this end, we first need to review the multivariate normal model, which is defined by real valued vectors X with parameters for the real n-vector μ and positive definite n x n matrix Σ with the pdf given in equation (F.61).

$$f\left(x\,|\,\mu,\Sigma\right)=\frac{1}{\sqrt{\left(2\pi\right)^{n}\left|\Sigma\right|}}e^{-\frac{1}{2}\left(x-\mu\right)^{T}\Sigma^{-1}\left(x-\mu\right)} \tag{F.61}$$

From the equation, it can be seen that, if μ and Σ are both single values, this function reduces to the representation in (I.C-9). The vector μ gives the mean of the model and the matrix Σ its variance-covariance structure.

If C is a matrix such that $\Sigma = CC^{T}$, then the modeler can simulate from the multivariate normal by calculating the vector $w = \mu + Cz$ where z is a real vector of n independent randomly selected observations from a standard normal model, that being a univariate normal model with mean 0 and variance 1. Thus, the ability to simulate from a multivariate normal reduces to the problem of factoring its variance-covariance matrix, which can now be addressed using Choleski's decomposition.[100]

Let us assume that the element in the ith row and j^{th} column of the matrix Σ is $\sigma_{i,j}$, and, as is the case for the variance-covariance matrix, that Σ is symmetric, i.e., $\sigma_{i,j} = \sigma_{j,i}$. Based on these assumptions, we can build a lower triangular component matrix with elements $c_{i,j}$ one row at a time, starting at the first row and first column using the relationships in (F.62).

$$c_{i,j} = \begin{cases} \dfrac{\sigma_{i,j} - \sum\limits_{k=1}^{j-1} c_{i,k}c_{j,k}}{\sqrt{\sigma_{j,j} - \sum\limits_{k=1}^{j-1} c_{j,k}^{2}}}, & 1 \leq j \leq i \leq n \\[4mm] 0, & 1 \leq i < j \leq n \end{cases} \tag{F.62}$$

F.6   Evaluation of models

Stochastic models allow us to extrapolate beyond actual data, creating a view of experience having varying degrees of accuracy. As such, actuarial models seldom capture all the critical aspects of underlying processes, and can constitute a significant leap of faith, if the appropriate model is not used, technically known as model uncertainty.

We have already seen that certain asymptotic properties of MLEs allow us to assess the reliability of the parameter estimates through the inverse of the Fisher information matrix. But there is still the matter of addressing model uncertainty.

There are a number of tests that will help measure the relative strength of one model over another. Some of these tests are model-specific and make extensive use of special properties of the underlying models. For example, classic tests of hypothesis as they relate to the difference between means of models rely heavily on properties of the normal and Student-t models. Such classic tests are not directly applicable to broader models. Other tests, often referred to as non-parametric tests, however, do not rely on such special characteristics of the underlying model. Several of these are discussed here.

One commonly used non-parametric test is the chi-squared test. This test is a one-parameter model, with the parameter ν often referred to as the degrees of freedom. Its popularity derives from the fact that the statistic

---

[100]   See for example, Wang, S.S., "Aggregation of Correlated Risk Portfolios: Models and Algorithms", *Proceedings of the Casualty Actuarial Society* LXXXV (1998): 848-939.

calculated has, under rather broad assumptions, a distribution which follows the chi-squared model with distribution function given in equation (F.63).

$$f(x|\upsilon) = \begin{cases} \dfrac{1}{2^{\frac{\upsilon}{2}} \Gamma\left(\dfrac{\upsilon}{2}\right)} x^{\frac{\upsilon}{2}-1} e^{-\frac{x}{2}}, x > 0 \\ 0, x \le 0 \end{cases}$$

(F.63)

Consider a simple example involving a die with six sides, two painted white and four painted red. Our initial hypothesis is the die is fair, providing the white side has a 1/3 chance of surfacing and red side, a 2/3 chance. To test the hypothesis, we throw the die n times and observe a white side o times. In the n throws, a white side would be expected $n/3$ times, and a red side $2n/3$ times. Thus, if o is "close" to $n/3$, we can draw some comfort in our assumption that the die is fair; if it is "far" from $n/3$, we will have reason to question our assumption. This can be tested in the statistic in equation (F.64), and under certain circumstances, will have an approximate chi-squared model with one degree of freedom.

$$\chi^2 = \frac{\left(o - \dfrac{n}{3}\right)^2}{\dfrac{n}{3}} + \frac{\left((n-o) - \dfrac{2n}{3}\right)^2}{\dfrac{2n}{3}}$$

(F.64)

If the calculation shows that χ^2 is so large its observation in a chi-squared model is not considered to be a chance event, then we should question our original assumption.

Suppose now, instead of two categories (white and red sides), there are a number of different possible states m assumed to have probabilities $p_1, p_2, \ldots, p_m$ that sum to 1 and N items with n_i of them in the ith category. In this case, the statistic in equation (F.65) will have an approximate chi-squared model with $m - 1$ degrees of freedom under certain conditions.

$$\chi^2 = \sum_{i=1}^{m} \frac{\left(Np_i - n_i\right)^2}{Np_i}$$

(F.65)

Until this point, there has been no indication of how the various probabilities are determined. In model testing, particularly when considering the distribution of claims sizes, this determination would depend on the nature of the underlying variable. For instance, if the counts are summarized by claims size, the result is a "natural" for the categories, and the probabilities can easily be calculated, assuming the model estimated is "correct." In the Pareto case, the equation (F.32) is used. If, however, the probabilities are estimated for a model with r parameters using MLE to fit the model, then the degree of freedom decreases to $m - r - 1$.

Throughout the discussion of the chi-squared test, the qualifications such as "under certain conditions" and "approximate" have been used with good reason. As a general rule of thumb, the results from a chi-squared test are less trustworthy, if any particular category has less than 5 expected observations. Let's review our general liability claims example above in the grouped data section. In this example, if we used our MLE estimates for the Pareto parameters, we would expect from 336 claims (the number in our sample) to see *four* claims in each of the $325,000-$475,000 and $1,000,000+ categories, and *two* claims in each of the $475,000-$675,000 and $675,000-$1,000,000 categories. For this reason we typically would need to combine a couple of these categories before applying the test. If we combined two successive categories, compressing these four into $325,000-$675,000 and $675,000+, we would obtain a chi-squared statistic for this model fit of 11.25. This number indicates there is little evidence to reject our assumption that the claims follow a Pareto model fitted to the data using MLE. This conclusion is based on the fact that approximately 51% of the values of a chi-squared model with 12 degrees of freedom are greater than 11.25.

The chi-squared test is quite flexible and can be applied in a number of situations, with one significant caveat: In addition to considering the expected number of observations in any single category, the choice of specific categories can also have significant impact on the test results. This shortcoming is of particular concern when testing the fitness of theoretical models whose categories have been controlled by the modeler. For example, it is quite possible that actual experience may reveal significant differences between model (expected) and actual (observed) claims frequency in adjacent size categories. But this difference could completely disappear if the two categories are combined. The first situation could result in a large chi-squared statistic, while the second, a smaller statistic, even though both are based on the same fit and the same data.

A test that overcomes this difficulty is the Kolmogorov-Smirnov (K-S) test, which can be applied if information about individual observations is available. Rather than comparing actual and expected frequency in categories, this test is based on the statistic shown in equation (F.66), which compares the empirical cumulative density function with that implied by the model.

$$D = \sup_x \left| F_n(x) - F\left(x \middle| \hat{\theta}\right) \right| \tag{F.66}$$

In (F.66), $F_n(x)$ represents the empirical cumulative density for the sample of size n, the portion of the observed n-item sample that is no more than x. This statistic measures the furthest distance the actual distribution varies from the model's forecast. It should be pointed out that the empirical cumulative density is largely a step function with jumps at the value of each data point. Thus, in calculating the value of D, comparisons both before and after the jumps need to be considered, with a particular focus on the difference at each data point, rather than between the jumps.

Under the null hypothesis that the data points actually follow the underlying model, we can test the relationship in (F.67), which provides information about the range of possible values for D for any value of t.[101]

$$\lim_{n \to \infty} \Pr\left(\sqrt{n}D \le t\right) = H(t) = 1 - 2\sum_{i=1}^{\infty}(-1)^{i-1} e^{-i^2 t^2} \tag{F.67}$$

Klugman et al.[102] provide the approximations for the term on the right in (F.67) at various critical values as summarized in the table in Figure I-1. Because the terms in the sum in (F.67) get small relatively quickly, the value of $H(t)$ can be reasonably approximated after a relatively small number of terms.

Figure I-1

Critical Values for K-S Test

$H(t)$	t
0.20	1.07
0.10	1.22
0.05	1.36
0.01	1.63

---

[101]   DeGroot, M.H. *Probability and Statistics*, p. 556. Addison-Wesley, Second Edition, 1989.
[102]   Klugman et al., ibid., p. 124.

In the first example for the Pareto with individual claims, we had 10 observations with a value for D of 0.440, and a value of $\sqrt{nD}$ of F.8. These would provide a sufficiently large sample, if the above table is used to reject the hypothesis at a 95% level of confidence, but not at 99%. As we noted above for the chi-squared test, Klugman et al. also cautions that this test is only valid in situations for which the null hypothesis is true. If the parameters tested are estimated from the data, then the relationship in (F.67) may not necessarily hold. One approach that can be used in this case is to estimate the parameters using a portion of the available data, perhaps half, and test the fit using all the data points.

Although this point is made relative to the K-S test, it has wider relative application. In general, fitting a model to data selects the "best" set of parameters for that model given the data observed. As such, it is difficult to consider the observations as truly random selections from a model that happens to have those parameters. This is one reason why the use of a "hold out" sample as described in the prior paragraph is encouraged. It also explains the further correction to the degrees of freedom in the chi-squared test, when the fit is measured against a model whose parameters were estimated from the data.

When considering model fits, the principle of parsimony comes into play. Briefly, this principle states that the model which best describes the data with the fewest parameters should be preferred, particularly in situations where conclusions are being made from data not directly available. This principle recognizes the dilemma posed by the addition of parameters, which can often make a model fit the data better, but simultaneously decrease the model's usefulness in understanding the underlying process. A classic example is that for any sample of n real measurements made over time, a modeler can always find an $n - 1^{st}$ degree polynomial that will exactly match those measurements at the times they were taken. Such a polynomial, though fitting the data exactly, probably has little or no value at predicting what the measurements would have been at any unobserved time.

Thus, tests for comparing how well different models reflect the structure in the underlying data should recognize the different number of parameters present in the respective models. Accordingly, parsimony would indicate that if two models "fit" the data equally well, then the one with the fewer parameters is preferred.

A number of measures contemplate the number of parameters in determining the fit of a model. While none have been universally accepted as an appropriate approach, two types of measurement – the Bayesian Information Criterion (BIC) and the Akaike Information Criterion (AIC) – are important to consider. Both begin with the negative-log-likelihood value for a particular fit and modify that value to reflect the sample size, n, and the number of parameters of the model that are fitted, r. The form often stated for the AIC is $2r - 2ln(L)$, where L represents the likelihood of the observed sample at the value of the fitted parameter. However, equation (F.68) gives a slightly modified version of this statistic that incorporates sample size. Equation (F.69) shows the BIC with these conventions.

$$AIC = \frac{2rn}{n-r-1} - 2\ln(L) \qquad\qquad (F.68)$$

$$BIC = r\ln\left(\frac{n}{2\pi}\right) - \ln(L) \qquad\qquad (F.69)$$

Although not directly comparable to one another, these measures can be used to compare different models as measured by the same data.

F.7 MLE, "exponential fit," and generalized linear models

In practice, the ease of calculations within a model and the ability to easily estimate its parameters may often have a greater influence on the selection of models than the characteristics of the underlying process being modeled. A slight digression will help illustrate this point.

Consider a simple problem in which observations from a certain phenomenon are expected to progress linearly such that constants a and b occur over time t equal to $a + bt$, graphically represented by a straight line. For any two observations at different points in time, we can uniquely calculate the values of a and b parameters that give rise to those two observations.

The problem becomes less certain for more than two observations, and even more difficult for observations that do not lie in a straight line. The heuristic solution would then be to find a straight line that is closest in some sense to all the observations. One measure of the distance between real numbers is the absolute value of their difference, or the square root of the square of their difference. Thus, one possible way to pick the parameters for the line is to minimize the total distance between sample points (t_i, y_i) and the line at the same t_i value, which can be analytically performed by finding the values of the parameters a and b that minimize expression (F.70).

$$SSE = \sum_{i=1}^{n} \left(y_i - \left(a + bt_i \right) \right)^2 \tag{F.70}$$

There is a relatively simple closed-form solution for the values of a and b that minimizes the sum-squared error (SSE). Most software packages, including Excel, SAS and R, contain functions to calculate them. The approach to solving this problem has *not* been stochastic, but rather deterministic. The formulas for a and b provide no direct information regarding the underlying stochastic models, nor do they hint at what the model actually is. This minimization problem is often referred to as "least squares fitting" and provides parameter estimates independent of any assumptions about an underlying stochastic model.

It is tempting to use the least-squares approach to fit more complex models to data. But estimated parameters from those models will have no a stochastic element, and, therefore, provide little information about what those estimates mean statistically, nor how "good" they actually are.

If the y_i values are instead assumed to be random observations from individual normal models with mean $a + bt_i$, and common variance σ_2, then we have turned a deterministic exercise into a stochastic model. We can then bring the power of MLEs to bear on calculating the negative-log likelihood, minimizing that function and deriving estimates of the parameters. In this example, it happens that the MLEs for the parameters are precisely those determined from the deterministic least-squares problem. This should not be surprising given the negative-log likelihood function for this problem as shown in equation (F.71).

$$\ell\left(y_1, y_2, \ldots, y_n \middle| \mu, \sigma^2 \right) = -\ln\left(L\left(y_1, y_2, \ldots, y_n \middle| \mu, \sigma^2 \right) \right)$$

$$= -\ln\left(\prod_{i=1}^{n} \frac{1}{\sqrt{2\pi\sigma^2}} e^{-\frac{\left(y_i - \left(a + bt_i \right) \right)^2}{2\sigma^2}} \right) \tag{F.71}$$

$$= \frac{n}{2}\ln\left(2\pi\sigma^2 \right) + \sum_{i=1}^{n} \frac{\left(y_i - \left(a + bt_i \right) \right)^2}{2\sigma^2}$$

For a given value of σ^2, the values of a and b that minimize (F.71) are the same as those that minimize (F.70). Thus the MLE for a linear regression problem with an underlying assumption of normal models has a convenient closed-form solution that happens to be the same as that of the least-squares problem.

To see how such convenience is often at the root of model selection, consider the typical estimate of annual inflation rate using an "exponential fit." The estimation begins with the deterministic model that the value of an item or index at one point in time is a constant (the inflation factor) times its value one year earlier. If x_0 represents the value of the index at time 0 and τ represents the annual rate of increase then, under this assumption, the value of the index at time t can be written as $x_0\tau^t$. In this case, the direct least-squares formula becomes much more difficult to solve directly. However, if instead of considering this relationship directly, we consider the natural logarithms of the observations, then we realize that $ln(y_i) = ln(x_0) + t\,ln(\tau)$, which is also a simple linear problem.

At this juncture, some might reason that the solution for the linear problem becomes a solution for the transformed problem. Thus, a common way to estimate the annual rate of increase τ is to estimate the linear parameters of the transformed problem, and then convert the estimate back by exponentiation. Although algebra is correct, this approach loses the essential properties of the MLE, because the estimate is no longer the MLE for the original problem. This fact is often too overlooked, causing some to deal with the resulting estimates in the same way as MLEs.

In these applications, it is tempting to simply take the exponential of the linear extrapolation and call it the "exponential" fit for the data. In reality, if we have a lognormal model with parameters μ and σ^2, then e^μ is the *median* and *not* the mean. Thus, the "exponential fit" represents the *median* and not the expected fit through the points. The appropriate expected value is shown in equation (I.C-11) and includes a term involving σ^2 too.

It should be pointed out that generalized linear models (GLMs) were designed for precisely this situation in which model-fitting can be cast as a linear problem using reasonably simple transforms. Under certain conditions on the transformation function (usually termed the "link function") and the underlying models, GLM theory derives MLE solutions, and thus recaptures the useful properties of MLEs, while maintaining some relative simplicity in calculating those estimates. GLMs gain this attribute at the expense of some potentially limiting restrictions, not the least of which is the ability or inability to transform the problem to a linear express by the use of reasonably simple link functions. There are also limitations on the underlying models assumed.

F.8   Some simple stochastic models plus their mixture

While there are countless models that can be used to estimate the distribution of claims sizes in different situation, only a relatively small number are used most often. The type of model used will depend on the objective. For example, discrete models are typically used to estimate the number of claims that might arise, while models defined by positive real value would be used to estimate the size of claims payments. In still other cases, loss-forecast models would be used to determine increments that can be either positive or negative.

Probably the most common model used to estimate the number of claims under a policy is the Poisson model shown in (F-73). Its application relies on whether a physical process generating occurrences (claims, for example) has the following three properties:

1.   **The number of occurrences in disjoint time intervals is independent, meaning the number of claims occurring one day is not dependent on the number occurring another day.**

2.   **The chance of an occurrence in a time interval is approximately proportional to the length of that interval. Stated mathematically, there is a constant λ such that for any interval of length**

t, the probability of at least one occurrence in that interval is $\lambda t + o(t)$. Here $o(t)$ represents a function of *t* that approaches 0 faster than *t* as *t* approaches 0, such that the following relationship holds:

$$\lim_{t \to 0} \frac{o(t)}{t} = 0 \tag{F.72}$$

3.   The chance of two occurrences in any interval of length *t* is $o(t)$.

Given these conditions, it is not difficult to see why a Poisson is often selected to model the number of claims. The following expressions summarize the Poisson model.

Poisson Model

$$f(x|\theta) = \begin{cases} \dfrac{e^{-\theta}\theta^x}{x!}, & x = 0, 1, 2, \ldots \\ 0 \text{ otherwise} \end{cases} \tag{F.73}$$

$$E(X) = Var(X) = \theta \tag{F.74}$$

It should be noted, however, that the mean and variance are equal in the Poisson model. Often either evidence or instinct would suggest that the variation in the number of claims is greater than what would be indicated by a Poisson, if for no other reason than the expected number of claims is itself uncertain. For this reason, other models of claims counts are sometimes used.

Consider the process outlined in Algorithm 4, as described by Heckman and Meyers.[103]

Algorithm 4

1.   Select χ at random from a gamma model with $E(\chi) = 1$ and $Var(\chi) = c$.

2.   Select the number of claims, *n*, at random from a Poisson model with parameter $\chi\lambda$.

In this case, the final number of claims *n* will have a negative binomial model with mean $E(n) = \lambda$ and variance $Var(n) = \lambda + c\lambda^2$. The pdf of the negative binomial can be expressed as in equation (F.75) with the mean and variance shown in equations (F.76) and (F.77).

Negative Binomial Model

$$f(x|\beta,r) = \begin{cases} (1+\beta)^{-r}, & \text{if } x = 0 \\ \dfrac{r(r+1)\ldots(r+x-1)\beta^x}{x!(1+\beta)^{r+x}}, & \text{if } x = 1, 2, \ldots \end{cases} \tag{F.75}$$

$$E(X) = \beta r \tag{F.76}$$

---

[103]   Heckman, P.E., and G.G. Meyers. "Calculation of Aggregate Loss Distributions from Claim Severity and Claim Count Distributions," *Proceedings of the Casualty Actuarial Society* LXX (1983): 22-61.

$$\text{Var}(X) = \beta r(1+\beta) \tag{F.77}$$

Using Algorithm 4 then results in a negative binomial with parameters $\beta = \lambda c$ and $r = 1/c$.

Algorithm 4 includes a gamma model denoted as two-parameter model with pdf given in equation (F.78), cumulative density function in equation (F.79), and moments in equation (F.80). The gamma model is also sometimes used to estimate claims size.

Gamma Model

$$f(x|\alpha,\theta) = \frac{\left(\dfrac{x}{\theta}\right)^{\alpha} e^{-\frac{x}{\theta}}}{x\Gamma(\alpha)} \tag{F.78}$$

$$F(x|\alpha,\theta) = \Gamma\left(\frac{x}{\theta};\alpha\right) = \frac{1}{\Gamma(\alpha)} \int_{0}^{\frac{x}{\theta}} z^{\alpha-1} e^{-z} dz \tag{F.79}$$

$$E(X^k) = \frac{\theta^k \Gamma(\alpha+k)}{\Gamma(\alpha)}, \, k > -\alpha \tag{F.80}$$

The two popular models used for this purpose are the Pareto model and the lognormal model, both of which have been discussed previously. The selection of lognormal is due to its close relationship to the normal model, and the fact that the sum of a large number of independent random variables tends to have an approximate normal model. If we assume the size of a claim to be the *product* of a large number of independent events, then the central-limit theorem would imply that the distribution of claims sizes might approximate a lognormal, which is summarized in the following:

Lognormal Model

$$f(x|\mu,\sigma^2) = \frac{1}{x\sqrt{2\pi\sigma^2}} e^{-\frac{(\ln(x)-\mu)^2}{2\sigma^2}} \tag{F.81}$$

$$F(x|\mu,\sigma^2) = \Phi\left(\frac{\ln x - \mu}{\sigma}\right) = \int_{-\infty}^{\frac{\ln x - \mu}{\sigma}} \frac{1}{\sqrt{2\pi}} e^{-\frac{z^2}{2}} dz \tag{F.82}$$

$$E(X^k) = e^{k\mu + \frac{k^2\sigma^2}{2}} \tag{F.83}$$

Claims-size models are often used to support pricing high-level insurance coverage. This type of coverage tends to have somewhat "thick" tails due to a few huge claims having a disproportional effect on the average. This phenomenon is not limited to insurance claims, as evidenced by the common use of the median in reporting housing values or incomes whose overall averages can be easily distorted by a relatively small number of very high-value homes or very high-income producing individuals. Because of this distortion, as well as the increased risk in pricing high levels of coverage and the additional parameter uncertainty, the tail of the lognormal is often viewed as not being thick enough to be used in practice. For this reason, many modelers favour the Pareto model, particularly in modeling the effects of very large claims, which is summarized as follows:

Pareto Model

$$f\left(x\middle|\theta,\alpha\right)=\frac{\alpha\theta^{\alpha}}{\left(x+\theta\right)^{\alpha+1}} \tag{F.84}$$

$$F\left(x\middle|\theta,\alpha\right)=1-\left(\frac{\theta}{\theta+x}\right)^{\alpha} \tag{F.85}$$

$$E\left(X^{k}\right)=\frac{\theta^{k}\Gamma\left(k+1\right)\Gamma\left(\alpha-k\right)}{\Gamma\left(\alpha\right)} \tag{F.86}$$

As two-parameter models, the gamma, Pareto, and lognormal effectively give the modeler only two "knobs" by which to tune the model. Once the parameters are selected, critical features such as skewness and kurtosis are fixed. This restriction gives rise to consideration of models with more than two parameters. Klugman et al.[104] provides a collection of families of parametric continuous models, many of which are used to model the size of insurance claims.

Rather than having to choose one model over another, there is also the possibility of assembling a single model from those under consideration and letting the data indicate how to combine them. This concept is addressed in a paper by Klugman and Rioux[105] that suggests considering a mixture of models with the cumulative density function presented in equation (F.87).

A Mixture of Models

$$\begin{aligned}F_{A}\left(x\middle|\mathbf{w},g,l,p,\ ,\alpha_{g},\theta_{g},\mu,\sigma^{2},\alpha_{p},\theta_{p}\right)=&\sum_{i=1}^{n}w_{i}\,F_{E}\left(x\middle|\theta_{i}\right)\\&+g\,F_{G}\left(x\middle|\alpha_{g},\theta_{g}\right)+l\,F_{L}\left(x\middle|\mu,\sigma^{2}\right)+p\,F_{P}\left(x\middle|\theta_{p},\alpha_{p}\right)\end{aligned} \tag{F.87}$$

In short, the cumulative density function of the mixture is simply a weighted average of cumulative density functions for a gamma (F_G), a lognormal (F_L), a Pareto (F_P) and a number of exponentials (F_E). The exponential model has the cumulative density function shown in equation (F.88).

$$F\left(x\middle|\theta\right)=1-e^{-\frac{x}{\theta}} \tag{F.88}$$

The paper's authors require that at least one of the g or l parameters be 0 – that is, that only one of the lognormal or gamma is allowed, not both – and that all weights (the parameters represented by roman letters) sum to 1. This approach affords considerable flexibility in the selection of models and gives a very rich set of possible tools.

---

[104] Klugman, et al., ibid., Appendix A.

[105] Klugman, S. and J. Rioux. "Toward a Unified Approach to Fitting Loss Models," *North American Actuarial Journal* Vol. 10, No. 1 (2006): 63. Also available at http://www.cbpa.drake.edu/MixFit/default.asp?id=0&ACT=19.

However, this flexibility comes at a price, since the approach requires a significant increase in the number of parameters estimated from the data.

F.9   Bayesian methods

Throughout the preceding sections we selected a model and used only the data at hand to estimate the parameters of that model. Presumably, our selection of a model may, in some sense, be guided by our prior experience with the data, but our discussion generally ignored prior experience. Items of import were defined by the boundaries of the cells and the presence or absence of a deductible or policy limit.

In practice, selection without consideration of prior experience is unrealistic. Questions would arise if patterns in the data did not support our experience in product. The same holds true in forecasting results from a complex and often incompletely understood process of generating claims. Under these conditions, we often apply a variety of different forecast methods and use "actuarial judgment" or prior experience to "select" a "best estimate." For example, when evaluating non-life unpaid claim liabilities in the United States, if multiple methods are not used, then additional disclosure is required under Actuarial Standard of Practice Number 43, "Property/Casualty Unpaid Claim Estimates."[106]

While some may question the appropriateness of prior experience in modeling, there are statisticians who believe that prior experience has a place in statistical analysis and should be formally recognized, even if it cannot be rigorously quantified. These statisticians are called Bayesians.

In a Bayesian world, a modeler might start with some sense of how likely a parameter will take on a particular value from a prior model of the parameter, and then review the data available, changing the assessment of this likelihood to arrive at a posterior model of the parameter. This is possible because of a fundamental Bayes' theorem, which we will summarize from Klugman, et al.[107] To better our understanding, we will first need a number of definitions. These include:

- The *prior distribution* is a probability distribution over the space of possible parameter values. It is denoted $\pi(\theta)$ and represents our opinion concerning the relative chances that various values of θ are the true value.

- An *improper prior distribution* is one for which the probabilities (or pdf) are non-negative, but their sum (or integral) is infinite.

- The *model distribution* is the probability distribution for the data as collected, given a particular value for the parameter. Its pdf is denoted $f_{x|\theta}(x|\theta)$. Note, this expression is identical to the likelihood function, and may also be referred to as such.

- The *joint distribution* has pdf

$$f_{X,\Theta}\left(\mathbf{x}|\theta\right)=f_{X|\Theta}\left(\mathbf{x}|\theta\right)\pi\left(\theta\right)$$

- The *marginal distribution* of x has pdf

$$f_X\left(x\right)=\int f_{X|\Theta}\left(\mathbf{x}|\theta\right)\pi\left(\theta\right)d\theta$$

- The *posterior distribution* is the conditional probability distribution of the parameters given the observed data. It is denoted $\pi_{\theta|X}\left(\theta|x\right)$.

---

[106] Section 3.6.1, Actuarial Standard of Practice No. 43.
[107] Klugman, et al., ibid., 107-108.

- The *predictive distribution* is the conditional probability distribution of a new observation y given the data x. It is denoted $f_{Y|X}(y|x)$.

Given this background we can now state Bayes Theorem as follows:

Theorem 3

The posterior distribution can be computed as

$$\pi_{\Theta|X}(\theta|x) = \frac{f_{X|\Theta}(x|\theta)\pi(\theta)}{\int f_{X|\Theta}(x|\theta)\pi(\theta)d\theta} \tag{F.89}$$

While the predictive distribution can be computed as

$$f_{Y|X}(y|x) = \int f_{Y|\Theta}(y|\theta)\pi_{\Theta|X}(\theta|x)d\theta \tag{F.90}$$

where $f_{Y|\theta}(y|\theta)$ is the pdf of the new observation, given the parameter value. In both formulas the integrals are replaced by sums for a discrete distribution.

Bayes' theorem, therefore, provides a way to let our prior assessment evolve with additional information, as well as to incorporate our stated uncertainty inherent in the estimation of the parameters directly into the assessment of possible future outcomes within the model's framework. In this way Bayes' theorem gives a posterior model of the parameter, rather than an estimate of the parameter itself, as in the MLE.

This principle allows for considerably more information, but also raises the question as to which single point on the model to use to represent the parameter. To address this issue, Bayesians may consider penalty functions, which involve selecting the value of the parameter, known as a Bayesian estimate of the parameter, that incurs the least expected penalty. One benefit of Bayesian estimates is that through a judicious choice of a penalty or loss function, one can reflect practical limitations and penalties inherent in misestimating a parameter.

The Bayesian estimator for a given loss function is then the value of $\hat{\theta}$ that minimizes a selected loss function p, which penalizes the user for an estimate $\hat{\theta}$ when the true value of the parameter is θ, i.e., the value of $\hat{\theta}$ that minimizes the expression in (F.91).

$$E_\theta\left(p\left(\theta,\hat{\theta}\right)\right) = \int p\left(\theta,\hat{\theta}\right)\pi(\theta)d\theta \tag{F.91}$$

There are an infinite number of such penalty functions; however, three have sufficiently convenient properties to warrant discussion here. These three functions are given in equations (F.92) through (F.94) and are sometimes referred to as the "square error," "absolute," and "zero-one loss" or penalty functions, respectively.

$$p\left(\theta,\hat{\theta}\right) = \left(\theta - \hat{\theta}\right)^2 \tag{F.92}$$

$$p\left(\theta,\hat{\theta}\right) = \left|\theta - \hat{\theta}\right| \tag{F.93}$$

$$p\left(\theta,\hat{\theta}\right) = \delta_{\theta-\hat{\theta}} \tag{F.94}$$

Sometimes called the "point mass," the function in equation (F.94) known as the Dirac delta function has the property shown in equation (F.95).

$$\int_S \delta_z(x)dx = \begin{cases} 1, \text{ if } z \in S \\ 0, \text{ if } z \notin S \end{cases} \tag{F.95}$$

These loss functions give rise to Bayesian estimates equal to the mean, median, and mode of the prior model, respectively.

The importance of the Bayesian approach becomes apparent when we step back and look at actuarial and related problems from a broader perspective. At the heart of classical non-Bayesian statistical analysis is the concept of "asymptotically," which suggests that a large enough number of observations from the same phenomenon will produce certain statistics with properties close to some convenient models; the more observations, generally, the closer the results will be to the "ideal." The concept works well for repeatable experiments, such as the toss of a coin, but it requires a leap of faith when only a relatively small number of observations are available for an ever-changing environment.

As noted above, Bayes' theorem does not require a "sufficiently large" number of observations and provides us with a useful model of the parameters, rather than the asymptotically normal model for MLE. However, Bayes' theorem does require a prior distribution of the parameter(s). And while it conveys how a model would evolve as more information becomes available, it does not provide a single point estimate for the parameters as does MLE.

An analyst's prior model may have a significant impact on the estimation of the parameters, particularly when empirical observed evidence is not plentiful.[108] Consider the following example of a friendly wage of $1.00 made between two friends on a coin toss. Immediately before the "money toss", the coin, which is known to be fair, is flipped three times. A 'head' is observed each time. Should either party to the bet change the wage? In a Bayesian sense, both have prior models about the chance of heads in a single toss, which concentrates near 50%, and thus are unlikely to appreciably change their assessment about that coin based on only three tosses.

Now change the example slightly. Instead of two friends, the wager is made between an Earthling and a Martian who has no experience with coins. After the three non-money tosses, the Martian, our surrogate for a true non-Bayesian statistician, might conclude, using a Bernoulli or binomial model, that there is a 50/50 chance that the true likelihood of a head is between 71% and 93%, and a 90% chance it will be above 55%. Based on this information, the Martian rejects the Earthling's proffered wager. Given this asymmetry of information, though, the Earthling might offer to reverse the wager, but request a $2.00 payoff for tails and give the Martian a $1.00 payoff for heads. The bet still looks quite favourable to the Martian with an actual expected gain for the Earthling of $0.50.

Thus, from a Bayesian point of view, the prior model is a powerful way for past experience to be brought to bear on a current problem. Indeed, Bayes' theorem gives a rigorous way to adapt that prior model for emerging "facts." Although a prior model can be subjective, some, including Rebonato,[109] require that it, in some sense, be real and verifiable in that it can be tested in the marketplace. As seen in our Martian example, someone with a better prior model can profit.

As a simple example of a Bayesian approach, let us consider this same Earthling-Martian coin-toss wager. If a trial can result only in success or failure, then the number of successes in n trials where the chance of success is θ can be modeled as a binomial model with parameters n and θ with discrete pdf given by (F.96).

[108] See, for example, Rebonato, R., Plight of the Fortune Tellers: Why We Need to Manage Financial Risk Differently: Princeton University Press, 2007.

[109] Rebonato, R., ibid.

$$f(x|n,\theta) = \begin{cases} \binom{n}{x}\theta^x(1-\theta)^{n-x}, & x = 0, 1, \ldots, n \\ 0 \text{ otherwise} \end{cases} \tag{F.96}$$

In this coin-toss problem, the parameter θ is unknown. If, like the Martian, we have no reason to believe that one value of θ between 0 and 1 is more likely than any other, then we would choose $\pi(\theta)=1$ for $0 \le \theta \le 1$, and 0 otherwise. In general, if we view x heads in n tosses from Bayes' theorem, we have the relationship in (F.97).

$$\pi_{\Theta|x}\left(\theta|x \text{ heads in } n \text{ tosses}\right) \propto \theta^x(1-\theta)^{n-x} \times 1 \tag{F.97}$$

The function on the right is also proportional to the pdf of a beta model with parameters $x + 1$ and $n - x + 1$, thus giving the equation (F.98).

$$\pi_{\Theta|x}\left(\theta|x \text{ heads in } n \text{ tosses}\right) = \frac{\Gamma(n+2)}{\Gamma(x+1)\Gamma(n-x+1)}\theta^x(1-\theta)^{n-x} \tag{F.98}$$

Using the three heads out of three tries, our revised prior model becomes (F.99).

$$\pi_{\Theta|x}\left(\theta|3 \text{ heads in 3 tosses}\right) = \frac{1}{2}\theta^3 \tag{F.99}$$

Thus, with a completely non-informative prior, the effect of observing three heads in three tosses is quite substantial. It should be pointed out that the uniform prior model over the unit interval is simply a special case of the beta model, wherein the parameters are both one. If, instead of our uniform prior model, the more general beta model is used, then the expression in (F.98) becomes the relationship in (F.100).

$$\pi_{\Theta|x}\left(\theta|x \text{ heads in } n \text{ tosses}\right) \propto \theta^x(1-\theta)^{n-x} \times \theta^{\alpha-1}(1-\theta)^{\beta-1} = \theta^{\alpha+x-1}(1-\theta)^{\beta+n-x-1} \tag{F.100}$$

This latter function is proportional to the pdf of a beta model with parameters $\alpha + x$ and $\beta + n - x$. In general, the posterior model of the parameter, after the observation of x successes in n trials, is again beta providing our prior model for the parameter of a binomial model has a beta model. This approach can be used to examine the impact of the observed three heads in three tosses on relatively certain priors.

If the two parameters of a beta model are equal, then the model is symmetric about 0.50. In a beta model with parameters $\alpha = \beta = 1,000$, about 92.6% of the model is between 0.48 and 0.52. This result might represent the prior experience the two friends had before observing the three flips. After the three heads were observed, the posterior model is again beta, but with parameters $\alpha = 1,003$ and $\beta = 1,000$, with virtually the same 92.6% between 0.48 and 0.52, resulting in little change in assessing the likelihood of heads for this coin toss.

This example demonstrates that with few observations, the prior model becomes important. The converse is also generally true: with many observations, the prior model is unimportant.

Now suppose we have a reasonably strong belief that the coin is biased to tails, and we express this belief as a beta with parameters $\alpha = 30$ and $\beta = 50$. In this case, about 90% of the values are between 0.29 and 0.47. If there are 1,000 coin tosses and heads are observed 500 times, then our posterior model will have a beta with parameters $\alpha = 530$ and $\beta = 550$, with about 89% of the values between 0.47 and 0.52. Conversely, if we had an equally strong prior belief that the coin is biased to heads, and we express this as a beta with parameters $\alpha = 50$ and $\beta = 30$, then the posterior is a beta model with parameters $\alpha = 550$ and $\beta = 530$, with roughly 88% of its values between 0.49

and 0.54. Thus, even though we had rather strong prior beliefs, the Bayesian approach allows substantial evidence to be reflected.

As noted above, Bayes' theorem provides models and not point estimates. As such, integration is a vital part of Bayesian analysis as indicated in Theorem 3. With multidimensional parameters, the integration becomes multidimensional, which can pose some barriers to applications of this approach.

The presentation in Section F.5, "MLE example – loss forecast models," used the asymptotic properties of the MLE, along with a rather convenient algorithm to derive estimates of the posterior model of reserves from a multivariate normal model, given a specific model and historical data observation. Just as simulation can be called upon in the MLE case, it can be a reasonably accurate approach in a Bayesian model, given a method known as the Gibbs Sampler.[110] The algorithm for a parameter vector of length k is given by Algorithm 5.

Algorithm 5

1.   Select initial values $\boldsymbol{\theta}^{(0)} = \left(\theta_1^{(0)}, \theta_2^{(0)}, \ldots, \theta_k^{(0)} \right)$.

2.   Set counter index $i = 0$.

3.   Simulate a sequence of random draws:

$$\theta_1^{(i+1)} \sim \pi \left(\theta_1 \Big| \theta_2^{(i)}, \theta_3^{(i)}, \ldots, \theta_k^{(i)} \right)$$

$$\theta_2^{(i+1)} \sim \pi \left(\theta_2 \Big| \theta_1^{(i+1)}, \theta_3^{(i)}, \ldots, \theta_k^{(i)} \right)$$

$$\theta_3^{(i+1)} \sim \pi \left(\theta_3 \Big| \theta_1^{(i+1)}, \theta_2^{(i+1)}, \theta_4^{(i)}, \ldots, \theta_k^{(i)} \right)$$

$$\vdots$$

$$\theta_k^{(i+1)} \sim \pi \left(\theta_k \Big| \theta_1^{(i+1)}, \theta_2^{(i+1)}, \ldots, \theta_{k-1}^{(i)} \right)$$

and form

$$\boldsymbol{\theta}^{(i+1)} = \left(\theta_1^{(i+1)}, \theta_2^{(i+1)}, \ldots, \theta_k^{(i+1)} \right)$$

4.   Increment index and return to step 3.

Note that we only need to simulate one parameter at any step, given fixed values for the remainder, which eliminates the need for multivariate simulation, as was the case in Section F.5. This sequence eventually reaches a steady-state that matches the posterior model of the parameters. This algorithm is reasonably simple to implement directly with software, for example in R (as included in the Web version of the Meyers *Actuarial Review* article), or in a separate software package such as WinBUGS.

From an actuarial perspective, a Bayesian approach can be quite rich, allowing a modeler to build up "experience" with a particular model from a range of different analyses and allow for current data to revise and refine the priors.

---

[110]   For an excellent overview of the Gibbs Sampler, see Meyers, G.G., "Quantifying Tail Risk with the Gibbs Sampler," *The Actuarial Review*, v. 35, no. 1 (February 2008). For a more complete description, see Scollnik, D.P.M, "Introduction to Markov Chain Monte Carlo Methods and Their Actuarial Applications," *Proceedings of the Casualty Actuarial Society* LXXXIII (1996): 114-165.

.